Highway Engineering

Highway Engineering

Robert Ashworth
M.Eng., Ph.D., M.I.C.E., A.M.Inst.H.E.
Senior Lecturer in Civil and Structural Engineering
University of Sheffield

Heinemann Educational Books Ltd
London

Heinemann Educational Books Ltd
LONDON EDINBURGH MELBOURNE TORONTO
SINGAPORE JOHANNESBURG AUCKLAND
IBADAN HONG KONG NAIROBI

SBN 435 72301 4
© R. Ashworth 1966
First published 1966
Reprinted with corrections 1969

Published by Heinemann Educational Books Ltd
48 Charles Street, London W1X 8AH
Printed in Great Britain by
Butler & Tanner Ltd
Frome and London

Foreword

by

Colonel S. M. Lovell

C.B.E., E.R.D., T.D., F.I.C.E., M.I.Mun.E.,
A.M.T.P.I., P.P.I.H.E.

County Engineer and Surveyor,
West Riding County Council

- -

Are you one of the band of keen young engineers who thinks the building of motorways and other new roads must be a fascinating occupation or are you already a practising Highway Engineer who has not yet had the good fortune to be associated with the motorway programme or other major improvement schemes? Perhaps you are still at university or technical college, learning the basic principles of highway engineering and looking forward to the time when you yourself will be in part responsible for the design, construction, and maintenance of our national highway network.

Whichever of these categories you fit into, this is a book that will not only interest you but will explain in simple language how it is done and what it means. It will explain the quite remarkable advances in highway engineering in the technological sphere, without getting you bogged down in detail yet at the same time acknowledging that this rapid advance is even accelerating. Furthermore it will emphasize the necessity of keeping not only up to date but in advance of the times, and point out the direction in which this is likely to lead you.

Let me give you a personal example to show, within a short span of years, the real progress which has been made in the field of highway engineering. As a young man I had to measure stones heaped on the side of the road and cracked there by stonecracker John. Yet today I expect my motorway work to start off with an aerial survey and by applying the engineer's skill in conjunction with the fullest use of a computer finish up with a bill of quantities straight off the computer ready to go to the contractor to price, at the same time producing as the end result a far more sophisticated scheme utilizing far fewer engineers and in a far shorter time than was possible even less than a decade ago. This then merely serves to emphasize the sort of progress that this fascinating book deals with.

We live in a democracy and certain rules and regulations known as Statutory Procedures have to be followed before roads can be built, and these rules are for the safeguard of the Mr and Mrs Browns of this world. Do not be surprised if you find this side of the business frustrating and perhaps even a little more difficult than the book would convey.

I have read this manuscript with very great interest and pleasure. My whole career, and I am still fully active in it, has been that of a Highway Engineer, and against that background I recommend this book to you all, even though you may have already built motorways or the like, without any reservation.

Preface

This book has been written primarily to provide an introduction to 'Highway and Traffic Engineering'. The subject is an extensive one, requiring not only an understanding of the basic principles of soil mechanics, surveying, and concrete technology, but also an insight into the more specialized fields of photogrammetry, statistics, and computer programming. It is perhaps a consequence of this diversity of interests that most textbooks which have appeared in recent years have sought to concentrate on a specific aspect of highway design or construction rather than attempt to cover the subject in its entirety. Whilst such books have proved valuable for the research worker and the practising engineer, those of us who are concerned with teaching the fundamental principles of highway engineering to students and young engineers have increasingly felt the need for an up-to-date British text providing a comprehensive treatment of the subject at an introductory level. This book seeks primarily to fulfil that need, though it is hoped it will also be found generally useful by the practising engineer.

The subject matter in this book has been arranged as far as possible to match the sequence of events leading up to the construction and completion of a new road. After an introductory chapter dealing with the administration of the road system in Great Britain, the first half of the book is devoted to various aspects of highway planning and design, leading to the location and setting out of the alignment. By contrast, the remainder of the book is concerned with constructional procedure and deals in turn with earth-moving operations, soil stabilization techniques, pavement design and construction, and surface water drainage. Although related essentially to British practice, considerable reference has been made to American design standards and much of the subject matter will be of interest to overseas readers. In particular, the chapter dealing with soil stabilization techniques has been extended to include methods of construction which are unsuitable for British climatic conditions but which are widely used in the developing countries.

One of the difficulties associated with a book of this nature is that design standards and specifications are constantly being revised. For this reason, I have attempted to develop the underlying principles governing the adoption of the current standards and have indicated where modifications and amendments may be expected in the near future. Those readers who are practising engineers should, of course, ensure that they have in their possession copies of the most recent design specifications.

In a book of this size it is not possible to give detailed treatment to every individual topic, but I have included an extensive list of bibliographical references which I hope will be useful to those readers wishing to pursue a specific item more deeply. In particular, special attention has been given to the research carried out in recent years at the British Road Research Laboratory and a considerable number of these bibliographical references relate to this work.

I am indebted to the many organizations and authorities who have assisted me in the preparation of this book by supplying photographs or by allowing me to reproduce design data, diagrams, and other copyright material. I am also grateful for the help and advice received from my publishers and from many friends and colleagues. It is impossible for me to mention all by name individually, but I should like in particular to thank Colonel S. M. Lovell for contributing the Foreword, Mr D. W. Bass and Mr B. J. Walker for reading the draft manuscript and offering critical comments, Mrs P. A. Kirby for typing the greater part of the manuscript, and finally my wife Kathleen for the help and encouragement which she has given to me during the time spent writing this book. Any success which this book may eventually achieve will be due as much to the assistance which I have received from others as to my own endeavours.

Note to 1969 Reprint

Since this book was first published, the Ministry of Transport *Memorandum on the Design of Roads in Rural Areas* (Memorandum No. 780) has been superseded by a new publication *Advisory Manual on the Layout of Roads in Rural Areas*. Whilst the design standards contained therein, apart from those relating to design capacities, are for the large part unchanged, the opportunity has been taken to incorporate such revisions into the text and references to the earlier memorandum have been deleted. In the same way, some of the earlier requirements for the design thickness of unreinforced concrete pavements given in *Road Note No. 29* have been replaced by more recent recommendations. It must be emphasized, however, that these changes do not represent a complete up-dating of the text and practising engineers concerned with other design standards and specifications should ensure that at all times they have copies of the most recent publications available to them.

R. ASHWORTH

Department of Civil Engineering,
University of Liverpool

Acknowledgments

I am indebted to the following organizations who have kindly provided photographic illustrations for this book: Leonard Fairclough Ltd (illustration on front of jacket); Aveling-Barford Ltd (Plates 8.1, 8.2, 8.3, 8.4, and 8.5); Stothert and Pitt Ltd (Plates 8.6, 8.7, 8.8, 11.2, 11.3, 11.5, and 11.6); Howard Rotavator Co. Ltd (Plates 9.1, 9.2, and 9.3); the Cement and Concrete Association (Plates 11.1, 12.1, 12.2, 12.4, 12.5, 12.6, 12.7 and back of jacket, 12.8, 12.9, 12.11, 12.12, 12.13, and 12.14); Bristowes Machinery Ltd and E.C.C. Quarries Ltd, Devon (Plate 11.4); Bristowes Machinery Ltd and Amey's Asphalt Co. Ltd. (Plate 11.7); the British Road Tar Association (Plates 11.8 and 11.9); the Road Surface Dressing Association Ltd (Plate 11.10); Concrete Sawing Equipment Ltd (Plates 12.3 and 12.10).

I should also like to thank the following for allowing the reproduction of diagrams, design data, and other copyright material from their publications: the American Association of State Highway Officials; the American Society of Civil Engineers; the British Road Federation; the British Road Tar Association; the Cement and Concrete Association; the Controller of H.M. Stationery Office; the Director of Road Research; the Highway Research Board; the Institution of Civil Engineers; the Institution of Highway Engineers; the Ministry of Transport; and the Steering Committee on Merseyside Traffic and Transport. Extracts from British Standard Specifications are reproduced by permission of the British Standards Institution, 2 Park Street, London, W.1, from whom copies of the complete Standards may be obtained.

Contents

List of Plates

xiii

1

Highway Development and Administration in Great Britain

The administration of the British road system is a complex procedure which has evolved from the gradual development of highways in this country throughout the years. At the present time, there are more than 1,200 highway authorities, each administering its own section of the national road network, and although the trend is towards some measure of national control of the highway system with larger administrative areas and consequently more uniformity in layout, design, and construction, the existing pattern seems likely to continue for many years. In order to appreciate how the complexities of the present system have come into being, it is necessary to consider each stage of highway development in relation to the traffic requirements of the day and the historical background of the period.

1.1 Roman roads

The earliest highways influencing our present system were those laid down by the Romans during their occupation of this country from A.D. 43 until the early fifth century. The Romans had previously constructed a network of roads covering Europe, North Africa, and part of Asia Minor, so that it was only natural for this system to be extended to cover those parts of Britain under Roman administration. These roads were constructed primarily for military purposes in order to improve communications between the various camps, and the majority radiated from the administrative centre of Londinium (London) in the south-east to the various provincial centres and from there to the Welsh and Scottish borders.

The Roman roads were in some instances aligned with existing tracks,

1

but were generally noted for their straight lines and their complete disregard of the natural contours of the countryside. The alignment of a number of these roads, now known by their early-English names such as Watling Street and Ermine Street, are still clearly distinguishable over considerable stretches and in some cases form the foundations for the modern roads. As already mentioned, Roman roads were constructed primarily for military purposes; chiefly to accommodate bodies of men marching on foot but also to allow for the transporting of equipment in heavy baggage wagons. The latter required substantial roads of adequate width and some authorities have suggested that the straight pattern of Roman roads may have resulted, to a considerable extent, from

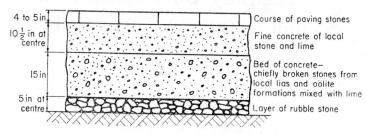

FIGURE 1.1 Fosse Way near Radstock (as described by J. McMurtrie[7])

the use of four-wheeled wagons which lacked a means of steering on the front axle and which could only negotiate corners with difficulty.

The Roman military engineers displayed an understanding of the principles of road construction which has not been excelled until comparatively recently. Their roads were usually built up of cemented stone layers set on a rubble foundation and surfaced with mortar-bound gravel or jointed stone slabs to an overall thickness of approximately 3 ft, but with the actual width of the surfacing rarely exceeding 14 ft. Generally local materials were used, and the constructional details were varied to suit local conditions, as for example during the building of the roadway across the Medway Valley, near Rochester, which was founded on oak piles driven into the soft, marshy ground. Margary[1] has described in detail the construction of this and other Roman roads, and Figure 1.1 is typical of many of the first-class roads of that period.

1.2 *Roads during the Middle Ages*

Following the Roman evacuation, Britain was divided into a number of small kingdoms between which there was little communication. For many years the roads were allowed to degenerate and no attempt seems to have been made to continue the road-building activities of the Romans. Maintenance was restricted to clearing away obstructions and occasionally filling up some of the larger holes which appeared, and in some instances the stone surfacing slabs were removed and used for other purposes. In time, many of the Roman highways were superseded by other tracks following the same general direction but having easier gradients.

The first recorded legislation dealing with highways, the Statute of Winchester (1285), ordered landowners to maintain the roads and bridges on their land in a fit state for traffic, and further required that highways between market towns be cleared of trees and bushes for a distance of 200 ft on either side in order to protect the wayfarer from attack. The tenants were no doubt obliged to undertake this task on the landowner's behalf without receiving any payment for their labours.

During the fourteenth and fifteenth centuries, the growth of a large number of provincial fairs and markets brought about an increase in the amount of traffic using the roads. Such was the state of the roads, however, that practically all travelling was either on foot or on horseback, with pack horses to transport goods, there being little wheeled traffic. With the dissolution of the monasteries during the reign of Henry VIII (1509–1547), the condition of the roads became even more deplorable since the monasteries had undertaken a good share of the maintenance work.

In 1555, a Statute of Philip and Mary placed the obligation of road maintenance upon each parish and the appointment of Highway Surveyors was authorized. The Highway Surveyor had no special qualifications and usually a landowner was given this honorary appointment. His duties were to see that the roads within the parish boundaries were kept repaired and were free from obstructions. To enable him to comply with these requirements, the Act also required each landowner to work for a number of days each year without pay on road maintenance under the direction of the Highway Surveyor, or else to provide the equivalent labour for this purpose. This forced labour became known as 'statute labour', and since there was no incentive for the parishioners to do more than the absolute minimum in maintaining existing roads, let alone building new ones, the country roads remained little more than rough tracks and travelling in winter was virtually impossible.

1.3 *The turnpike system*

Following the introduction of coach travel in the early seventeenth century and the general increase in trade that was taking place between the towns and the surrounding countryside, a heavy burden was placed on those parishes which happened to lie on one of the 'through' roads. The parishioners resented repairing the road for others to use, with the result that the condition of the roads deteriorated still further.

To arrest this decay, the turnpike system was introduced in the eighteenth century for the purpose of maintaining roads from tolls collected from the people using the road, the toll charge varying according to the type of vehicle. Trustees were appointed in charge of each section of turnpike, which were usually from 15 to 20 miles in length, to administer and repair the road. The first turnpike was established by Act of Parliament in 1706, and eventually there were more than 1,100 separate trusts controlling some 22,000 miles of road. The Highway Surveyors employed by the trustees rarely possessed any professional qualifications and were generally unable to bring about any improvement in road conditions. In addition, there was a good deal of dishonesty and mis-use of the funds on the part of the trustees, which incensed the road users and aroused much hostility towards the turnpikes. As the number of turnpike trusts increased, so the cost of travelling rose and the hostility became greater, giving way eventually in some instances to serious violence and the breaking down of the toll gates.

1.4 Nineteenth-century roads—Telford and McAdam

Although the first serious attempt at road building since Roman times took place in Scotland during the eighteenth century where General Wade began a system of metalled roads to improve communications in the Highlands, primarily for military purposes during the Jacobite trouble, it was not until the following century that any real effort to reconstruct the road system was attempted.

Early in the nineteenth century, Thomas Telford (1757–1834), a famous engineer who later became the first President of the Institution of Civil Engineers, constructed a further 1,000 miles of new roads in the

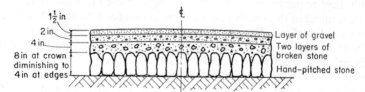

FIGURE 1.2 Telford's construction

Highlands and at the same time cut the Caledonian Canal. Later, he moved southwards and reconstructed the London to Holyhead road, including the erection of the Menai Straits suspension bridge, to provide the Postmaster General of the day with improved communications with Ireland.

Telford gave careful attention to the alignment of his roads and reduced the gradients as much as possible so as to assist the speeding-up of coach travel. His method of construction (Figure 1.2) was to excavate down to a level formation, on top of which were placed hand-packed stones varying in depth from about 8 in at the centre of the road to about 4 in at the haunches, giving a 4 in crossfall over the half width of the road. These stones were not more than 4 in wide and were laid with their broadest end downwards, the spaces between being filled with fine chippings. On top of this foundation, two layers of broken stone, 4 in and 2 in thick respectively, were placed in the central 18 ft of the road and compacted by traffic. At the sides of the road the stones were placed in a single layer 6 in thick. The final surfacing layer of gravel, 1½ in thick, was then placed over the full width of the road, watered, and left to be compacted by traffic.

At the same time that Telford was occupied with this work, another famous engineer, John Loudon McAdam (1756–1836), was carrying out his own experiments on road construction. McAdam, a turnpike trustee, was eventually granted charge of roads in the Bristol area and was able to put into practice his own principles of construction. McAdam's construction (Figure 1.3) differed from that of Telford in

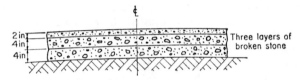

FIGURE 1.3 McAdam's construction

that he dispensed with the carefully prepared foundation layer and instead dug the formation to the required surface camber, which was only about half that provided by Telford. On top of the formation he placed two 4 in layers of broken stone, and finally covered these with a surfacing layer 2 in thick, formed by angular fragments of broken stone not greater than 1 in in size. This layer was compacted in the first place by ramming and later by traffic. Following the success of his methods of construction, McAdam was appointed Surveyor-General of Roads in 1827 and 'macadam' roads were soon in existence throughout the country.

The work of Telford and McAdam opened up a vast improvement in communications and, for the first time for many years, roads were being provided to suit the requirements of the traffic, including steam carriages which were in the experimental development stage at that time. Unfortunately, this era coincided with the birth of the railways which brought about an immediate reduction in the number of passengers carried by the stage coaches. Many important coaches had to be withdrawn on financial grounds, the turnpike trusts became consequently insolvent as a result of the loss of revenue and could no longer carry out their duties of repairing the roads, and so the liability for road maintenance reverted once again to the parish.

1.5 Highway legislation

The Highways Act of 1835 retained the parish as the administrative unit for all roads, other than turnpikes, within its boundaries, but authorized the formation of groups of parishes into Joint Highway Boards. Salaried officers were appointed and statute labour was replaced by hired labour, rates being levied by the Highway Surveyor to meet the expenses. Few parishes, however, took advantage of this opportunity to link with neighbouring parishes, so the Highways Act of 1862 gave Local Justices the power to combine parishes into Highway Districts in an effort to improve road conditions by enlarging the impossibly small administrative area of a single parish, but not all Justices took the necessary action.

In the meantime, the winding up of the turnpike trusts added further to the burden of local rates as these roads came under the administration of the local parish or Highway District, and from 1876 onwards, a Government grant of £200,000 per annum was made to ease the rate-payers' burden on the disturnpiked roads. In addition, the Highways and Locomotives Act of 1878 adjusted the burden between different parishes in the county by requiring half of the maintenance costs for roads disturnpiked after 1870 to be contributed from county funds.

County Councils were created by the Local Government Act of 1888 and were required to pay the full maintenance costs for all main roads in the county, other than those lying within the boundaries of the County Boroughs which were given powers equivalent to those of a County Council. Main roads included all disturnpiked roads together with any others which it was felt desirable to classify as main roads. In addition, contributions could be made towards the upkeep of secondary roads.

A further Local Government Act of 1894 abolished both Highway Parishes and Highway Districts and constituted the present Urban and Rural District Councils in an attempt to give wider areas of administration for the network of minor roads. In the meantime, the few remaining turnpike trusts were being gradually abolished—the last one to be wound up being the Anglesey section of the Holyhead road in 1895—so that at the turn of the century road administration was vested in the County Councils, the County Borough Councils, the Urban District Councils, and the Rural District Councils.

1.6 Development of mechanical traction

The early attempts to apply mechanical traction to road vehicles had been thwarted by road conditions, by the popularity of the railways, and by restrictive legislation governing the size, weight, and speed of road vehicles, so that it was not until the 'Man and Red Flag Act' of

1864 had been repealed in 1896 that the development of the motor vehicle really began. With the rapid increase of motor traffic that took place in the following years, road surfaces began to disintegrate and break up, and an additional problem, that of dust raised by fast-moving vehicles, proved a new source of annoyance to both travellers and roadside dwellers. Efforts had therefore to be made to strengthen the road construction and also reduce the dust nuisance, and the cost of this work had to be borne by the ratepayers who begrudged this extra payment and pressed the Government to provide some measure of relief.

Eventually this pressure led to the Development and Road Improvement Funds Act of 1909, which created the Road Board, the first national road authority in the country, and placed at its disposal the bulk of the proceeds of motor vehicle licence duties and a 3d. per gallon petrol tax. It was intended that this money should be used in connection with certain classes of road improvement work such as widening, levelling, and treatment to reduce dust, but not for routine maintenance work. The Board had powers to assist highway authorities in the construction of new roads, both financially and technically, and with the latter purpose in mind, constructed and tested a large number of experimental sections incorporating new surfacing materials. Before many of these schemes could be started, however, war broke out and road development was arrested.

1.7 Progress in the inter-war years, 1918–1939

At the end of the war in 1919, the newly-created Ministry of Transport took over the work of the Road Board and proposals for an extensive scheme of road improvements were carried out, partly to cater for the expanding motoring population (Figure 1.4) and also to relieve unemployment. Financial restriction prevented these improvements keeping pace with the increase of traffic however.

Under the Ministry of Transport, main roads were divided into two classes, Class I and Class II, whilst the remaining roads such as country lanes and residential streets in towns were placed in the category of Unclassified Roads. The latter formed about 75% of the total length of public highway.

In a further effort to reduce the number of highway authorities, the Local Government Act of 1929 transferred control of all roads in rural areas to the County Council, but allowed Non-County Boroughs and Urban Districts with a population in excess of 20,000 to claim the right to administer their own main roads in addition to the secondary ones already under their control.

The lack of uniform standards of design and construction created difficulties for travellers using the main through routes, since practice varied from one authority to the next and such roads might come under the control of several authorities within the space of a few miles. In order to provide some degree of uniformity along the main national highways, the Ministry of Transport, by virtue of the Trunk Roads Act of 1936, took over as highway authority for 4,505 miles of main roads in England, Scotland, and Wales, but not including any main roads within the boundaries of the City of London, County Boroughs in England and Wales, and Large Burghs in Scotland. Also in 1936, the

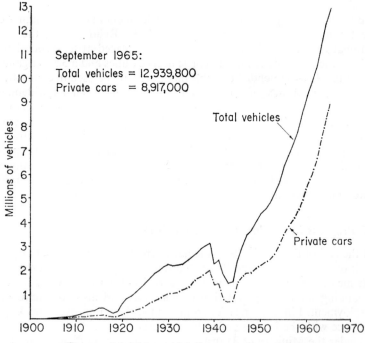

FIGURE 1.4 Motor vehicle licences in Great Britain

Budget speech had included the announcement that the Road Fund was no longer to receive the bulk of the proceeds from motor vehicle licence duties directly (which were then amounting to some £30 million per year), but that this money would be paid into the National Exchequer, and grants would be voted annually to the Road Fund through the Civil Estimates according to its requirements.

About this same time, the construction of the German autobahnen solely for the use of high-speed motor traffic, coupled with the alarming increase of road accidents in this country, led to strong pressure on the Government for the creation of a similar system of motor roads in

Great Britain. These demands came not only from the general public but also from the country's leading highway engineers, and in 1938 the County Surveyors' Society produced a scheme showing proposals for about 1,000 miles of motorway covering the whole of England and extending to South Wales and Southern Scotland. These motorways were intended to by-pass all the large towns, but would be connected to them by link roads. Access to the motorway would be restricted to specific junctions with important main roads, and other minor roads would be taken over or would pass under the motorway with no connecting links.

1.8 Post-war developments

The outbreak of war in 1939 brought a further period of stagnation in road development, though there was a temporary relief in the build-up of motor vehicles using the roads as a result of petrol rationing (Figure 1.4). Immediately after the war, in May 1946, the Minister of Transport submitted plans for a ten-year highway programme to the House of Commons. The first stages of the programme were to be devoted to completing the arrears of maintenance work and making good war damage, whilst the later stages were to cover a comprehensive reconstruction of the major national traffic routes, including the provision of a limited number of new motor roads.

The 1946 Trunk Roads Act provided for a further 3,685 miles of main road being taken over by the Ministry of Transport. On this occasion, roads within County Boroughs were taken over, and the total length of trunk roads was thus extended to 8,190 miles. The Ministry of Transport, as highway authority, is responsible for the full maintenance and improvement costs of trunk roads and authorizes such work as is necessary, although the actual undertaking of this work is normally delegated to the County Council or County Borough Council concerned, who acts as agent and carries out the work to the Ministry specifications. For trunk roads in Scotland and Wales, the respective Secretaries of State act in a similar capacity as the Minister of Transport in England.

Other legislation in 1946 created the category of Class III roads covering a number of previously unclassified roads which were of more than purely local value. These were added to the other previously designated County Roads, Class I and II, giving the present classification system for the 200,704 miles of all-purpose roads:

1. Trunk Roads—national system of main through traffic routes (8,349 miles, 4·2% of total mileage).
2. County Roads, Class I—all other important roads linking large centres of population (19,860 miles).
3. County Roads, Class II—other main roads linking Class I roads with smaller centres of population (17,642 miles).

4. County Roads, Class III—not main roads, but of more than purely local value (48,998 miles).

5. Unclassified Roads—country lanes, town streets, suburban roads and all other roads not previously classified (105,855 miles, 53% of total mileage).

(The mileage figures given above are taken from *Basic Road Statistics, 1966*,[2] and are applicable to the year ended 31st March, 1965.)

For approved works of improvement or maintenance, the County Roads qualify for an Exchequer grant of 75% for Class I roads, 60% for Class II roads and 50% for Class III roads, except that in areas where road maintenance is covered by a block grant the rates apply only to improvements. New legislation proposes that with effect from 1st April 1967 the present system of classification for County Roads will be replaced by a single category of 'principal roads', the total mileage of which will be initially about the same as that of the present Class I roads and which will qualify for a 75% grant for improvements.

1.9 *Motorway plans*

Despite the high hopes of the early post-war years and the rapidly increasing vehicle population, the economic situation soon led to a marked reduction in the planned expenditure on roadworks and the postponement of the new motorway projects. Legislation was passed, however, in the form of the Special Roads Act, 1949,* to make motorway construction possible. Until that time, all types of highway users, including pedestrians, had as much right to use any public highway as the motor vehicle. The Special Roads Act provided for the construction of new roads or the appropriation of existing roads reserved for special classes of traffic, as authorized by the Ministry of Transport. A schedule of the same Act prescribed classification of traffic into nine groups covering various types of motor vehicles and also including horse-drawn vehicles, pedal cyclists, pedestrians, and driven animals. Special Roads can therefore be reserved exclusively for a particular class or classes of traffic, and such restrictions are in fact now applied on motorways.

Although the first Order under the Act was made later that year, it was not until December 1953 that the Government announced a road programme including the first sections of motorway—the Preston and Lancaster By-passes and the Ross Spur Motorway. A further programme announced in July 1957 was based on five main objectives,[3] namely:

1. The improvement of the Great North Road from London to Newcastle.

---

* Now consolidated in the Highways Act, 1959.

2. A motorway from London to the North-West.
3. Better communications between the Midlands and South Wales.
4. Better roads to the Channel Ports.
5. A new outlet from London to the West.

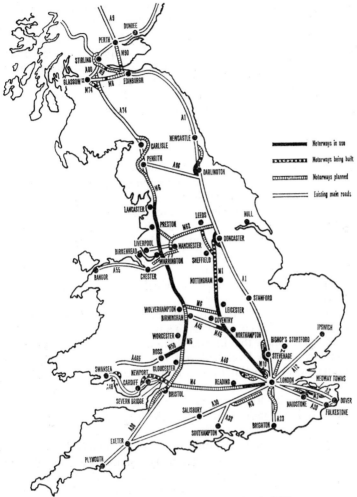

FIGURE 1.5 British motorways: March 1966

This programme included the London–Birmingham and Birmingham–Preston Motorways, part of the Bristol–Birmingham Motorway, several shorter lengths of motorway such as the Doncaster By-pass, the Medway Towns Motorway, the Slough and Maidenhead By-passes, and also the new Severn Bridge. These schemes were delegated to the County Councils concerned who acted as agents for the Ministry of Transport, or in some cases consulting engineers were appointed to act on the latter's behalf. At the time of writing, much of this work has been completed and since the opening of the first section of motorway, the Preston By-pass, in December 1958 more than 380 miles of motorway have been completed and a further 150 miles are under construction.

Plans for an extension to the motorway system outlined above have now been put into effect. These include the completion of the London–Yorkshire Motorway and the extension of the Birmingham–Preston Motorway northwards to Carlisle. In some cases work has already started, whilst in others the line has now been fixed. The present state of progress and future proposals are shown in Figure 1.5.

1.10 The years ahead

In spite of this rural motorway programme and many other small but important improvement works being carried out simultaneously on the all-purpose road system, little is being done by way of new construction to improve traffic conditions in urban areas. There have been, of course, isolated schemes such as the Hammersmith Flyover and the Hyde Park Corner Underpass in London and the Birmingham Ring Road which have reduced congestion over a limited area, but it is unfortunately all too apparent that the improvement of the British road system is not keeping pace with the number of vehicles coming onto the roads (Figure 1.4).

In September 1965, there were 12·9 million licenced motor vehicles in Great Britain which corresponds to a population–vehicle ratio of 4·1. American figures show that in 1963 there was one vehicle per 2·3 population and saturation level had still not been reached.[4] The recent Buchanan report[5] has estimated that in this country the eventual level of vehicle ownership may reach saturation level by A.D. 2010, by which time there could be 40 million motor vehicles for a population of 74 million. This is an indication of the challenge confronting the new generation of highway and traffic engineers.

Although lack of funds and difficulties in land acquisition are probably the major reasons for this delay, many engineers including Colonel S. M. Lovell, the County Engineer and Surveyor for the West Riding of Yorkshire, have drawn attention to the unwieldy administrative structure that exists at present.[6] Because of this arrangement, many proposed schemes are delayed for several years as a result of the backwards and forwards movement of documents and plans between the authorizing authority and the agent authority acting on the former's behalf, or between different authorities each concerned with one section of a particular scheme.

In April 1965, there were 1,231 highway authorities in Great Britain, comprised as follows:[2]

England

Ministry of Transport	1
County Councils and G.L.C.	48
London Borough Councils	32
County Borough Councils	78
Non-County Borough Councils	244
Urban District Councils	474
Total	**877**

Scotland

Scottish Development Department	1
County Councils	31
Large Burgh Councils	24
Small Burgh Councils	175
Total	**231**

Wales

Welsh Office	1
County Councils	13
County Borough Councils	4
Non-County Borough Councils	32
Urban District Councils	73
Total	**123**

This arrangement can only result in administrative difficulties, and suggestions have been put forward for a national authority with direct control, both administratively and financially, over the main development schemes such as motorways and trunk road improvements. This authority could work either on a central or on a regional basis and would be responsible for the planning, design, and supervision of new roads, which would be constructed by contractors. On completion, the roads would be handed over to the local highway authorities for future maintenance.

It would seem that if any progress is to be made in the attempt to catch up with the backlogs of the highway system then such a step must eventually come about, and the sooner this happens then the greater is the chance that this country will one day possess a highway system to suit the demands of the traffic.

REFERENCES

1. MARGARY, I. D., *Roman Roads in Britain* (London: Phoenix House Ltd, vol. 1, 1955; vol. 2, 1957)
2. BRITISH ROAD FEDERATION, *Basic Road Statistics, 1966* (London: British Road Federation, 1966)
3. BAKER, J. F. A., 'The General Motorway Plan', *Proc. Instn. civ. Engrs.* (London: vol. 15, 1960, pp. 317–32)
4. TANNER, J. C., 'Forecasts of Vehicle Ownership in Great Britain', *Roads and Road Construction* (London: vol. 43, 1965, pp. 341–7 and 371–6)
5. MINISTRY OF TRANSPORT, *Traffic in Towns* (London: H.M.S.O., 1963, p. 26)
6. LOVELL, S. M., 'The Suitability of the Existing Highway Organization to Deal with an Expanding Programme of Road Construction', *Conference on the Highway Needs of Great Britain 1957* (London: Instn. civ. Engrs., 1958, pp. 173–88)
7. MCMURTRIE, J., 'The Fosse Road at Radstock', *Proc. Somerset archaeol. Nat. Hist. Soc.* (Taunton: vol. 30, Part II, 1884, pp. 76–82)

BIBLIOGRAPHY

JEFFREYS, REES, *The King's Highway* (London: Batchworth Press Ltd, 1949)
CROSS, C. A. (Ed.), *Encyclopedia of Highway Law and Practice*, vols. 1 and 2 (London: Sweet and Maxwell, 1965)

2

Traffic Surveys and Road Capacity

Before any road scheme is seriously contemplated—irrespective of whether it is simply the realignment of an existing road or an extensive new motorway—a traffic survey of one kind or another should be carried out. This survey will provide the data on which the proposed road layout can be based, and failure to obtain this information may lead to a false assessment of the potential traffic requirements of the road, resulting in its inability to handle the volume of traffic subsequently wishing to make use of that route.

2.1 Nature and extent of traffic surveys

In many instances it is sufficient for design purposes if the survey is confined to a study of traffic volumes, measured on a daily or hourly basis and possibly broken down into the numbers of each type of vehicle. On other occasions, however, these volume studies have to be supplemented by information concerning such topics as vehicle speeds, journey times, delay times at intersections, parking studies, accident records, pedestrian movements, and various aspects of vehicle performance. It is the intention in this chapter to limit description to two types of survey, namely volume and speed surveys, but many of the techniques adopted are, of course, applicable to other types of studies. For a more comprehensive treatment of the subject, particularly in relation to urban development, the reader is referred to a recent Ministry of Transport memorandum.[1]

In any traffic survey it is rarely possible to collect information concerning every individual vehicle or driver, since there are usually limitations in the amount of money and time which can be devoted to the task, in addition to which the question of public inconvenience must be seriously considered. For these reasons, a sampling procedure is often introduced. Care should be taken, however, to ensure that all the necessary information is collected in the course of the survey, and on this account a pilot survey to decide the scope and pattern of the full survey and also to allow the investigators to experiment with various sampling techniques is useful.

Conversely, it should be remembered that all the data collected has to be analysed if it is to be of any use, and therefore a more extensive and complicated survey than is really necessary will increase not only the costs of conducting the survey but also the subsequent analysis, and may in fact result in the essential items being clouded with obscure detail. The investigators must therefore have a clear understanding of the purpose of the survey before commencing the work, and the survey should be planned accordingly to give no more than the relevant data.

It is helpful in many surveys to obtain the co-operation and goodwill of the general public, and this can often be achieved by advanced publicity in the local newspapers. Care should be taken though to avoid any statements which might distort the normal pattern of movements of both vehicles and pedestrians, and for this reason it is advisable to omit precise details concerning the time of the survey and the location of the survey stations.

VOLUME SURVEYS

2.2 *Types of volume surveys*

The type of traffic volume survey which is required in a particular case depends on the extent of the new construction or improvement work proposed and its location with respect to other similar roads in the area. In rural areas where the main traffic routes are often some distance apart, a relatively small scheme such as the reconstruction of a short length of the existing alignment to by-pass a village or to avoid a long, steep gradient would be unlikely to attract a significant amount of traffic from other roads in the area. Thus the anticipated volume of traffic along the new section of road could be determined simply by counting the traffic using the existing road and allowing for the normal growth of traffic over the next twenty years or so.

On the other hand, if the scheme involved a considerable length of improvement works or concerned an entirely new road such as a motorway, then it is likely that traffic would be drawn from other roads in the area and therefore the traffic survey should embrace all these alternative routes. In urban areas, this is particularly true for even very small improvement schemes, and cases may be cited where the conversion of a stretch of road from single to dual carriageway layout or the installation of traffic signal control at an isolated intersection has resulted in a considerable redistribution of the traffic pattern in the locality.

In these circumstances, a comprehensive traffic survey over a wide area, rather than a simple count at one point, is necessary. This would normally take the form of an origin and destination survey (O–D survey), since it is only with the additional information concerning the general direction which a driver is following that the probability of him choosing to use a particular section of improved road can be assessed in advance with any degree of confidence.

2.3 Volume counts

The volume of traffic using a section of road can be measured by counting vehicles passing a fixed point in both directions. Counting may be carried out manually or by automatic means and both methods have certain advantages.

(a) Manual methods
In this method, the passing of a vehicle is recorded by an enumerator on a specially prepared form or on a series of hand tallies, the vehicles being simultaneously classified into a number of predetermined groups. For the sample survey taken in 1960, the Ministry of Transport adopted a classification system with nine vehicle groups ranging from pedal cycles to heavy articulated commercial vehicles, and whilst there are arguments for using this same system for all counts, there are many instances when a breakdown into fewer classes is sufficient.

For many purposes it is usual to convert the actual number of vehicles into equivalent passenger car units (p.c.u.); these values being determined by the relative effects of different types of vehicles on traffic flow. Since the effect of a bus or heavy commercial vehicle in a traffic stream varies according to the precise road and traffic conditions, it is not possible to give general values to suit all purposes. Table 2.1

TABLE 2.1 *Vehicle equivalents in passenger car units*[1]

Traffic conditions	Cars, light vans and m/c combinations	Goods vehicles (medium and heavy)	Buses and coaches	Solo motor cycles	Pedal cycles
Rural roads	1·0	3·0	3·0	1·0	0·5
Urban streets between intersections	1·0	2·0	3·0	0·75	0·33
Roundabouts	1·0	2·8	2·8	0·75	0·5
Traffic signals	1·0	1·75	2·25	0·33	0·2

shows the values agreed between the Road Research Laboratory, the Ministry of Transport, and other highway authorities.[1]

On account of the labour involved in the conducting of a manual count, the period of counting has generally to be limited to a few days. Observations are usually made over the 16-hour period from 6 a.m. to 10 p.m. and should preferably continue over seven consecutive days. If that is not possible, then the count should take place on at least three consecutive days inclusive of Saturday and Sunday, and the average daily flow may be deduced by considering the flow on the weekday covered by the census to be representative of the Monday to Friday volumes and dividing the total weekly flow by seven.

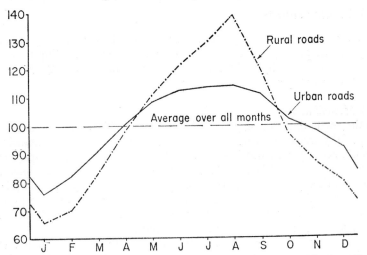

FIGURE 2.1 Seasonal patterns on urban and rural roads (vehicle-miles per standard week in each month, averaged over 1956 to 1960, expressed as a percentage of the average over all months)[2]

Since traffic flows vary from month to month throughout the year, being generally at their lowest in January and reaching a peak in August, the volume count should be taken at the busiest time of the year or else the figure should be adjusted to take account of this seasonal fluctuation. This can be done by making use of the results of the continuous count by automatic traffic counters at fifty points on classified roads throughout the country, conducted by the Road Research Laboratory.[2] These points have been selected at random and cover trunk, Class I, Class II, and Class III roads in both urban and rural areas. The counters are read daily at 8 a.m., and in addition to showing traffic trends from year to year, the results give seasonal distribution patterns. These patterns differ for urban and rural conditions, the amplitude of the latter being larger and the peak more pronounced (Figure 2.1), but are remarkably alike at similar locations, and so can be used to estimate seasonal variations at other census points on roads having similar traffic characteristics.

It is possible to estimate approximately the average daily flow from a count taken on a single da or even for only a few hours, applying the information from other census points in the area with regard to weekly and daily traffic fluctuations, but these results are necessarily of limited value since the accuracy is bound to be influenced by weather conditions and other local factors. Such information is sometimes useful in the preliminary stages of planning when money is not available for a more complete survey or time is limited, provided that more accurate figures are obtained at a later date.

(b) Automatic methods
The passing of vehicles can be recorded automatically by special equipment used in conjunction with some form of vehicle detector. The type most commonly used is a pneumatic detector, which consists of a length of thick-walled rubber tubing about $\frac{1}{4}$ in internal diameter fastened down to the surface of the road perpendicular to the direction of the traffic. The passage of a vehicle axle over the tube transmits a pressure pulse through the tube which operates an electrical contact on a diaphragm switch, so actuating a counter which is arranged to register every other pulse in order to correspond to one count per vehicle.

Other types of detectors have incorporated an energized wire loop buried in the road surface or a photoelectric cell arrangement set a few feet above the road surface. Both devices transmit a signal to the counter when a vehicle passes, though the photoelectric cell method suffers from the disadvantages that directional flows on a single carriageway layout cannot be separated and also the beam can be triggered off by pedestrians. This latter difficulty can be overcome by using a double beam detector in which two parallel beams set some three feet apart must be broken simultaneously before the counter is actuated.

The simplest types of recording equipment merely totalize the input signals and have to be read at predetermined intervals. More elaborate instruments incorporate a clock mechanism and print out hourly or daily totals automatically, whilst others can be pre-set to record for a selected period of the day only.

Automatic methods of counting have the advantage that little attendant labour is required, particularly with the more elaborate types of counters, and therefore measurements can be made for long periods. Such counters are thus ideally suited for the continuous measurement of seasonal and annual trends at the selected sites previously referred to. The chief disadvantage is that these counters are not able to give a classification breakdown, and therefore the results must generally be supplemented by a sample manual count. Other disadvantages are that

B

errors can be incurred with multi-axle vehicles and also with light vehicles such as pedal cycles and mopeds which may fail to register when using pneumatic detector tubes. Difficulties may also occur in finding suitable sites for the equipment in localities where wilful damage is likely to be encountered.

2.4 Origin and destination surveys

It has already been mentioned that an O–D survey is necessary where it is anticipated that traffic will be drawn from a number of existing routes onto a new or improved road. By means of this type of survey it is possible to estimate the number of drivers travelling on each of the existing routes who will choose to use the new road in future.

The O–D survey obtains, in addition to a straightforward count of vehicles on each road, further information concerning the place of origin and destination of each journey and the location of any intended intermediate stops within the survey area. The origin of the journey is in this instance the last fixed point of call prior to entering the area covered by the survey and the destination is the next point of call after leaving the area. These are not necessarily the same as, and must not be confused with, the origin and the destination of the overall journey.

Survey stations must be established on all the main roads entering and leaving the area concerned, so forming a cordon or screen line. Sites for these stations should be on straight, level sections of road with good visibility and, if vehicles are to be stopped, the carriageway should be sufficiently wide for some form of sampling to be used if necessary. There are a number of basic methods by which the required information may be obtained, namely:

1. By roadside interview.
2. By the use of prepaid postcards.
3. By attaching coloured tags or stickers to vehicles.
4. By observing vehicle registration numbers.
5. By selective interview at home or at the place of employment.

(a) Roadside interview

In this method, vehicles are stopped and the drivers are questioned as to the origin and destination of the journey and the location of proposed intermediate stops. The questions must be carefully worded without ambiguity and be kept to a minimum so that drivers are not unduly delayed. Additional questions regarding the purpose of the journey, for example, business or pleasure, may be asked. The interviewer enters these particulars on a specially printed form or card, and also notes other information such as the time of day, the direction of travel, the type of vehicle, and the number of passengers.[3]

To obtain the full co-operation of drivers in this and other methods which involve stopping vehicles, it is advisable to display prominent warning signs in advance of the survey station and it is often necessary to obtain the assistance of the police to control and direct traffic. This is particularly important when the traffic flow is so heavy that some kind of sampling procedure has to be introduced to avoid long delays.

The sampling technique may be carried out on either a numerical or a time basis, but in all cases the system should be prearranged and used consistently. One method is to stop every nth vehicle, whilst another is to stop all vehicles arriving within certain fixed time limits. Both methods have the disadvantage that queues may form during times of heavy flows, and a third method which involves stopping the next vehicle arriving after the completion of each successive interview may be preferred. In all cases at least two people are required—one to carry out the interviews and one to count and direct traffic, and often it may prove advisable to use more than one interviewer. Each enumerator can conduct 100 to 150 interviews per hour depending on the number of questions asked.

(b) Prepaid postcards

To reduce the delays which are necessarily introduced in the roadside interview method, an alternative system is to hand each driver a business-reply-type prepaid postcard, suitably numbered to indicate the survey station and the approximate time of day, as he enters the survey area. Questions similar to those asked by the interviewer are tabulated, and the driver is requested to answer these and also supply the additional information concerning the type of vehicle and number of passengers before returning the card by post to the survey headquarters.

In practice, this method often results in a poor response and is liable to lead to biased results since certain classes of the community are more likely to return the cards than are others.

(c) Coloured tags on vehicles

At the incoming survey station, a tag of distinctive colour is stuck on the windscreen of each vehicle entering the survey area; a different colour and shape being used at each point. Observers at the outgoing survey stations note the colour designation for each vehicle leaving the survey area, and, if desired, other observers at selected points within the area may be used to help trace the routes followed by the vehicles.

This method can be further extended to give information on journey times by giving each driver a time-stamped card bearing the survey station number at the point of entry and collecting these at the exit point, where the observer records the time and survey station number. This procedure requires each vehicle to be stopped twice, however

(d) Registration numbers

The three methods mentioned above all suffer from the disadvantage that vehicles have to be stopped to some extent. In addition, drivers are aware of the survey taking place and may for this reason avoid the survey area on purpose. An alternative method in which the registration numbers of vehicles passing the survey stations are noted avoids these disadvantages. Intermediate observers may be used to trace the paths of vehicles within the survey area, and journey times may be obtained by recording the times at which the vehicles pass the survey stations.

To work effectively in heavy flows, two observers are required, one reading the registration numbers of passing vehicles and the other noting them down. In this way about 300 vehicles per hour can be recorded. Alternatively, a single observer can record the information into a portable tape recorder. To save time, it is often sufficient to note only the last letter and the three figures of the registration number rather than the complete number. In very heavy flows some form of sampling technique previously agreed by all observers, such as noting only vehicles with registration numbers ending in the figure 3 or 7, may be employed.

The main disadvantage of this method is the amount of correlation and analysis of data which is involved. Methods (c) and (d) suffer from a further disadvantage as compared with (a) and (b) in that all observations must be taken during the same period, which requires a large team of trained observers. For the roadside interview and prepaid postcard methods, a smaller team of enumerators can occupy different survey stations in turn on successive days and this overcomes the difficulty of selecting an 'average' day for a one-day survey.

(e) Selective interview

In this method a random sample of population is interviewed either at home or at the place of employment to obtain information concerning details of all journeys made by the person or family concerned on a particular day or days. The method is especially suited to studying the traffic demands of large urban areas and, as in the case of the Greater London Traffic Survey, may be spread over many months.

The population sample may be determined from the electoral roll, in which case the interviews would take place at the homes of the families selected, or a number of places of employment may be chosen at random and the interviews conducted at work. The latter method has the advantage of including people living outside the immediate area of the town or city but takes no account of pleasure trips, such as for shopping and entertainment purposes.

2.5 *Analysis and presentation of data*

Having completed the survey, the records must then be analysed to give the required information. This analysis is most easily carried out by transferring the details from the survey sheets onto a set of punched cards, using one card per vehicle. These cards have usually 40 or 80 columns with 12 lines per column, and therefore a large number of separate items of information may be recorded on each card. The survey data must be coded so that, for example, each vehicle type, each origin zone, and each destination zone has a distinguishing number which can be punched in the appropriate card column(s). In some circumstances it is possible to record directly on cards using a portable punch or, alternatively, by making a pencil mark in the appropriate square and using a special machine which can sense the presence of the mark, the information can be reproduced on a punched card.

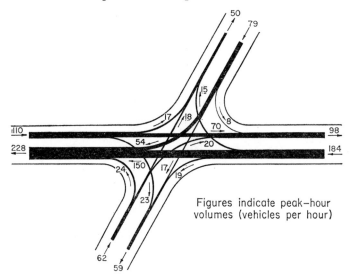

FIGURE 2.2 Flow band diagram for a four-way intersection

Once the data has been recorded, the punched cards can be processed and analysed by automatic machines which can sort, count, and tabulate the required information, operating at speeds of up to 2,000 cards per minute. The results of the survey may be shown as 'flow bands' on a map of the existing road or street network, the band widths being proportional to the hourly or daily volumes of traffic using each road (Figure 2.2).

Alternatively, if a wider area is being considered, the information may be represented on a 'desire line diagram'. Straight lines are drawn between each of the origin and destination zones using the flow band technique to depict the volume of traffic involved in each case. This method is particularly useful when considering the site for a new tunnel or bridge crossing for a river, since the diagram will show at a glance the most useful location. Such a study has been made with regard to the proposed second Mersey crossing (Figure 2.3).[4]

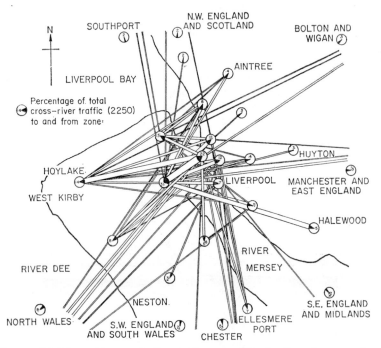

FIGURE 2.3 Merseyside conurbation traffic survey: Desire lines for cross-river vehicular traffic during average off-peak hour[4]

2.6 *Design volume*

Following the collection and analysis of the survey data, the design volume for each part of the road network under consideration must be chosen. Since the traffic volume on any road varies continually throughout the day (Figure 2.4), it is firstly necessary to decide upon a time interval for design purposes. This interval must be of sufficiently short duration for the flow to remain sensibly constant, otherwise the design volume determined from the average flow would be appreciably less than the peak flow during that period.

In general, for most roads, the average flow over a one-hour period is acceptable, although this may be too long in certain locations such as the approaches to large factories and industrial areas and in the business areas of city centres where the flows measured over a shorter period of time during the rush hour may be up to four times the average for that hour. In these circumstances, design on an hourly basis would result in severe congestion at the times of peak flow and would lead to unacceptable delays.

In addition to the volume of traffic actually measured at any particular count or survey, allowance must be made for an increase in traffic volume on account of:

(*a*) *The normal growth* in the number of licensed motor vehicles from year to year (Figure 1.4), which has resulted in an increase of 67% in vehicle mileage on trunk and classified roads in Great Britain over the years 1958–1965.[5]

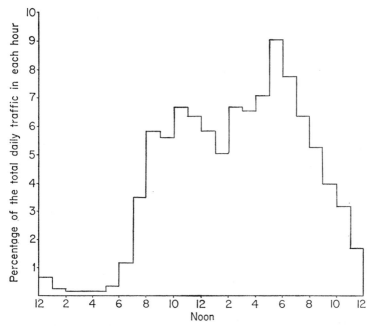

FIGURE 2.4 Typical daily traffic pattern for a weekday in summer on a rural road

The *Advisory Manual on Traffic Prediction for Rural Roads*[6] recommends that a design period of 15 years should normally be used in the planning of large schemes so as to provide sufficient capacity for future traffic growth, this period commencing from the first year in which the improvement is likely to be in use. Based on national forecasts, this provision will allow for a 63% increase of traffic volumes over the period 1970–1985.

(*b*) *The transference of vehicles* from other roads in the area to the road under consideration following the completion of the improvement work. This factor, as already mentioned, is the purpose of the O–D survey.

It has been found in America that the decision which a motorist makes with regard to choosing a certain route is essentially determined on a time-factor basis. Where two alternative routes, one of which is a freeway, each take the same journey time, then irrespective of the actual mileage involved approximately half the drivers will choose the freeway. When the freeway route reduces the journey time by 20%, then 75% of drivers will choose that way, and when the journey time is only 40% of that along the alternative route then 95% of drivers will use the quicker route (Figure 2.5).[7]

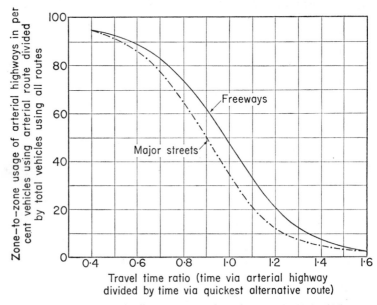

FIGURE 2.5 Traffic diversion curves for urban arterial highways[7]

(c) *The inducement or generation of additional traffic* as a result of the mprovement works, since it may be assumed that travelling time over specific distances will be reduced and therefore business interests in the area will be able to extend their radius of activities or else increase the number of daily trips. In addition, motorists will be tempted to travel further afield on pleasure trips. An example of the latter can be seen with the M.6 motorway through Lancashire which has now put the Lake District and the North Lancashire coast resorts within easy reach of Manchester and Merseyside. It is difficult to estimate the magnitude of the induced traffic component, but American experience suggests that it may increase (a) and (b) by as much as 30–50%, and this has been confirmed by measurements taken on British motorways.

(d) *The changes in traffic* arising out of alterations in land use and the development of land served by the road. Here again, it is difficult to set a precise figure for this factor, but consideration of the general development proposals for the area may give some indication with regard to future trends.

2.7 Design procedure

Having taken all these factors into account to assess the expected volumes of traffic using the road at some future date, there are basically two procedures for determining the volume for design purposes. Both methods assume that it would be uneconomical to provide sufficient capacity to meet the volumes occurring just once or twice a year, and therefore a lower volume is selected as the design volume. These methods are:

(a) Thirtieth highest hourly volume method[8]
If for any road, a graph is drawn showing the hourly traffic volumes against the number of hours during the year when that volume is reached or exceeded, then a curve similar to those shown in Figure 2.6 is obtained. It can be seen that the flow occurring for just one hour in the year is about twice the volume which is exceeded on a hundred hours during the year, and that there is a marked change of slope around the thirtieth highest hourly flow. From this change of slope, it is inferred

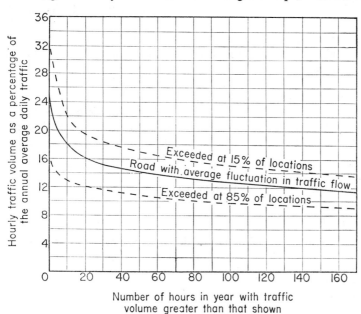

Number of hours in year with traffic
volume greater than that shown

FIGURE 2.6 Relation between peak hourly flows and annual average daily traffic volumes on rural highways (American data)

B*

that it would be uneconomical to provide capacity to suit traffic volumes occurring on less than thirty hours per year, but that little would be saved in constructional costs by providing capacity which would be exceeded on, say, fifty or a hundred hours during the year compared with thirty, when balanced against the increased congestion which this would entail. The design is thus based on the thirtieth highest hourly flow during the year, and to obtain this figure it is usual to measure or estimate the annual average daily traffic volume (A.A.D.T.) for the site concerned and take an appropriate percentage of this figure as indicated by the relation between the thirtieth highest hourly volume and the A.A.D.T. at another location with similar traffic characteristics.

(b) Ministry of Transport method
This method is based on the results of a count of traffic during one of the busiest weeks of the year, and unless other information is available, it is usually assumed that any week during the month of August is acceptable. The average daily flow (16-hour day) is deduced from these counts, as mentioned earlier in this chapter, and since measurements at various locations have shown that the peak hour flow during such a week is about 10% of the average daily flow for the week, then the design hourly volume can be obtained.

This hourly volume is likely to be exceeded only on a limited number of hours during the year, and although little data have been published to enable a comparison of the two design methods to be made, there is probably little difference in the design volumes given by the two approaches.

Unless there is reason to apply different growth, generation, and land use factors to each of the existing roads which will eventually feed traffic onto the road under consideration, the thirtieth highest hourly flow or 10% of the average daily flow can be deduced firstly for the existing flows and then corrected to take account of these factors.

SPEED SURVEYS

2.8 *Speed definitions*

Measurements of speed of an individual vehicle or the average speed of a number of vehicles can be expressed in three distinct ways:

1. Mean journey speed.
2. Mean running speed.
3. Instantaneous or spot speed.

The mean journey speed is often required for 'before-and-after studies' in which the economic value of a particular scheme is being considered, and is derived from measurements of journey time between two points a known distance apart, delays arising from traffic control measures and congestion being included in the journey time. The journey time may be measured by an observer moving in the traffic stream who adjusts the speed of his vehicle so that the number of overtaking vehicles is equal to the number overtaken.[9] Other methods of measuring journey time include noting the time of passing and the registration numbers of vehicles at two or more points, and, for intersection studies in urban areas, observing the vehicles from a high vantage point overlooking the intersection.

The mean running speed is deduced by a moving observer in the same manner as the mean journey speed, except that all periods of time when the vehicle is actually stationary are deducted from the total journey time. Delays caused by congestion and other factors which slow down the vehicle without actually stopping it will still be included, however. Care must therefore be taken when interpreting this measure of speed, since it is conceivable that a traffic control measure which results in vehicles moving continuously but slowly rather than by a stop-start motion may, in fact, produce a lowering of the mean running speed but an increase in the mean journey speed.

Instantaneous or spot speed refers to the speed of a vehicle at one particular instant of time and can be measured directly by various methods. The simplest methods are based on timing the vehicle over a short distance, often a multiple of 147 ft for easy conversion to miles per hour, using a pair of marks on the road surface or, more accurately to avoid parallax errors, with an enoscope (an optical arrangement with a large mirror to turn the observer's line of sight through 90°) and stop watch. Spot speed measurements can also be made using electronic, optical, or radar speedmeters or a time-lapse camera.[1]

Individual spot speed measurements are useful for design purposes, since it is desirable where possible to base the geometrical design of the road on a speed value which will only be exceeded by a small proportion of vehicles, say 10 or 15% of private cars. Care must be taken, however, to ensure that where existing speeds are measured these speeds are in fact those which are desired rather than those which are governed by gradients, limited overtaking opportunities, and other prevalent factors along the existing route.

2.9 Space–mean speed and time–mean speed

When stating the average speed of a number of vehicles, it is important to distinguish whether a time or a space basis has been used for measurement. The difference between the two can be illustrated by considering a set of vehicles spaced a uniform distance apart along an infinite length of road and all moving at the same speed V_1 together with a second set of vehicles superimposed on the first and also spaced uniformly but moving at a constant speed V_2. If speed measurements are made on all vehicles within a fixed length L of road at a particular instant of time then the average speed or *space–mean speed* V_S is given by:

$$V_S = \frac{mV_1 + nV_2}{m + n} \tag{2.1}$$

where there are m vehicles moving at speed V_1 and n vehicles at speed V_2 within this length at any given time.

Now suppose that instead of measuring the speed of all vehicles within the fixed length L, measurements are made on all vehicles passing a fixed point during a time interval t. There will be mtV_1/L vehicles in this time moving at speed V_1 and ntV_2/L vehicles moving at speed V_2. Therefore the average speed or *time–mean speed* V_T is given by:

$$V_T = \frac{V_1(mtV_1/L) + V_2(ntV_2/L)}{mtV_1/L + ntV_2/L} = \frac{mV_1^2 + nV_2^2}{mV_1 + nV_2} \tag{2.2}$$

In a specific example, if $m = 100$, $n = 50$, $V_1 = 30$ m.p.h. and $V_2 = 60$ m.p.h., then:

$$V_S = \frac{mV_1 + nV_2}{m + n} = \frac{100(30) + 50(60)}{100 + 50} = 40 \text{ m.p.h.}$$

$$V_T = \frac{mV_1^2 + nV_2^2}{mV_1 + nV_2} = \frac{100(30)^2 + 50(60)^2}{100(30) + 50(60)} = 45 \text{ m.p.h.}$$

In all practical cases of steady flow conditions involving vehicles travelling at different speeds, V_T will exceed V_S, since the faster moving vehicles which pass the measuring point during a fixed time interval will stretch over a greater length of road than the slower moving vehicles and therefore will give additional weight to the mean speed measurement.

Wardrop[10] has shown that in these circumstances $V_T = V_S + \sigma_S^2/V_S$, where σ_S is the standard deviation of the space distribution of speeds, and that V_T is usually 6–12% greater than V_S.

In all of the methods of speed measurement mentioned previously, the speeds of successive vehicles passing a fixed point are obtained, and therefore these average out to give V_T. If, however, the speeds of a number of vehicles are determined from a pair of aerial photographs taken a fixed time interval apart then these will give as the mean value V_S. Distinction between the two methods of measurement is therefore important, particularly where before-and-after studies are involved.

ROAD CAPACITY

2.10 *Types of road layout*

Following the determination of the design volume of traffic along a new section of road, the next stage in highway planning is to decide on the type of layout which will be required in order to accommodate this amount of traffic. The most usual forms of layout adopted in this country are:

1. Two-lane carriageways.
2. Three-lane carriageways.
3. Dual two-lane carriageways.
4. Dual three-lane carriageways.

In past years, a number of four-lane single carriageway roads have been constructed, but, because of the high accident rate of these roads compared with the dual two-lane carriageway layout, their construction is no longer recommended, and many are now being converted to dual carriageway layout.

Multi-lane carriageways do have one advantage over a dual carriageway layout in urban areas in that allowance may be made for the 'tidal flow' which occurs during the morning and evening rush hours by using the centre lanes for incoming vehicles in the morning and for outgoing traffic during the evening. This practice is common in many American cities and has also been used in the Mersey Tunnel and on certain London bridges in this country.

Three-lane single carriageway layouts are highly controversial, both in this country and abroad. The present Ministry of Transport policy is to construct these roads where the anticipated traffic volume exceeds the capacity of a two-lane layout but does not warrant dual carriageway construction, the argument in favour being that the accident rate on three-lane roads per million vehicle-miles is no greater than on two-lane roads. Whilst this is true of many three-lane roads which are operating with volumes below their design capacity, there is nevertheless a great danger of head-on collisions in the centre lane when the traffic volume exceeds the design capacity and opportunities for overtaking are consequently restricted. With the continual increase of traffic, more and more three-lane roads are becoming consistently overcrowded, and unless a watchful eye is kept on them with a view to conversion to dual carriageway layout before such a state of affairs is reached, then there appears to be a potential danger in adopting this form of layout.

Dual carriageway layouts have been used in all cases for motorway construction in this country, and although two-lane carriageways were provided on some of the earlier motorways, it now seems likely that the greater part of the motorway system will be constructed with three lanes in each direction on account of the greater capacity and safety which this provides.

2.11 Highway capacity studies

A number of theories, some with supporting experimental evidence, have been put forward in an attempt to determine the capacity of various forms of road layout, capacity being defined as the maximum number of vehicles per hour passing a fixed point. Some of these theories have been concerned with a single line of traffic moving under ideal or near-ideal conditions, and headway–speed or volume–concentration–speed relationships have been examined. Other work has been concerned with the overall capacity of particular forms of layout with traffic moving under more normal conditions, and from these studies speed–volume (or speed–flow) relationships have been derived.

2.12 Headway–speed relationships

Space headway is defined as the distance from the front of one vehicle to the front of the vehicle immediately preceding it, and consequently if a stream of vehicles is travelling at a speed V m.p.h. with a uniform space headway h_S ft, then the traffic volume per hour $Q = 5,280V/h_S$.

If it is assumed that a driver will so position his vehicle that, in the event of the driver ahead making an instantaneous emergency stop, he will be able to stop before striking the vehicle in front, then this headway can be expressed as the sum of three components. The first of these terms corresponds to the average vehicle length bumper to bumper, the second represents the distance travelled during the time that a driver realizes that the vehicle ahead has stopped and transfers his foot to the brake pedal, whilst the third term represents the actual braking distance.

The average reaction time for a number of drivers has been measured as 0·71 seconds,[11] and therefore for a speed V m.p.h. the reaction time distance is given by 1·04V ft.

In braking to a stop from an initial speed v ft/sec the distance covered is given by $v^2/2f$, where f is the deceleration. f is not a constant, but it is usual to assume a constant value corresponding to the mean overall deceleration, and Starks and Lister[12] have shown that $f = 0.63g$ for a car fitted with conventional drum brakes braking at speeds of up to 60 m.p.h. on a dry road surface, which gives a braking distance of 0·053V^2. Later work by Kemp[13] on a car fitted with disc brakes has shown that this relationship still generally holds good for speeds of up to 100 m.p.h.

If the average vehicle length is 20 ft then the safe headway is given by:

$$h_S = 20 + 1.04V + 0.053V^2 \tag{2.3}$$

and therefore:

$$Q = \frac{5,280V}{20 + 1\cdot04V + 0\cdot053V^2} \tag{2.4}$$

The maximum capacity given by this equation occurs for $V = 20$ m.p.h. and $Q_{max} = 1,700$ vehicles per hour.

To determine the minimum headways adopted by drivers at various speeds, the Road Research Laboratory[14] carried out observations of traffic moving under actual road conditions. Since there was some difficulty in deciding whether or not a particular driver was trying to maintain the minimum headway, these tests were supplemented by controlled experiments on a disused airfield. In these controlled tests, the drivers were instructed to maintain the minimum spacing which would normally be used when driving along a road, and measurements were taken at various speeds. The results of the controlled tests and the road measurements gave the relationship for the most frequent headway as

$$h_S = 17\cdot5 + 1\cdot17V + 0\cdot008V^2 \tag{2.5}$$

The maximum theoretical capacity obtained from this equation is 2,750 vehicles per hour at a speed of 47 m.p.h.

It can be seen that the two headway relationships given above are similar as regards the first two terms, but that the third term in the experimental equation is much smaller than its theoretical counterpart. This is no doubt the result of drivers assuming that their own vehicle had a braking efficiency as good as or only slightly worse than the preceding vehicle and knowing that as an added safety factor they could normally pull out and stop alongside the vehicle ahead. Such emergency action would not be possible in practice in times of heavy flows and, since the braking distances for individual vehicles differ greatly, it is obviously an unsatisfactory basis for design.

2.13 *Volume–concentration–speed relationships*

Concentration is defined as the number of vehicles per unit length of road, and is therefore the reciprocal of the mean space headway.

Volume, concentration, and speed are connected by the basic relationship

$$Q = KV \tag{2.6}$$

where Q is the volume (vehicles per hour), K the concentration (vehicles per mile), and V the speed (m.p.h.).

The form of the volume–concentration relationship must be as Figure 2.7, since $Q = 0$ for $K = 0$ and also for $K = K_J$ (jam concentration) when vehicles are packed so closely along the road that movement is impossible. Between these limits, the volume must have a maximum value Q_{max}.

The volume–concentration curve has been called the fundamental diagram of road traffic and much effort has been devoted to determining a mathematical function to describe this relationship. Suitable forms of the diagram, as a whole or in part, have been derived by a wide variety of methods; for example, by the application of car-following theories, by the analogy of a compressible fluid subject to shock waves, by the choice of appropriate mathematical functions satisfying the boundary conditions, or by empirical methods based on experimental data. To be applicable over the whole range from $K = 0$ to $K = K_J$, each of these relationships should satisfy the boundary conditions $Q = 0$, $V = V_M$ (mean free speed) for $K = 0$ and $Q = 0$, $V = 0$ for $K = K_J$. In addition, since the addition of a small volume of traffic to an empty road

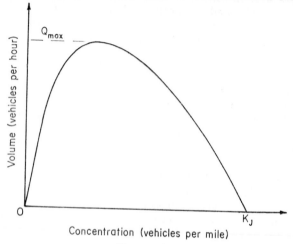

Concentration (vehicles per mile)

FIGURE 2.7

will not affect the mean free speed V_M, a fifth boundary condition, $dV/dK = 0$ at $K = 0$, should be fulfilled.

Haight[15] has critically examined a number of proposed mathematical relationships between volume, concentration, and speed and has shown that none of these functions entirely satisfied all these boundary conditions and was therefore acceptable over the whole range of K. In addition, he has pointed out that the diagram is characteristic of a particular place at a particular time with a particular vehicle composition, and it would be a mistake to assume that one form of relationship would be universally applicable.

A number of experimental relationships between volume and concentration have been derived from studies of traffic behaviour in road tunnels where lane changing is prohibited. In one such study carried out in the Holland Tunnel, New York, Edie and Foote[16] found that high traffic flows of 1,400 vehicles per hour or more in the fast lane were associated with speeds of around 20 m.p.h. and concentrations of about 70 vehicles per mile. By using speed-controlled eleven-car platoons travelling at 20–25 m.p.h. with New York Port Authority vehicles at the head and tail, it was found that the peak hour volume in this lane could be increased to about 1,800 vehicles per hour.

In some recent experiments with controlled traffic in a single lane at the Road Research Laboratory's research track, measurements were taken on vehicles travelling on circular paths at fixed concentrations and also on straight and circular paths at fixed speeds. The vehicles used were generally private cars or light vans, though medium goods vehicles were included in some of the tests. The tests indicated that jam concentration occurred with approximately 300 vehicles per mile and that flows of 1,800 vehicles per hour (light traffic) and 1,500 vehicles per hour (mixed traffic) were possible at speeds in the range 20–40 m.p.h.[17]

2.14 Speed–flow studies

Relationships between the mean running speed of vehicles and the flow have been given by Wardrop and Duff[18] for rural roads and for lengths of urban streets between major intersections (Figure 2.8). The diagram

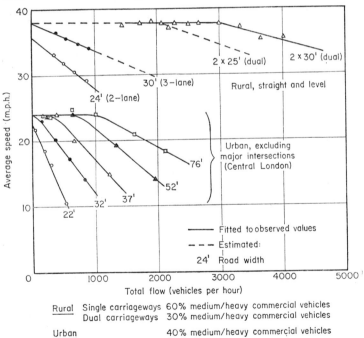

FIGURE 2.8 Relation between speed and flow on roads in Great Britain[18]

shows the general reduction in mean speed in urban areas compared with rural areas, and also the effect of carriageway width on the total flow.

The relationship for urban streets is given by the formula:[10]

$$V = \left(31 - \frac{Q + 430}{3(w - 6)}\right) \text{ or 24 m.p.h., whichever is the less} \quad (2.7)$$

where V is the mean running speed (m.p.h.), Q the total two-way volume (vehicles per hour), and w is the carriageway width (ft).

Equation 2.7 applies provided that w is at least 20 ft and the resulting speed is not less than 10 m.p.h., but is strictly valid only when the traffic conditions are similar to those experienced during the study.

2.15 Capacity and level of service

It is obvious from the foregoing sections that the volume of traffic which a road (or a single lane) will carry is largely dependent on the conditions imposed upon the traffic using the road, in so far as this volume can be greatly increased by forcing vehicles to adopt a particular uniform running speed and prohibiting overtaking. Hence it is necessary to define the meaning of the term *capacity* rather more precisely.

The *Highway Capacity Manual*[8] defines capacity as 'the maximum number of vehicles which has a reasonable expectation of passing over a given section of a lane or a roadway in one direction (or in both directions for a two-lane or a three-lane highway) during a given time period under prevailing roadway and traffic conditions'. Thus capacity represents a definite quantity—the maximum traffic volume which a given roadway can handle under a given set of conditions. When traffic volumes are below the capacity of the roadway then, in general, speeds are higher and a better *level of service* is provided.

Six levels of service, designated A–F from best to worst, are proposed in the *Manual* to identify the operating conditions existing under various combinations of speed and volume. These six levels cover the entire range of traffic conditions which may occur. Level of service A describes a condition of free flow with low volumes and high speeds which is attainable on freeways and other high-speed rural highways. At this level, operating speeds of over 60 m.p.h. are possible and the traffic volume is only about one-third of the capacity. (*Operating speed* is, by definition, the highest overall speed at which a driver can travel on a given highway under favourable weather conditions and under prevailing traffic conditions without at any time exceeding the safe speed as determined by the design speed on a section-by-section basis.)

Levels of service B, C, and D reflect increased volume/capacity ratios and progressive reductions of operating speed as an unstable flow condition represented by level of service E is approached. The latter level of service denotes conditions with the traffic volume at or near to the capacity of the highway and operating speed is of the order 30–35 m.p.h. Level of service F corresponds to the right-hand side of the volume-concentration curve shown in Figure 2.7 with a condition of forced flow at low speeds and high concentrations with volumes below the capacity of the road.

2.16 Design capacity for rural roads

For multi-lane highways, observations have shown that the greatest number of vehicles that can pass a point one behind the other in a single lane averages between 1,900 and 2,200 passenger cars per hour. This volume is attainable only in exceptional circumstances when there are at least two lanes exclusively for traffic in one direction, traffic is comprised entirely of passenger cars, lane widths and edge clearances are adequate, and there are no restrictive sight distances, gradients, or intersections. Under ideal conditions, the capacity of a multi-lane highway may thus be considered to be 2,000 passenger cars per hour per lane, but in practice such conditions are rarely fulfilled and a more realistic figure for capacity is 1,500 passenger cars per hour per lane. Similarly for two-lane single carriageways, the capacity under ideal conditions is 2,000 passenger cars per hour (total for both directions, regardless of distribution), but this again is rarely achieved in practice.

Suitable values for the design capacity of rural roads suggested by various authorities are given in Table 2.2. These figures are for the total two-way volumes in passenger cars per hour, except where otherwise indicated. The British figures allow for mixed traffic composition on the basis of equivalent passenger car units as given in Table 2.1 for

TABLE 2.2 *Design capacity for various types of rural roads* (*two-way total*)

Type of road	Roads in Rural Areas[19]	Highway Capacity Manual[8]
	(passenger cars per hour)	
Two-lane carriageway	900	900
Three-lane carriageway	1,500	1,500
Dual two-lane carriageway	3,300	⎫ 1,000 per lane in
		⎬ direction of
Dual three-lane carriageway	5,000	⎭ heavier flow

rural roads, whilst the American figures specifically apply to flows which exclude medium and heavy commercial vehicles but take account of mixed traffic by applying an appropriate correction factor; for example, 0·42–0·83, depending on the type of terrain, for a 20% commercial vehicle composition on multi-lane highways. In all cases, the figures are based on free-flowing conditions with adequate lane widths and assume the absence of restrictive features such as steep gradients, insufficient visibility distance, and appreciable cross-traffic.

The *Highway Capacity Manual* uses the term *service volume* in preference to design capacity, and the values shown in Table 2.2 are those corresponding to level of service B which allows operating speeds of 50 m.p.h. or more in typical rural conditions. On divided highways with full control of access somewhat greater volumes are possible when there are three or more lanes in each direction.

The Ministry of Transport design capacity figures are set out in the *Advisory Manual on the Layout of Roads in Rural Areas*[19] in terms of p.c.u.'s per 16-hour day (6 a.m.–10 p.m.) as follows:

Two-lane 24 ft carriageway: 9,000 p.c.u.'s per 16-hr day
Three-lane 33 ft carriageway: 15,000 p.c.u.'s per 16-hr day
Dual two-lane 24 ft carriageways: 33,000 p.c.u.'s per 16-hr day
Dual three-lane 36 ft carriageways: 50,000 p.c.u.'s per 16-hr day

These values have been arrived at by taking the maximum hourly capacities and multiplying by a factor of 10, since, as previously explained on page 28, the peak hour flow can be considered to be approximately 10% of the average daily flow during a 'busy week'. In the case of dual carriageways, a 60/40 directional split is assumed with a lane capacity of 1,000 p.c.u.'s per hour in the direction of the heavier traffic flow.

It can be seen from Table 2.2 that the revised Ministry of Transport design capacities are now in line with their American counterparts for rural highways, whereas those given in the earlier Memorandum No. 780[20] (now superseded) were appreciably lower. This reflects a more realistic appraisal of the effects of high standards of geometric design on highway capacity.

Discussions of road capacity have so far been restricted to uninterrupted flows, and are therefore applicable mainly to rural conditions and urban motorways. In practice the capacity of any urban road network is limited by the overall capacity of its intersections. The treatment of the capacity of intersections, whether controlled by traffic signals or uncontrolled (roundabout or priority flow), is a complex subject which is outside the scope of this book, and the reader is referred elsewhere for a full discussion of this topic.[8, 21, 22]

REFERENCES

1. MINISTRY OF TRANSPORT and SCOTTISH DEVELOPMENT DEPARTMENT, *Urban Traffic Engineering Techniques* (London: H.M.S.O., 1965)

2. TANNER, J. C. and SCOTT, J. R., '50-Point Traffic Census—the First 5 Years', *Department of Scientific and Industrial Research, Road Research Technical Paper No. 63* (London: H.M.S.O., 1962)
3. COBURN, T. M., 'The London–Birmingham Motorway, Traffic and Economics, Part I, Traffic Investigation', *Department of Scientific and Industrial Research, Road Research Technical Paper No. 46* (London: H.M.S.O., 1960, pp. 1–41)
4. STEERING COMMITTEE ON MERSEYSIDE TRAFFIC AND TRANSPORT, *Interim Reports of the Mersey River Crossing Committee and the Transport Committee* (Liverpool: Steering Committee on Merseyside Traffic and Transport, 1963)
5. BRITISH ROAD FEDERATION, *Basic Road Statistics, 1966* (London: British Road Federation, 1966)
6. MINISTRY OF TRANSPORT, SCOTTISH DEVELOPMENT DEPARTMENT, THE WELSH OFFICE, *Advisory Manual of Traffic Prediction for Rural Roads* (London: H.M.S.O., 1968)
7. AMERICAN ASSOCIATION OF STATE HIGHWAY OFFICIALS, *A Policy on Arterial Highways in Urban Areas* (Washington, D.C.: American Association of State Highway Officials, 1957, p. 111)
8. HIGHWAY RESEARCH BOARD, 'Highway Capacity Manual 1965', *Highway Research Board Special Report 87* (Washington, D.C.: National Academy of Sciences—National Research Council, 1965)
9. WARDROP, J. G. and CHARLESWORTH, G., 'A Method of Estimating Speed and Flow of Traffic from a Moving Vehicle', *Proc. Instn. civ. Engrs.* (London: vol. 3, Part II, 1954, pp. 158–71)
10. WARDROP, J. G., 'Some Theoretical Aspects of Road Traffic Research', *Proc. Instn. civ. Engrs.* (London: vol. 1, Part II, 1952, pp. 325–62)
11. DUFF, J. T., 'Standards of Design of Rural Roads', *Paper presented to the Institution of Civil Engineers Traffic Engineering Study Group*, 10th December, 1959 (Unpublished)
12. STARKS, H. J. H. and LISTER, R. D., 'Experimental Investigations on the Braking Performance of Motor Vehicles', *Proc. Instn. mech. Engrs., Automobile Division* (London: 1954–5, pp. 31–44)
13. KEMP, R. N., 'Stopping from 100 m.p.h.', *Automobile Engineer* (London: vol. 51, 1961, pp. 48–9)
14. SMEED, R. J. and BENNETT, G. T., 'Research on Road Safety and Traffic Flow', *Instn. civ. Engrs., Road Engineering Division Paper No. 29* (London: Instn. civ. Engrs., 1949)
15. HAIGHT, F. A., *Mathematical Theories of Traffic Flow* (New York: Academic Press, 1963, ch. 3, pp. 67–95)
16. EDIE, L. C. and FOOTE, R. S., 'Experiments on Single-Lane Flow in Tunnels', *Proc. Symposium on the Theory of Traffic Flow, Warren, Michigan, 1959* (Amsterdam: Elsevier, 1961, pp. 175–92)
17. WARDROP, J. G., 'Experimental Speed/Flow Relations in a Single Lane', *Proceedings of the Second International Symposium on the Theory of Traffic Flow, London, 1963* (Paris: The Organization for Economic Co-operation and Development, 1965, pp. 104–19)
18. WARDROP, J. G. and DUFF, J. T., 'Factors Affecting Road Capacity', *Proc. Third International Study Week in Traffic Engineering, Stresa, 1956*

(London: World Touring and Automobile Organisation (OTA), 1956, not consecutively paginated) also *The Surveyor* (London: vol. 115, 1956, pp. 819–22)

19. MINISTRY OF TRANSPORT, SCOTTISH DEVELOPMENT DEPARTMENT, THE WELSH OFFICE, *Advisory Manual on the Layout of Roads in Rural Areas* (London: H.M.S.O., 1968)

20. MINISTRY OF TRANSPORT, 'Memorandum on the Design of Roads in Rural Areas', *Ministry of Transport Memorandum No. 780* (London: H.M.S.O., 1961)

21. ROAD RESEARCH LABORATORY, *Research on Road Traffic* (London: H.M.S.O., 1965, p. 215)

22. DAVIES, E. (Editor), *Traffic Engineering Practice* (London: Spon, 1968 (2nd edition), p. 129)

3

Route Planning

- -

Once the need for a new road has been established by the methods outlined in the previous chapter, the precise location of the alignment must
be determined as quickly as possible so that negotiations can proceed
for the purchase and acquisition of any land required. It should be
noted that this phase of the procedure can be a prolonged one—
especially when the authority concerned is acting as agent and the proposals have to be sent backwards and forwards to obtain the views of
the authorizing authority—and construction work may not start for
perhaps three to five years.

THE RECONNAISSANCE SURVEY

3.1 *Survey objective*

The first step towards fixing the road alignment is to take an overal
look at the area concerned, select what appear to be possible routes
between the terminal points, and then closely examine each of these in
turn to decide which will be the most suitable, without actually determining the precise centre-line. This stage of the procedure is termed the
reconnaissance survey and the form which it takes depends to a great
extent on whether or not large-scale contoured maps of the area are
already available.

3.2 *Ground reconnaissance*

In Great Britain, as in most other developed countries, large-scale maps
will be readily obtainable and much of the reconnaissance work can be

carried out in advance of a visit to the site by examining the Ordnance Survey 2½ in to 1 mile or 6 in to 1 mile sheets. All are contoured at 100-ft vertical intervals, whilst some of the latter series show contours at 25-ft intervals. By inspecting these maps and drawing longitudinal sections along possible alignments, a number of alternative routes can be considered, all of which must satisfy the required engineering design standards for horizontal curve radii and gradients. In some cases there will be no restrictions, other than topographical ones, on the alignment between the two terminal points, whilst in other instances traffic considerations may dictate the route to some extent; for example, the road may be required to pass to a particular side of a certain town in order to intercept the heavy traffic flows to and from that direction.

Unless the engineer is familiar with the area concerned it is essential to supplement the office work with a 'walking' reconnaissance, the object of which is to note any development which has taken place subsequent to the Ordnance Survey sheets being issued and also to make a preliminary examination of subsoil conditions. In addition, the county planning department and any other local authorities concerned should be consulted in order to learn of proposals for future development which may affect the routes under consideration.

In comparing alternative alignments, it will be necessary to estimate the cost of each scheme, taking into account such factors as the subsoil conditions, drainage considerations, the amount of earthworks involved, the number of bridges and road intersections, the overall length of the proposed road and any diversions of existing roads, and the number of buildings to be demolished. Any difference in overall cost can then be weighed against other considerations such as the agricultural value of the land to be used, the effect of severance on farmland and on the rural community structure, and the relationship between the road and the surrounding landscape. From these deliberations, one particular route will normally emerge preferable to all others, but in a few cases lack of detailed knowledge of subsoil conditions and the consequent inability to estimate costs reliably may result in two or more alignments appearing equally feasible, in which case a more extensive site investigation will be required in order to decide between them.

Overseas, the reconnaissance survey follows a similar pattern except that it is not quite so easy in an area which has not previously been mapped. In a small scheme the most suitable route may be readily picked out by eye, but on a larger scale it is impossible to compare all the alternatives and ensure that the engineering requirements are satisfied simply by a visual examination of the area, and therefore some form of rough survey is needed to assist in this choice. In this survey it is only necessary to plot the positions of the more important topographical features—particularly any high ground, wide rivers, and areas of swamp and dense forest which would form a barrier to the road alignment—though in addition it may be found useful to note sources of roadmaking materials. Plane table or ground photographic methods of survey may be usefully employed, distances being measured by range-finder, elevations by aneroid barometer or Abney level, and bearings by prismatic compass.

3.3 Photographic reconnaissance

In many overseas countries where there are no suitable maps available, the only satisfactory method of carrying out the reconnaissance survey for a sizable scheme is by means of aerial photography. The photographs are normally taken with the axis of the camera perpendicular to the terrain and the aircraft flies along a series of parallel strips at a predetermined height and at constant speed taking photographs at fixed time intervals. The spacing of these strips and the timing sequence are so arranged that each photograph overlaps its neighbours by approximately 60% in the forward direction and 30% laterally in order to give full stereoscopic coverage of the area and allow for variations in the flight path of the aircraft and the effect of tilt.

For the reconnaissance survey, it is necessary to obtain block coverage of the entire area lying between the terminal points of the projected road and including all possible deviations and connecting routes. Since for a particular camera, the negative scale is related directly to the flying height of the aircraft, it follows that the number of photographs required to cover a given area decreases with the square of the flying height. To minimize expense at this early stage, a negative scale of 1 : 80,000 may be chosen, since this can now be achieved by an aircraft with a ceiling height of 23,000 ft using a camera with a super-wide-angle lens. Before the introduction of this type of lens, such a scale would have required a flying height of 40,000 ft and consequently a much more expensive jet aircraft. This negative scale would allow subsequent mapping to be carried out at a scale of say 1 : 25,000 with a contour interval of 25 ft.

In some circumstances it may be desirable to obtain a mosaic, or photoplan, of the area to assist in the early stages of the reconnaissance survey. A mosaic is made up from a set of 9-in square contact prints which may be simply 'laid-down' with approximate matching at the edges, or, if desired, some degree of control can be applied to the photographs to rectify for tilt of the aircraft and scale variations. It should be appreciated, however, that these 'controlled' mosaics are bound to include some displacement of features as a result of height distortion where there is considerable topographical relief, and must therefore not be regarded as being equivalent to an accurately plotted map.

The advantage of the mosaic at this stage over the conventional map produced from aerial photographs lies chiefly in the greater speed and lower cost at which it can be made available, in addition to which it is ideal for showing features such as existing development, surface vegetation and topography, cultivation boundaries, and drainage patterns. Experience has also shown that a trained interpreter with some knowledge of local conditions can build up a very useful picture of surface geology from aerial photographs by noting tonal changes, typical land-form characteristics, gully shapes and gradients, and the type of vegetation growth.

This type of information is particularly useful in overseas countries where it is important that a new road alignment is planned so that suitable roadmaking materials are available locally. For example, in Northern Borneo, the 'kerangas' soils, which are of special interest to the road engineer since they provide a good level foundation, support relatively thin and stunted vegetation compared with that covering the adjacent podzolic soils and can be readily distinguished from the latter on aerial photographs by an experienced interpreter.[1]

Normally black-and-white film is used for aerial photography, although colour film offers distinct advantages for identifying rock and mineral types and distinguishing different types of vegetation growth. There are, however, some disadvantages when using colour film; the chief being the increased cost of processing and the more critical exposure setting compared with panchromatic film.

THE PRELIMINARY SURVEY

3.4 Object of survey

Although the reconnaissance survey will have indicated the most suitable route for the road to follow, it will still be necessary to make a closer examination of the topographical features along this route in order to determine the best location for the centre-line, both in plan and elevation, within this relatively narrow strip. Since the contour interval on the 6-in Ordnance Survey maps is too wide for them to be used for this purpose, a more detailed survey using either ground or aerial methods must be employed. This survey is termed the *preliminary survey*.

Before the planning of this survey has advanced too far, it is a good idea to make contact with those authorities and individuals who will eventually be affected by the proposed scheme, and who may be intending to raise objections to the alignment at a later date. Such bodies include, where applicable, those responsible for the administration of national parks and for the preservation of ancient monuments and buildings of special architectural or historic interest, the Forestry Commission and the Ministry of Agriculture, various public undertakings such as the British Railways Board, the Central Electricity Generating Board, local river boards and catchment authorities, and publicly-sponsored bodies such as the Council for the Preservation of Rural England who are concerned with the landscaping aspects of the alignment. In many instances, minor adjustments can be made to the provisional alignment without impairing the layout or materially increasing the cost, and an exchange of views with those parties concerned may enable difficulties to be resolved and objections forestalled.

It is also advisable at this stage to consider the location of possible borrow pits and tips for waste material and ascertain the attitude of the owners. Although the ultimate responsibility for such matters rests with the contractor, any difficulties encountered will be reflected in his tender rates and hence will affect the overall cost of the work. On many major road schemes, the contractors often have to pay exorbitant rents for the use of land surplus to the actual work requirements, such as for offices, access points, and topsoil storage, and thought is now being given to buying land surplus to the requirements for this purpose.

3.5 Ground survey methods

This survey will usually be based on an open traverse in which angular measurements are made with a theodolite and distances are measured by steel banding or by one of the more modern self-reducing tacheometers; an overall accuracy of 1 in 3,000 being desirable. The traverse will follow as closely as possible the suggested alignment, but may have to diverge from this line in places where buildings, hedges, and other features obscure the lines of sight.

The width of the strip which it is necessary to survey depends to a large extent on the degree of flexibility in the proposed alignment at a particular point. In some instances, the road may have to pass through a gap between two buildings, in which case an overall width of 300 ft would be sufficient, whilst at other points it may be desirable to survey up to 400 ft either side of the provisional centre-line. In particular, where the new road crosses existing roads which may have to be re-aligned for some considerable distance either side of the intersection, the overall width of the survey strip may approach ¼ mile.

The amount of detail which has to be picked up in the ground survey can be greatly reduced by making use of existing survey sheets if these are available. In Great Britain, 1 : 2,500 O.S. sheets (uncontoured) have been produced for the whole country, excepting moorland and mountainous areas, in the County Sheet lines series and work is in hand on a revised series on National Grid sheet lines. In addition, built-up areas are being mapped to a 1 : 1,250 scale, also on National Grid sheet lines.

The general plan for a road scheme will normally be drawn to a 1 : 2,500 or 1 : 1,250 scale, with intersections detailed separately at 1 : 500, and, if necessary, these other scales can be obtained from the existing 1 : 2,500 sheets by photographic enlargement. Using such plans, the ground survey serves as a revision to these sheets and also enables contours to be established at 5-ft vertical intervals over the strip, together with spot levels along existing roads.

3.6 *Aerial survey methods*

As an alternative to the ground survey described above, aerial survey methods are now being used to an increasing extent. Air photography has the advantage that the survey can be carried out without the land-owners' knowledge, so avoiding controversy at a stage when the precise route is still uncertain, in addition to which trained staff can be released from survey duties and used elsewhere for design and supervisory work.

For these large-scale surveys, the aircraft flies at a predetermined height and at constant speed along a series of parallel strips taking vertical photographs at fixed time intervals as for the small-scale reconnaissance surveys mentioned previously. In the first place, a band of country of width sufficient to include any deviation from the provisional alignment is covered and 1 : 2,500 scale plans contoured at 5-ft intervals are prepared. Often in developed countries such as Great Britain this will amount only to a revision of existing survey plans with the addition of contours, and because of the limitations imposed on the choice of the alignment by features other than topographical ones a single strip coverage will be sufficient in many cases. Overseas, difficulties have sometimes arisen as a result of the surveyed strip being of insufficient width to include even the smaller culvert catchment areas, and in these circumstances it is desirable to specify as wide a coverage as economy will allow.

Once this survey has been studied and the alignment selected within narrow limits, new large-scale photographs can be taken from a flying height of approximately 1,500 ft and 1 : 500 plans contoured at 1- or 2-ft vertical intervals can be prepared for all intersections, bridges, and service areas. These large-scale plans can also be used to provide ground levels for earthwork calculations (see page 114) and an accuracy corresponding to a standard error of ± 4 in in plan and elevation is claimed for this work.

The flying height of the aircraft is determined by the scale of the map required and the contour interval, the type of camera and aircraft available, the nature of the terrain, and the type of plotting equipment to be used. There is often a conflict between these factors and a compromise has to be accepted. Table 3.1 gives an indication of flying heights for different scales of mapping and contour intervals using a modern camera with a 6-in focal length and first- or good second-order plotting equipment.[2] In some cases the plan scale is the controlling factor whilst in other instances the contour interval determines the flying height. It should always be appreciated, however, that specifying a larger scale or a closer contour interval than is actually required may lead to substantially increased costs.

Plotting of aerial surveys to scales of 1 : 500 and larger is now possible as a result of post-war developments in cameras and lenses which together with modern high-speed emulsions allow exposure times of

TABLE 3.1 *Flying heights for different scales and contour intervals*[2]

Scale of map	Vertical contour interval (ft)	Flying height (ft)
1:25,000	25	25,000
1:10,000	20	20,000
1:10,000	10	12,500
1:5,000	10	12,500
1:5,000	5	7,500
1:2,500	10	6,000
1:2,500	5	6,000
1:1,250	5	3,500
1:1,250	2	2,000
1:1,250	1	1,200
1:500	5 or 2	1,500
1:500	1	1,200

1/1,000 second to be used. This enables photography to be undertaken at very low flying heights of about 1,000–1,500 ft with no visible movement of the image during exposure. Furthermore, the introduction of new emulsions with high-resolution characteristics has greatly reduced the effects of haze and cloud and has allowed photographic work to be carried out over a much wider range of weather conditions, thus ensuring more economic use of the expensive equipment involved and consequently lower costs.

3.7 Plotting techniques

Aerial photogrammetry is undertaken by a number of specialist firms who carry out the dual tasks of obtaining the photographic negatives and producing from these, by means of a stereoscopic plotting machine, an accurately contoured plan. In these plotting machines, of which the Wild Autograph A8 is typical, successive pairs of photographs are held in their correct relative positions to reconstruct the original camera air base and are viewed stereoscopically in a binocular system. Each photograph is capable of rotation in three directions about its optical centre to correct for variations in swing (movement in the horizontal plane), tip (fore and aft movement), or tilt (lateral movement) during the aircraft's flight, these data being recorded on the film together with the time of the exposure, the altitude, and any other necessary information. When the two photographs are correctly oriented, the observer is provided with a three-dimensional view of the ground surface and any point can be plotted directly onto the survey plan at the required scale by means of a system of mechanical rods which pivot about points corresponding to the optical centres of the two camera positions.

Elevations are obtained from the three-dimensional model using a 'floating' reference mark which can be set at any desired height relative to the survey datum. When the mark is set at the same elevation as the ground surface it appears to the observer to rest in contact with the ground at this point, hence it is possible to trace out a contour line by keeping the reference mark in apparent contact with the ground surface.

Further description of stereo plotting machinery and photogrammetry theory is outside the scope of this book and reference should be made to a standard text for more detailed information.

3.8 *Ground control*

In all aerial surveys it is necessary to have a number of ground control points to enable the scale of the survey plan to be correctly established. When elevations are also required, spot levels on these control points serve to provide a series of datum points for contouring work. Ground control points may be established prior to the aerial survey, termed *pre-pointing*, or by *post-pointing* after the photographs have been examined, when use is made of a number of clearly defined marks such as corners of fence lines, road gullies, or manhole covers. The latter has many advantages and is preferred for normal practice since the control points can be located at suitable positions in relation to the photo strips. Where existing features are lacking then pre-pointing may have to be adopted, marks being made on the ground surface by removing turf to form a regular figure such as a cross or circle.

Distances between control points have in the past been measured by steel bands suspended in catenary, but this is nowadays being replaced by electronic methods of distance measurement using equipment such as the Geodimeter or the Tellurometer.[3] Differences in elevation between control points are normally determined by conventional levelling or by measuring the vertical angles along control lines.

Improved methods of aerial navigation are now allowing the number of ground control points to be greatly reduced, and for elevation control in medium- and small-scale mapping work abroad the Airborne Profile Recorder (A.P.R.), which consists of a precise radar altimeter and a highly sensitive hypsometer to record differences above or below a predetermined pressure surface, may be used to give a continuous profile along the aircraft flight path. A recent survey carried out in Africa using this equipment between terminal control points 80 miles apart showed a standard error of ± 4 ft for the A.P.R. heights when compared subsequently with ground levelling. This was well within the tolerance allowable at that stage of the work.[2]

3.9 Selection of centre-line

Having completed the preliminary survey by ground or aerial methods, the plans can then be studied to obtain the best location of the road centre-line within the surveyed strip. This process is largely one of trial and error, the provisional horizontal and vertical alignments being adjusted until a reasonable economy of earthworks has been obtained consistent with satisfying geometric design standards and landscaping requirements.

The final alignment, in particular the vertical profile, will be governed to a considerable extent by subsoil conditions and there is little point in attempting to achieve even an approximate balance of cut and fill before an investigation has been carried out to assess the nature and quality of the material to be excavated. However, unless there is reason to believe that existing ground conditions will be a major factor, it is better to fix the horizontal alignment with a reasonable degree of accuracy before starting the soil survey, and use the results chiefly to make adjustments to the profile. In some circumstances the soil survey may be delayed until the centre-line has been set out in the field, provided that minor adjustments of the alignment are still possible should unexpectedly bad ground be encountered.

THE SOIL SURVEY

3.10 Soil survey procedure

The soil survey involves an exploration of the soil conditions along the proposed road alignment by means of boreholes or trial pits to obtain samples which can then be examined and tested in the laboratory. The objects of the survey are to assess the suitability of the route for the proposed works and to enable an adequate and economic design to be prepared. In addition, the information provided by the survey may help to foresee constructional difficulties and assist the contractor in programming the sequence of operations.

Some preliminary information on soil conditions can be obtained by studying the Geological Survey maps of the area (both solid and drift) and by inspecting neighbouring quarries and existing cuttings.

Unpublished information relating to borehole records may be obtainable from the Geological Survey Office, whilst in mining areas the records of the National Coal Board should be consulted. Topographical features such as a marked change in vegetation may be an indication of a change in the underlying geological structure.

The water level in rivers and streams should be noted, although this should not be taken as a firm indication of the depth of the water table in the ground, since movements of ground water are largely independent of surface flow and the water table may be higher or lower than stream level depending on the nature of the strata.

Extended sites such as those for road schemes require a large number of relatively shallow borings to enable a section to be drawn indicating all the strata which will influence constructional work, including information on ground water conditions.

The spacing of boreholes is largely determined by financial considerations and the anticipated variability of the underlying soil in the horizontal direction. As a general guide, a spacing of 300 ft along the centre-line, or in the form of a grid where a wider strip is being investigated, is typical for the initial survey with additional borings superimposed between these in any sections warranting further investigation.

A post-hole auger, 4- or 5-in diameter, is normally used for shallow borings in soft soils. This hand tool is suitable for putting down holes to a depth of about 20 ft, using lining tubes if required, but for deeper borings and in harder materials, power-operated machines will be needed. Boreholes should generally be taken to a depth of 4 to 5 ft below existing ground level at points where the road is to be carried on an embankment, with an occasional deeper boring, but should continue to a depth 4 to 5 ft below the road formation level if the road is to be in cutting. Samples of soil should be taken from each strata encountered in the borehole and at vertical intervals not exceeding 5 ft in an apparently homogeneous material. These samples should be placed in airtight sample tins which should be carefully labelled to indicate the location of the borehole and the depth of the sample below the ground surface. A full description of sampling procedure and soil classification is given elsewhere.[4, 5, 6]

If there is no trace of water in the borehole then it may be backfilled at once, but otherwise the hole should be left for between 12 and 24 hours to allow the water to reach its final level, which should then be measured and noted on the boring record.

Trial pits may be preferred to boreholes in dry ground needing little support for exploration at shallow depths of up to 10 ft, particularly at important points such as bridge sites, since they enable the soil or rock to be exposed and examined *in situ*. The cost of trial pits increases rapidly with depth, however, especially in water-bearing ground, and is normally prohibitive at depths exceeding 20 ft.

3.11 Information from soil survey

The information obtained from the soil survey should be presented on a record drawing showing the location of the boreholes and trial pits in plan and giving a profile of the soil types encountered along the proposed centre-line of the road. An accompanying report can describe generally the topography and soil types, noting in detail any important features and setting out the principal recommendations for the design points under consideration.

The soil survey should provide information on the following points:

1. The suitability of the proposed alignment both horizontally and in profile. The alignment in plan should preferably avoid peat, soft clay, and waterlogged ground, and the vertical profile should be arranged so that, where possible, high embankments are avoided on poor foundation material and cuttings are reduced in depth where expensive rock excavation is entailed. Consideration should be given to placing the road on a low embankment where the water table is high, so avoiding the provision of extensive subsoil drainage.
2. The nature of the material to be handled. Excessive volumes of peat or rock will increase constructional costs, and any excavated material which can successfully be used to form embankments will reduce the volume of imported filling material. This information will also help in the selection of suitable side slopes for embankments and cuttings and will be of use to the contractor in deciding the types of excavation plant to be used (see page 153), and possibly in selecting sites for borrow pits.
3. The foundation conditions which will be encountered at bridge sites. This will influence the design of these structures as regards provision for settlement of the abutments.
4. The type and thickness of the road pavement, as indicated by C.B.R. tests (see page 185) taken in the laboratory from borehole samples or *in situ* at or near formation level.

In conclusion, it should be emphasized that the soil survey comprises only a small fraction of the total cost of the scheme and that failure to carry out a thorough investigation in the early stages of planning can result in heavy expenditure at a later date.

REFERENCES

1. CLARE, K. E. and BEAVEN, P. J., 'Roadmaking Materials in Northern Borneo', *Department of Scientific and Industrial Research, Road Research Technical Paper No. 68* (London: H.M.S.O., 1965)

c

2. MOTT, P. G., 'Aerial Methods of Surveying for Civil Engineering', *Proc. Instn. civ. Engrs.* (London: vol. 26, 1963, pp. 497–512)

3. SANDOVER, J. A. and BILL, R., 'Measurement of Distances by Radio Waves and its Application to Survey Problems', *Proc. Instn. civ. Engrs.* (London: vol. 24, 1963, pp. 11–28)

4. ROAD RESEARCH LABORATORY, 'Soil Survey Procedure', *Department of Scientific and Industrial Research, Road Research Technical Paper No. 15* (London: H.M.S.O., 1954 (2nd edition))

5. THE COUNCIL FOR CODES OF PRACTICE, 'Site Investigations', *British Standard Code of Practice CP2001: 1957* (London: British Standards Institution, 1957)

6. BRITISH STANDARDS INSTITUTION, 'Methods of Testing Soils for Civil Engineering Purposes', *B.S. 1377: 1961* (London: British Standards Institution, 1961)

4

Geometric Design of Roads
in Rural Areas

Geometric design of roads includes such features as cross-sectional lay-out, horizontal and vertical curvature, superelevation, gradients, visibility distances, and layout of intersections. These topics are examined in this chapter, apart from intersection design which is the subject of Chapter 5.

CROSS-SECTIONAL LAYOUT

4.1 Lane width

The four basic types of road layout have already been referred to in Chapter 2, namely:

Two-lane carriageways.
Three-lane carriageways.
Dual two-lane carriageways.
Dual three-lane carriageways.

Lane width has an important bearing on highway capacity,[1] and the standard now recommended in *Roads in Rural Areas*[2] for important classified roads is 12-ft wide lanes in all cases, except on three-lane single carriageways when an overall width of 33 ft should normally be used. Widths may be less in special circumstances but a minimum width of 18 ft should be provided on two-lane roads.

On sharp radius curves, extra lane width should be provided to allow for the increase in the effective width of commercial vehicles traversing these curves. For roads with 12-ft lanes, the carriageway should be

widened by 1 ft for each traffic lane on curves sharper than 500 f
radius. With lane widths less than 12 ft in the circumstances state
above, then each traffic lane width should be increased by 1 ft on curve
sharper than 1,500 ft radius, by 1 ft 6 in where the radius is less than
1,000 ft, and by 2 ft where the radius is less than 500 ft.

4.2 *Central reserve*

In the case of dual carriageway layouts, a wide central reserve o
median strip should be provided to separate the two carriageways an
so reduce the chance of a vehicle skidding across the reserve into th
face of oncoming traffic.

In theory, there is no reason why this central reserve should assum
a constant width, and many of the more pleasing alignments have bee
obtained with the carriageways set at different levels and following un
related paths, so making use of any topographical variation in leve
across the section and including features such as clumps of trees in th
central reserve. In practice, however, in this country, the agricultura
value of land is so great that most dual carriageway alignments hav
followed a rigid pattern with parallel carriageways set at the same leve
either side of a narrow central reserve, although the Oxford By-pas
(A40) is a notable exception.

Central reserves should preferably have a minimum overall width o
15 ft, but on sites where topographical, agricultural, or other con
siderations prevent this width from being obtained, then 10 ft shoul
be considered the minimum for new alignments and 4 ft where road
are being widened on an existing alignment. Many practising engineer
feel that these Ministry of Transport standards are too low, particularl
on high-speed motorway layouts, and it is interesting to note that th
comparable American standard[3] specifies a 36-ft wide median in fla
and rolling topography and at least 16 ft in urban and mountainou
areas. In any case, greater widths may be required at intersections t
provide shelter for turning vehicles and cross traffic, and also wher
subsequent widening of the carriageways is envisaged at some futur
date.

4.3 *Verges, footways, and cycle tracks*

A level verge should be provided alongside all classified roads in rura
areas, preferably having a minimum width of 12 ft of which the 4 f
adjacent to the carriageway is clear of footways, lighting standards, an
other obstacles which provide marginal friction and so reduce th
capacity of the road. The verge assists visibility on horizontal curve
and also provides a space onto which snow can be thrown.

Where required, footways and cycle tracks can be incorporated i
the verge, the former normally being necessary only in the vicinity o

villages and the latter where the average daily flow exceeds 1,000 cycles per 16-hour day or where a heavy peak flow is anticipated, as may be the case if schools or factories are sited nearby. Cycle tracks were commonly provided on many roads built in the 1930's, but recent changes in travelling habits have since led to them becoming obsolete and many have now vanished as a result of road-widening schemes. If provided, cycle tracks should be one-directional with an absolute minimum width of 6 ft, but normally 9 ft wide, and footways should be at least 5 ft wide. Grass verges separating the cycle track from the carriageway and footway should have minimum widths of 6 ft and 3 ft respectively, and a combined cycle track and footway should not be adopted.

1.4 Kerbs and shoulders

Kerbs are used to define the limits of the carriageway and contain the road construction and are particularly useful to drivers in fog and during hours of darkness. Kerbs may be vertical, splayed, or flush, and on through routes continuity and uniformity of practice is desirable. Standard sections of concrete kerbs are given in B.S. 340.[4]

Vertical kerbs are necessary only where a footway adjoins or is very close to the carriageway and at places where it would be dangerous for a vehicle to leave the carriageway. In most cases, a height of 4 in above the carriageway surface is sufficient for any raised kerb, whether splayed or vertical. Since all forms of raised kerb induce 'kerb shyness' to some extent and reduce the effective road width, flush kerbs are preferable wherever possible. These should provide sufficient contrast in colour and texture to define the edge of the carriageway and it will generally be advisable to harden the verge for a limited distance behind a flush kerb to prevent damage from rutting by vehicles over-running the kerb. Experimentally, flush kerbs have been formed with a corrugated or indented surface to warn drivers whose vehicles are straying from the carriageway.

On motorways and on other important classified roads where the breakdown of a vehicle on the carriageway would provide an unacceptable obstruction to traffic flow, a surfaced shoulder should be provided adjacent to the carriageway to allow drivers to make an emergency stop. These shoulders were originally constructed to a width of 8 ft with a grass surface, but a 10-ft paved shoulder is now considered necessary. The shoulder is separated from the carriageway by a 12-in wide flush marginal strip contrasting in colour with the road surface.

4.5 Camber and crossfall

Provision must be made for the run-off of surface water from the carriageway, shoulders, cycle tracks, footways, and verges by shaping the road cross-section to give the necessary falls into the channels, gullies, and ditches which together form the surface water drainage system. The carriageway may have a straight crossfall (usually 1 in 40 or 1 in 48 depending on the type of surfacing material) between the two channels or marginal strips, or alternatively, a cambered section falling in both directions from the road crown may be adopted.

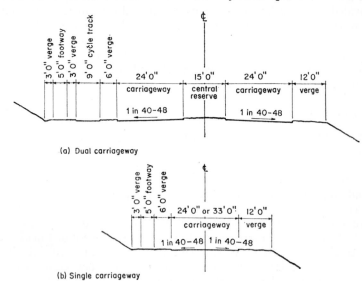

(a) Dual carriageway

(b) Single carriageway

FIGURE 4.1 Typical layouts of all-purpose rural roads

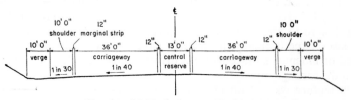

FIGURE 4.2 Typical motorway layout

A cambered section has a relatively flat portion over the centre of the road with steeper falls adjacent to the kerbs, and for this reason excessive camber may induce drivers to use the crown of the road in order to lessen the risk of skidding. Since the transverse surface gradient varies across a cambered section, crossfall is defined as the gradient of the line joining the crown of the road to the channel. A straight crossfall makes any future widening of the carriageway an easier task, but has the disadvantage that the surface run-off from two or three lanes is all taken to one side of the road.

Figures 4.1 and 4.2 show typical cross-sectional layouts of an all-purpose road and a motorway on tangent (straight) sections of the horizontal alignment.

HORIZONTAL ALIGNMENT

4.6 Design speed

The design speed is a speed selected for the purpose of correlating those features of a highway such as curvature, superelevation, and visibility distance upon which the safe operation of vehicles is dependent. It is the *highest* continuous speed (not the average speed) at which individual vehicles can travel with safety upon the highway when weather conditions are favourable, traffic density is low, and the design features of the highway are the governing factors for safety.

Roads in Rural Areas recommends that the design speed for new construction and for the improvement of existing trunk and classified roads should, where possible, be as follows:

1. Dual carriageways.   70 m.p.h.
2. All 33-ft single carriageways and trunk and principal roads with 24-ft single carriageways.   60 m.p.h.
3. Other roads with two-lane single carriageways.   40 or 50 m.p.h.

These design speeds may not always be justified on economic grounds in difficult country, and, in this case, lower values may have to be adopted. The above figures apply, of course, only to rural roads where there is no restrictive speed limit.

4.7 Superelevation

A vehicle of weight W travelling around a horizontal curve radius R ft, with a speed v ft/sec experiences an outward horizontal centrifugal force Wv^2/gR, where g is the acceleration due to gravity (ft/sec²). If the vehicle speed is expressed as V m.p.h., then the outward force is

$$\frac{W(88V/60)^2}{gR} = \frac{WV^2}{15R} \text{ (approximately)} \quad = \frac{WV^2}{127.2R} \quad \text{where } V \text{ is in km/h}$$

When the road surface is banked at an angle x to the horizontal (Figure 4.3), the resultant force parallel to the road surface is

$$\frac{WV^2}{15R} \cos x - W \sin x$$

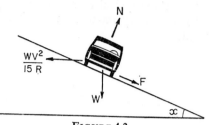

FIGURE 4.3

Provided that no slipping takes place, this force is balanced by the frictional force F between the tyres and the road surface.

It is evident from the above expression that for a given curve with R and x fixed there is a particular speed $V = \bar{V}$ for which $F = 0$. $\bar{V}$ is given by

$$\frac{W\bar{V}^2}{15R} \cos x - W \sin x = 0$$

i.e.
$$\bar{V} = \sqrt{(15R \tan x)} \tag{4.1}$$

$\bar{V}$ is termed the *self-steering speed* (or 'hands-off' speed) for the curve.

For a curve of fixed radius R ft, the amount of superelevation, represented by the angle x, can be varied within practical limits to make the self-steering speed correspond with any pre-desired value. By making $\tan x = V_D^2/15R$, the self-steering speed could be equated to the design speed V_D m.p.h., but since for operational purposes it is more desirable that the self-steering speed should correspond to the average speed of vehicles travelling along the road rather than the maximum or design speed, current practice recommends that superelevation be provided such that

$$\tan x = V_D^2/37R \tag{4.2}$$

within the limits of maximum superelevation 1 in $14\frac{1}{2}$ and minimum superelevation equal to the normal crossfall for the road surface.

For such curves, the self-steering speed is given by

$$\bar{V} = \sqrt{(15R \tan x)} = \sqrt{(15R \times V_D^2/37R)} = 0.64 V_D$$

and hence for a dual carriageway layout with a design speed $V_D = 70$ m.p.h., the self-steering speed on superelevated curves will be 45 m.p.h., which is approximately the average speed for vehicles on this type of layout.

The maximum superelevation of 1 in $14\frac{1}{2}$ in this country is introduced to reduce the chances of slow-moving vehicles sliding sideways on an icy road surface or overturning when carrying exceptionally high loads. Many other countries allow a slightly greater superelevated angle to be used, particularly when snow and ice conditions are not prevalent, and in these circumstances a maximum superelevation rate of up to 0.12 ft per foot is common.

Roads in Rural Areas recommends that adverse camber and crossfall should be eliminated on all curves of radius less than four times the desirable minimum curve radius given in Table 4.1, and for aesthetic reasons this same treatment is sometimes applied on long curves of greater radii.

4.8 Minimum curve radius

All vehicles travelling at a speed in excess of the self-steering speed for a particular curve experience an outward force parallel to the road surface as given by

$$F = \frac{WV^2}{15R} \cos x - W \sin x \qquad (4.3)$$

The force normal to the road surface is

$$N = \frac{WV^2}{15R} \sin x + W \cos x \qquad (4.4)$$

To prevent the vehicles from sliding sideways, the ratio F/N must not exceed the coefficient of friction μ between the tyres and the road surface.

For design purposes, the critical value of F/N will be that for vehicles travelling at the design speed V_D m.p.h., and therefore

$$\frac{(WV_D^2/15R) \cos x - W \sin x}{(WV_D^2/15R) \sin x + W \cos x} \not> \mu$$

i.e. $$\frac{V_D^2/15R - \tan x}{(V_D^2/15R) \tan x + 1} \not> \mu$$

Since tan x has a maximum value of 0·07 (equivalent to a super-elevation of 1 in 14½) and, as will be shown later, $V_D^2/15R$ cannot exceed 0·22, the denominator can be taken as unity and the condition to be satisfied is that $V_D^2/15R - \tan x \not> \mu$.

μ is termed the *sideways force coefficient* or *cornering factor* and is dependent on the type and state of the road surface, the condition of the vehicle tyres, and the vehicle speed.

Values of μ have been determined for various surfacing materials by the Road Research Laboratory using specially adapted vehicles.[5] The earlier measurements were made with a motor cycle and sidecar combination in which the sidecar wheel could be set at an angle to the normal position so that forward movement of the vehicle produced a combination of rolling and sliding motion on this wheel. Forces acting on the wheel were measured by dynamometers and values of μ were calculated for a series of trial runs made at various speeds up to 30 m.p.h. along sections of road surfaced with different materials. Some of these surfacings were newly-laid, whilst others had become smooth and polished after several years' use.

c*

The tests showed that all hard-surfaced roads had a uniformly high skidding resistance when dry, but, when wet, slipperiness was caused by the lubricating effect of the film of water between the tyre and the road surface. The degree of slipperiness varied widely between different surfacing materials and in all cases became more evident as speed increased (Figure 4.4). Throughout the tests, smooth tyres were used so as to reproduce the worst possible combination of conditions and also eliminate the effect of changes in performance resulting from wear of the tyre tread.

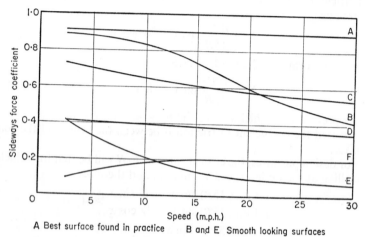

A Best surface found in practice   B and E Smooth looking surfaces

C and D Rough coarse-textured surfaces   F An ice covered surface

FIGURE 4.4 Typical relations between sideways force coefficient and speed for wet surfaces

In more recent tests, the motor cycle unit has been replaced by a test car which has the measuring wheel set within the car body, and a continuous record of the skidding resistance of the surface under test can be obtained at speeds up to 50 m.p.h.

Roads in Rural Areas recommends that R and x be chosen such that

$$V_D^2/15R - \tan x \ngtr 0.15 \tag{4.5}$$

This is the same as accepting a minimum value $\mu = 0.15$. From Figure 4.4, this would seem reasonable for most surfacing materials, although it should be noted that this value may not be achieved on smooth polished wet surfaces with a vehicle having worn tyres and travelling at a high speed, nor on ice-covered surfaces at quite low speeds.

It is also relevant to note that the frictional force can be equated to the lateral acceleration parallel to the road surface α by the relationship $F = \alpha W/g$. Leeming and Black[6] have termed the ratio F/W the *lateral ratio* and have suggested from observations that a lateral ratio not exceeding 0·15 provides a reasonable standard of comfort for passengers in vehicles travelling around the curve.

From equation 4.3, at the design speed,

$$\frac{F}{W} = \frac{V_D{}^2}{15R} \cos x - \sin x \not> 0.15$$

Since x is small, this is virtually the same requirement as equation 4.5 above.

As already stated, $\tan x$ has a maximum value of 0·07 corresponding to a superelevation of 1 in $14\frac{1}{2}$. Hence $V_D{}^2/15R$ should not exceed 0·22, and thus for a particular design speed there is a minimum curve radius given by the relationship $R_{min} = 0.3V_D{}^2$ (Table 4.1).

TABLE 4.1 *Minimum curve radii for various design speeds*[2]

Design speed V_D (m.p.h.)	Minimum curve radius (ft)	
	Absolute minimum with superelevation 1 in $14\frac{1}{2}$ R_{min}	Desirable minimum with superelevation 1 in 21 R_D
70	1,500	2,800
60	1,100	2,100
50	750	1,450
40	500	900

In addition to these absolute minimum values, the advisory manual gives a set of desirable minimum radii corresponding to a ratio $F/N = 0.07$ and so providing a greater factor of safety against sideways sliding. In this case, the superelevated angle is not at its maximum value and is therefore given by $\tan x = V_D{}^2/37R$.

Hence
$$\frac{V_D{}^2}{15R} - \tan x = \frac{V_D{}^2}{15R} - \frac{V_D{}^2}{37R} = 0.07$$

i.e.
$$R_D = 0.57V_D{}^2$$

At this radius,
$$\tan x = V_D{}^2/37R_D = 1/21.$$

4.9 Transition curves

The change in direction of a vehicle from a straight path on the tangent section of the alignment to a curved one on the circular arc cannot be made instantaneously, since the driver has to alter the position of the steering wheel between the two sections. Normally the steering wheel movement is gradual so as to avoid abrupt changes in radial acceleration which can cause discomfort to passengers, and during this time the vehicle is steered along a transition curve which has a radius decreasing from infinity on the tangent to a fixed value on the circular arc.

If the road layout is in the form of circular arcs leading directly from and into the tangents, then the vehicle is bound to steer a path in which the distance from the kerb or marginal strip varies. So as to enable the driver to maintain a constant distance from the kerb line, the road alignment may include transition sections between the tangents and the circular arcs. The use of a transition curve improves the appearance of the road alignment in addition to which the transition section provides a convenient means of attaining full superelevation before the commencement of the circular arc.

Roads in Rural Areas recommends that transition curves be used where the radius of the circular arc is less than the value given in Table 4.2 according to the design speed.

TABLE 4.2 *Limiting radii for use of transition curves*[2]

Design speed (m.p.h.)	Transition curves to be provided with curves of radius less than (ft)
70	5,000
60	4,500
50	4,000
40	2,000

4.10 *Form of transition curve*

The radial acceleration experienced by a vehicle travelling at v ft/sec changes from zero on the tangent to v^2/R on the circular arc. It is suggested that the form of transition curve be such that the rate of change of radial acceleration is constant.

For a transition curve length L_s, then the change of radial acceleration per unit length is v^2/RL_s and at any point distance l from the start of the transition the radial acceleration is v^2l/RL_s. Now if the instantaneous radius of curvature at this point is r, then the radial acceleration is v^2/r;

i.e.

$$\frac{v^2l}{RL_s} = \frac{v^2}{r}$$

or the form of the transition curve is given by

$$\frac{1}{r} = \frac{l}{RL_s} \qquad (4.6)$$

This curve is known as a *transition spiral* or *clothoid*.

Other curves in which the above condition is approximately fulfilled are the cubic parabola and the lemniscate and these are sometimes used in setting out calculations (see page 100).

4.11 Transition curve design

From time to time various formulae have been proposed by which the length of the transition curve can be deduced. Some of the earliest work on the subject was carried out on unsuperelevated railway curves by Shortt[7] who concluded from his observations that, for the comfort of passengers, the length of transition curve should be such as to limit the rate of change of radial acceleration to a value not greater than 1 ft/sec³.

Since the total change of radial acceleration is v^2/R, and the time taken to traverse the transition curve is L_s/v, then the rate of change of radial acceleration is a constant C given by

$$C = \frac{v^2/R}{L_s/v} = \frac{v^3}{RL_s}$$

Hence
$$L_s = \frac{v^3}{CR} = \frac{3 \cdot 15 V_D{}^3}{CR} \qquad (4.7)$$

where V_D is the design speed (m.p.h.).

Using Shortt's suggested value, $C = 1$, $L_s = 3 \cdot 15 V_D{}^3/R$.

For highway transition curves, a value $C = 2$ has sometimes been adopted since the former tends to give excessively long transitions.

Smirnoff[8] has given a modified version of Shortt's formula:

$$L_s = \frac{3 \cdot 15 V_D}{Q} \left(\frac{V_D{}^2}{R} - 15 \tan x \right) \qquad (4.8)$$

where Q is the rate of change of lateral acceleration and x the angle of superelevation.

This formula takes account of the reduction in sideways force obtained by superelevating the circular arc, and replaces the rate of change of radial acceleration by the rate of change of lateral acceleration which is measured parallel to the road surface. Q is again limited to a value between 1 and 2 ft/sec³ but, because of the allowance for superelevation, a shorter transition length is obtained.

A number of highway engineers have questioned the application of Shortt's work to highway design in the absence of supporting experimental data and, for this reason, Leeming and Black[6] carried out a large number of measurements on vehicles traversing horizontal curves. In these experiments, continuous readings were taken of lateral acceleration and passengers were asked to classify the ride as comfortable or otherwise. The measurements were taken on a number of curves at varying speeds, and from the graphical records produced the maximum lateral acceleration on the circular arc and its rate of change along the transitional path were easily deduced. Analysis of the results showed that comfort appeared to be related solely to the maximum value of lateral acceleration or lateral ratio (see page 60) experienced on the circular arc and not to its rate of change along the transition. This work therefore casts considerable doubt on the use of Shortt's formula, or its modified version, to calculate transition curve lengths.

Alternative methods of calculating the length of transition curves are based on the rate of attainment of superelevation, since the two factors are normally related, but before these can be examined it is necessary to consider the manner in which superelevation is applied. In any case, it should be appreciated that on highways, unlike railways, a driver can vary the path followed by his vehicle to a considerable extent without encroaching on the adjacent traffic lane or over-running the kerb and therefore the use of a precisely calculated transition length is unwarranted. Whilst there are considerable variations of opinion regarding the method of calculation, most authorities agree that the transition sections should be as short as possible and wholly transitional curves should be avoided.

4.12 *Attainment of superelevation*

Basically there are three methods, shown diagrammatically for a dual carriageway layout in Figure 4.5, by which superelevation may be applied:

1. By rotation of each carriageway about its centre-line.
2. By pivoting each carriageway about the edge adjacent to the central reserve.
3. By pivoting each carriageway about the edge which is on the inside of the curve.

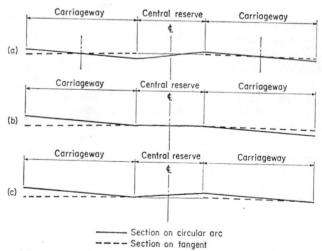

——— Section on circular arc
– – – – Section on tangent

FIGURE 4.5 Methods of applying superelevation on a dual carriageway layout

The first and second methods result in depressing the edge of the carriageway in places relative to the normal road gradient and may interfere with drainage provisions. On the other hand, the first and third methods may result in large level differences across the central reserve, and for this reason the second method is the one normally adopted in Great Britain where central reserves are usually narrow. On single carriageways, normal practice is to pivot about the inside edge of the carriageway (after removing adverse camber) or rotate about the centre-line.

Considering the level along the outer edge of the left-hand carriageway in Figure 4.5(b), the attainment of superelevation may be by a straight run-on with vertical curves at both ends or by a reverse vertical curve. An example of the latter is the curve

$$h = \frac{Hl^2}{L^2}(3 - 2l/L) \qquad \text{(Figure 4.6)}$$

where L is the overall length of the curve, H the overall rise of the outer edge of the carriageway relative to the inner edge, and h the rise at a point distance l from the start of the curve.

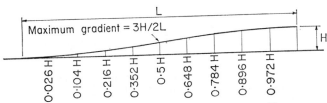

FIGURE 4.6 Typical superelevation run-on profile

The running-on of superelevation should take place over a sufficient length so as to be pleasing in appearance to the road user whilst giving a feeling of safety and comfort when the vehicle is being driven at the design speed. There are no completely rational methods of determining the required length and current practice is to take account of the rate of rotation of the carriageway. American standards[9] suggest a maximum slope difference between the carriageway edges as shown in Table 4.3,

TABLE 4.3 Lengths of superelevation run-on[9]

Design speed (m.p.h.)	30	40	50	60	70
Maximum relative slope in per cent gradient between edges of two-lane carriageway	1·33	1·14	1·00	0·89	0·80
Minimum length of run-on (ft)	100	125	150	175	200

subject to minimum lengths which correspond approximately to the distance travelled in two seconds at the design speed. For three-lane highways, the length of run-on should be at least 1·2 times that for a two-lane highway.

Cram[10] has proposed that the rate of change of gradient along the outer edge of the superelevation run-on profile should not exceed a value $m\%$ per 100 ft, and for a reverse circular curve profile has shown that this corresponds to a minimum length

$$L = \sqrt{(40,000H/m)} \qquad (4.9)$$

where H is the overall rise of the outer edge of the carriageway relative to the inner edge.

A maximum value $m = 1$ is suggested, whilst $m = 0·5$ and $0·25$ would be preferable on important trunk roads and motorways respectively.

On horizontal curves without transitions, adverse crossfall is eliminated on the tangent and the carriageway is rotated to give full superelevation at some point along the circular arc. Practice varies between

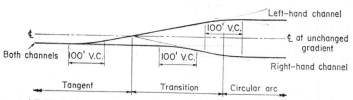

FIGURE 4.7 Typical superelevation run-on profile for a single carriageway road (American practice)

different authorities as to the amount of superelevation provided by the start of the circular arc, but it is usually about 80% of the full superelevation value.

On horizontal curves with transitions, the running-on of superelevation invariably takes place along the transition curve. Common British practice is to begin eliminating adverse crossfall at the start of the transition curve and provide full superelevation by the start of the circular arc, whilst in America adverse crossfall is usually eliminated before the start of the transition curve, as shown in Figure 4.7 for a section where superelevation is applied by rotation about the centre-line. Whichever method is adopted, the lengths of superelevation run-on and transition curve are obviously interrelated and, depending on the criteria adopted for design purposes, the transition curve length follows from the former or *vice versa*.

VISIBILITY ON HORIZONTAL CURVES

4.13 *Visibility restrictions on curvature*

A further restriction on the radius of horizontal curves may arise from considerations of visibility. This is particularly important on curves in deep cuttings, especially when sharp curvature to the left coincides with a falling gradient, although visibility may be restricted by other features such as buildings and trees.

On a horizontal curve radius R (Figure 4.8), the visibility distance s is given by

$$(s/2)^2 = (2R - d)d \qquad (4.10)$$

where d is the distance between the centre-line of the nearside lane and the obstruction limiting visibility, measured at the driver's eye level, which in Great Britain is now taken as 3 ft 6 in above the road surface.[2]

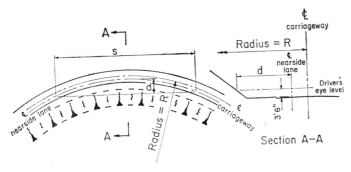

FIGURE 4.8

Since d is normally small in comparison with R, $s = \sqrt{(8Rd)}$, so that once the radius of the curve has been fixed, s can only be increased by increasing d. This may, however, not be possible in a partially built-up area, nor economical where extensive rock excavation would be required on the inside of a curve, and in such cases the alignment may have to be rerouted or a lower design speed accepted. The latter solution should be avoided if at all possible on safety considerations, particularly when the remainder of the alignment is laid out to encourage high speeds. In planning the highway layout, care must be taken to avoid artificial restrictions on visibility by badly-sited fence lines and boundary hedges or by tree planting schemes, and particular attention should be given to the siting and design of overbridges on sharp horizontal curves.

4.14 Minimum stopping visibility distance

As a minimum requirement, a driver must be able to see along the road for a sufficient distance so that when travelling at the design speed he is able to bring his vehicle to stop before striking a stationary vehicle or other obstacle which appears in the road ahead of him. This distance is known as the minimum stopping visibility distance and on dual carriageway alignments is the sole requirement for visibility.

This topic has already been discussed in Chapter 2 in connection with theoretical headway spacings of vehicles for capacity considerations. In these circumstances, average performance on a dry road surface was considered, corresponding to a driver's reaction time of 0·71 seconds and a vehicle deceleration of 0·63g (see page 32). Geometric design, however, must be based on extreme rather than average performance.

Reaction time, which is composed of perception time, foot-transfer time, and any time lag in the brake actuation system, varies within the range 0·25 to 2 seconds for the majority of drivers and hence the latter figure may be considered a satisfactory basis for geometric design. The braking performance of a vehicle decreases markedly on a wet road surface, particularly at high speeds, compared with that possible on a dry surface. The braking distance d ft is given by

$$d = v^2/2\mu g \qquad (4.11)$$

where v is the vehicle speed when the brakes are applied (ft/sec), μ the braking force coefficient, assumed constant, and g the acceleration due to gravity (ft/sec²).

Measurements have shown that the braking force coefficient is virtually identical with the sideways force coefficient for smooth tyres,[11] which again may be considered to represent the extreme condition for design. On this basis, an average braking force coefficient of $\mu = 0·3$ (corresponding to an average deceleration of 0·3g) may be used to calculate the braking distance on roads with a design speed up to 50 m.p.h., but a lower overall deceleration rate is required at higher speeds.

For a reaction time of 2 seconds and a mean deceleration of 0·3g, the minimum stopping distance s ft at a speed V m.p.h. is given by

$$s = 2·93V + 0·111V^2 \qquad (4.12)$$

TABLE 4.4 *Minimum stopping visibility distances*

Design speed (m.p.h.)	Minimum stopping visibility distance (ft)	
	Roads in Rural Areas[2]	A.A.S.H.O. geometric design[9]
70	950	600
60	650	475
50	425	350
40	300	275

Table 4.4 shows the recommendations for minimum stopping visibility distance given in *Roads in Rural Areas*. For comparison, the equivalent American standards for rural highways[9] are also shown. These are

less exacting than the British counterparts and the difference arises chiefly from using a speed value for wet surface conditions which is lower than the design speed (e.g. 59 m.p.h. for roads with a design speed of 70 m.p.h.). This, it is claimed, is justified by observations of vehicle speeds under such conditions.

4.15 Minimum overtaking visibility distance

On single carriageway roads, sufficient opportunities for safe overtaking should be provided over as great a proportion of the alignment as possible. This requires visibility distances over these sections in excess of those required for safe stopping.

The Road Research Laboratory has carried out observations on over-taking movements under controlled conditions and these have been described by Crawford.[12] These experiments showed that at speeds in the range 30–50 m.p.h., drivers were prepared to overtake a vehicle ahead when there was a time interval of 8 seconds or more before the next oncoming vehicle passed the overtaken vehicle. Thus for a driver to be able to overtake safely, the visibility distance along the road must be not less than the sum of the distances covered by the overtaken and the oncoming vehicles in this time interval, plus the initial distance be-tween the overtaken and the overtaking vehicles.

For design purposes, the oncoming vehicle must be considered to be travelling at the design speed for the road, although a slightly lower speed can be assumed for the overtaken vehicle. On this basis, the total visibility requirement is approximately equal to the distance covered by a vehicle travelling at the design speed in a time of 16 seconds, and the recommendations given in *Roads in Rural Areas* are derived accord-ingly (Table 4.5). No standard is given for 70 m.p.h. since it is considered

TABLE 4.5 *Minimum overtaking visibility distances*[2]

Design speed (m.p.h.)	Minimum overtaking visibility distance (ft)
60	1,400
50	1,200
40	950

that such a design speed is unsuitable for single carriageway roads. Many drivers are, of course, prepared to start overtaking when visibility is considerably less than the distances shown in the knowledge that should an oncoming vehicle appear during the early part of the manœuvre, they can always brake and fall back into line.

VERTICAL ALIGNMENT

4.16 Gradients

Steep gradients present the greatest barrier to free-flowing conditions in mixed traffic, since the speed difference between heavy goods vehicles and private cars is accentuated and more overtaking opportunities are required. From the vehicle operation viewpoint, gradients should be as flat as possible, and should ideally allow all vehicles to ascend in top gear and descend without the need to restrict speed by braking or by the use of a lower gear. Economical considerations of earthworks, however, normally necessitate steeper gradients.

Most private cars are capable of ascending a long sustained gradient of 1 in 15 at a speed of not less than 30 m.p.h., but with medium-powered goods vehicles, an approach speed of 40 m.p.h. will be reduced to less than 30 m.p.h. over a distance of 2,000 ft along a gradient of 1 in 50 and over a distance of 600 ft along a gradient of 1 in 20.[1] From such considerations, *Roads in Rural Areas* recommends that a gradient of 1 in 25 (4%) should generally be regarded as the maximum to be provided on a new road, although it is recognized that in hilly country a steeper gradient may have to be adopted for economic reasons. On motorways, gradients have been permitted to exceed 1 in 33 (3%) only exceptionally.[13]

Where steep gradients have to be adopted, particularly on two-lane single carriageway roads, an extra lane should be provided for ascending traffic wherever possible. An extra lane may also be justified on long gradients flatter than 1 in 25 where there is a large proportion of slow-moving traffic.

The braking distance of a vehicle is reduced on an uphill gradient and increased on a downhill gradient from $d = v^2/2\mu g$ (see page 68) to

$$d = v^2/2g(\mu \pm G) \qquad (4.13)$$

where G is the road gradient 1 in x expressed as the ratio $1/x$.

Thus the visibility requirements on a horizontal curve which coincides with a steep gradient may be adjusted to take account of this factor.

For surface water drainage purposes, a minimum longitudinal gradient of 1 in 250 is desirable, otherwise special provision will have to be made by forming the channels to alternate summits and valleys in order to secure adequate drainage.

4.17 Vertical curves

A vertical curve is used wherever two gradients intersect on the longitudinal profile of the road and, depending on the gradients concerned, will be either a summit (or crest) curve or a valley (or sag) curve. Although both types of curve are of the same form, they must be treated separately for design considerations, since in the former case the length of curve is normally determined by visibility requirements, whilst comfort of passengers and general appearance form the design criteria for valley curves.

The vertical curve is usually parabolic in shape and extends for an equal distance either side of the vertical intersection point. It is normal practice to denote the two intersecting gradients as grades $G_1\%$ and $G_2\%$ (i.e. gradients 1 in $100/G_1$ and 1 in $100/G_2$ respectively). A positive grade signifies a rising gradient and a negative grade a falling gradient in the direction of forward chainage.

4.18 Visibility considerations

For summit curves, the relationship between curve length L and visibility distance s is dependent on whether L is greater or less than s. In British practice, intervisibility is measured between two points 3 ft 6 in above the carriageway level and the formulae are:

$$L = s^2G/2,800 \text{ (where } L \geqslant s) \tag{4.14}$$

$$L = 2s - 2,800/G \text{ (where } L \leqslant s) \tag{4.15}$$

where G is the algebraic difference between the grades, i.e. $G = G_1 - G_2$.
A derivation of these formulae is given in Appendix I, page 271.

Given values of s and G, the required curve length L can be obtained by substituting in the appropriate formula above, or, alternatively, Figure 4.9 may be used. The visibility distances required for vertical curves are exactly the same as for horizontal curves, and wherever possible the greater distances allowing for safe overtaking should be provided on single carriageway roads (see Tables 4.4 and 4.5).

Recently revised American standards[14] now require vertical curve lengths calculated from minimum stopping sight distances to be based on intervisibility between the driver's eye level (assumed 3 ft 9 in) and an object 6 in high on the carriageway ahead, whilst those providing minimum overtaking sight distance are determined from intervisibility requirements between the driver's eye level and a point 4 ft 6 in above the carriageway, representing the minimum height of a vehicle.

There appears to be considerable merit in adopting an object height smaller than 3 ft 6 in for calculations involving minimum stopping visibility distances, since this increases the distance at which an approaching driver can see an obstacle in the road ahead such as merchandise which has fallen from a commercial vehicle or an injured cyclist or motor cyclist whose machine may have skidded. At the same time, there would be a greater measure of safety during hours of darkness when only the rear lights of a stationary vehicle are readily visible, although it may be argued that speeds would be lower under these conditions and stopping distances correspondingly shorter. With a smaller object height, curve lengths would have to be increased to provide the same visibility distances and earthworks would be accordingly greater.

Where visibility considerations indicate a very short or even no vertical curve, as is the case with a small algebraic difference in the

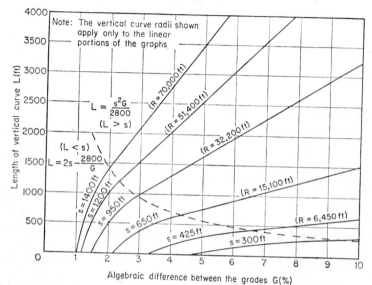

FIGURE 4.9 Relations between curve length, visibility distance, and the algebraic difference between the grades for summit vertical curves

grades (Figure 4.9), then summit curves should be designed from comfort and appearance considerations as for valley curves. On the other hand, if a valley curve is crossed by an overbridge then a check should be made to ensure that visibility requirements are satisfied between a point 6 ft above the road surface (eye level of truck driver) and an object 18 in high (tail light of vehicle).[9]

4.19 Minimum vertical curve radius

Any parabolic vertical curve approximates to a large radius circular arc of radius R ft, and the vertical acceleration experienced by passengers in a vehicle travelling at a speed V m.p.h. is equal to $2 \cdot 15 V^2 / R$ ft/sec². Cram[10] has suggested from experimental observation that this vertical acceleration should not exceed $1 \cdot 5$ ft/sec² for reasons of comfort, which means that for a particular design speed there is a minimum curve radius as given in Table 4.6. From these values the minimum length of vertical curve for any change of grade can be obtained from the relationship $R = 100L/G$. $R.\theta \doteq L$.

TABLE 4.6 Minimum vertical curve radii for comfort

Design speed (m.p.h.)	Minimum vertical curve radius (ft)
70	7,000
60	5,200
50	3,600
40	2,300

As indicated on Figure 4.9, curve radii for visibility requirements always exceed those derived from considerations of comfort, and some authorities prefer to adopt the same minimum radius for valley curves as used in summit curves in order to produce a smooth flowing alignment. For motorways, it is recommended that valley curves should be greater than 30,000 ft radius wherever possible and that summit curves should have a desirable minimum radius of 60,000 ft and a length in excess of 1,000 ft.[13] On other all-purpose roads, it is suggested that no vertical curve should ever be shorter than 200 ft long.

MISCELLANEOUS STANDARDS

4.20 Road markings

Road markings are used to indicate to drivers those sections of the road alignment where horizontal or vertical curvature reduces visibility below certain acceptable limits. Since new roads designed in accordance with the earlier recommendations of this chapter will normally have adequate visibility, except possibly where the requirements for safe overtaking have not been fulfilled for economic reasons, road markings are particularly applicable to existing alignments.

Guidance on markings is given in Chapter 5 of the *Traffic Signs Manual*.[15] In the system described there are three types of lines— compulsory or prohibitory lines, warning lines, and lane lines.

(a) *Compulsory lines* are continuous and always form part of a double line installation. They should be used where the visibility on horizontal and vertical curves is less than the following criteria; the visibility distances being measured between points 3 ft 9 in* above the road surface along the centre-line.

Speed (m.p.h.)	30	35	40	45	50	55	60
Visibility distance (ft)	200	250	300	350	425	525	650

The speed value used to ascertain the required visibility distance is not

* This value is likely to be amended (see page 67).

the design speed of the road but the actual speed of vehicles observed at the approach to that particular hazard. Since vehicle speeds will vary over a considerable range, the speed to be used is the 85 percentile speed (i.e. that not exceeded by 85% of drivers) on a dry road and under normal free-flow conditions. The same speed value should not be assumed to apply throughout a length of road and should be measured in each case, since it will depend largely on the nature of the alignment immediately preceding the approach.

The second line in a double line installation where visibility is better than the prohibitory criterion should be broken with a 1-yard mark and a 5-yard gap.

(b) *Warning lines* are single broken lines with the mark approximately twice as long as the gap (normally 6-yard mark, 3-yard gap in rural areas). These should be used where visibility is better than the prohibitory criteria given above, but less than the following:

Speed (m.p.h.)	30	35	40	45	50	55	60
Visibility distance (ft)	300	350	425	525	650	800	950

The speed values to be used are again the 85 percentile speeds.

Warning lines may be used between sections of double line marking but should never form part of a double line installation. In addition, warning lines should be used on the approaches at both sides of a road junction for a distance varying between 60 and 260 ft depending on vehicle speeds and the location.

(c) *Lane lines* are broken lines with a 1-yard mark and an 8-yard gap, and are installed where compulsory or warning lines are not required. Where a change from lane lines to compulsory lines has to be made, an intermediate section of warning lines would result in a too frequent change of the marking pattern, and it is recommended that arrows be used on the approaches to direct drivers towards the near side of the road.

Double line markings should not normally be used when the road width is less than 20 ft, on account of the width required by commercial and public service vehicles, and a single warning line should be used instead.

4.21 Lay-bys and stopping places

The provision of paved lay-bys to accommodate vehicles whose drivers wish to stop from time to time along the road should be regarded as an essential feature of any rural highway design. In addition to these lay-bys, sufficient space with suitably hardened parking areas should be provided off the carriageway at any places of particular scenic interest where drivers may be tempted to stop for a considerable time.

Where possible, lay-bys should be located alternately on either side of the road at approximately equal intervals. If lay-bys have to be sited in pairs, then they should be intervisible and staggered so that emerging vehicles draw away from each other. *Roads in Rural Areas* recommends that two lengths of lay-by per mile, each about 100 yards long, should be provided on each side of three-lane and dual carriageway roads. On two-lane single carriageway roads, shorter lay-bys, spaced at intervals of one mile upwards depending on traffic volume, will normally be sufficient.

Lay-bys should not be sited on the inside of a bend, nor in close proximity to a road junction, and should never be formed within the central reserve on a dual carriageway road. Advantage can sometimes be taken of short lengths of disused carriageway when an existing road is being realigned.

The width of a lay-by should normally be 10 to 12 ft with an absolute minimum width of 8 ft. The length should not be less than 100 ft, exclusive of any tapered entry and exit sections. Surfacing the lay-by with a material which contrasts in colour with the main carriageway is sometimes an advantage, but care should be taken to avoid using an inferior type of surfacing which is less attractive to drivers.

On motorways, continuous hard shoulders are provided to cater for emergency stopping of vehicles and a similar type of layout may be desirable on some heavily trafficked all-purpose roads, such as important trunk roads and motorway feeder routes. In addition to these shoulders, provision must also be made at regular intervals for routine stops by constructing service areas where refreshments and petrol may be obtained.

It is intended to provide service areas at approximately 12-mile intervals on the completed British motorway network, with parking, petrol, and other facilities available on both sides of the road so that right-turning movements across the opposing traffic stream are not necessary. Considerable thought and attention has been given to the siting and design of the service areas already in use, of which the overhead restaurant spanning the motorway at Charnock Richard, and the restaurant and roof terrace carried on a tower 100 ft above the motorway at Forton, both on the Lancashire section of the M.6, are of particular interest.

4.22 Bridge loadings and clearances

Although it is not intended that this book should attempt to deal with the structural design of bridges, it is considered relevant to geometric design that some mention should be made of the loadings and clearances adopted by the design engineer concerned with such structures.

Recommendations for highway bridge loadings are given in Memorandum No. 771.[16] The normal design loading is Type HA as defined in

B.S. 153: Part 3A: 1954,[17] although on motorway contracts, accommodation or occupation bridges giving farm access have been designed for half the Ministry standard. In addition to the standard loading, all bridges carrying motorways and trunk roads are checked for 45 units of Type HB loading (37½ units for Class I and Class II roads), and the central reserve and hard shoulders, which are continuous over the bridge, are designed to carry the same standard loading as the carriageways.

Footbridges are designed to carry a live load of 100 lb/sq ft of deck area, placed so as to produce maximum moment and shear values at any section, and should be checked for horizontal wind load as defined in B.S. 153.

The ruling dimension for bridges on the most recent three-lane sections of motorway is 119 ft; this applying to the width between parapets for bridges carrying the motorway and to the square distance to be spanned by overbridges. This allows a distance of 5 ft from the back of the hard shoulder in which to erect a safety fence in the former case or accommodate drainage and services in the latter. On other types of roads, a minimum distance of 4 ft should be provided between the edge of the carriageway and the face of the bridge abutment or parapet, though a somewhat greater distance will be necessary where there are footways or cycle tracks.

The required headroom for road traffic at bridges is 16 ft 6 in minimum over the full width of the carriageways and any shoulders, whilst for cyclist and pedestrian subways the recommended headroom is 7 ft 6 in and 7 ft 0 in respectively.[18]

ROAD LANDSCAPING

4.23 The road and the landscape

So far in this chapter, geometric design has been based largely on considerations of the safety and comfort of drivers and passengers in vehicles using the highway and little attention has been paid to the manner in which the road blends itself into the landscape. Horizontal and vertical alignments have been treated separately and no attempt has been made to correlate these two features. Spencer[19] has demonstrated that such lack of coordination can give an apparently kinked appearance to the road alignment and has shown that where horizontal and vertical curves occur at approximately the same chainage, a more pleasing sweeping alignment can be obtained by making coincident the points at which changes occur in both the horizontal and vertical planes.

Such coordination naturally requires the use of longer curves than would otherwise be necessary and the siting of curves in positions which are not necessarily the most economical locations. This increases the cost of the roadworks, as is evident from the comparative figures for a 28-mile length of the M.1 motorway in Northamptonshire which showed that earthworks would be increased by more than 40% if all mutually visible change points in the horizontal and vertical alignments were to be correlated as opposed to using minimum radii on both horizontal and vertical curves.[20] In this instance, a compromise solution in which coordination of curves was made a primary consideration only when the horizontal curve radius was less than 6,000 ft and the vertical curve radius less than 42,000 ft was preferred.

Other aspects of landscaping which help to blend the road into the surrounding countryside have already been mentioned in relation to the use of variable-width medians and the siting of the carriageways at different levels to suit the existing contours. Wherever possible, any natural features close to the road alignment such as groups of trees should be retained, and efforts should be made to avoid breaks in the skyline by forming the road on a curve when it cuts deeply through a ridge. Similarly, a road passing through a wood should also be set on a curve to preserve an unbroken background.

Horizontal and vertical curves should be as long as possible and curves in the same direction linked by a short straight should be avoided. Gently curving alignments are preferred to long, straight stretches of road on which the driver's senses may become numbed, although it should be added that straight sections of considerable length are in most cases not possible in this country.

One of the most criticized aspects of British motorways has been the sharp demarcation between the side slopes of cuttings and embankments and the existing ground, the rigid adherence to uniform side slopes largely irrespective of the height of the bank, and the siting of the curtilage fences at a fixed distance from the top of the cutting or the toe of the embankment. One distinguished landscape architect, Miss Sylvia Crowe, claims that greater attention to these details on the M.1 would have improved the appearance of the motorway enormously, and a comparison is made with newly constructed German autobahnen which have rounded side slopes flowing smoothly into the adjacent countryside.[21] Bridges, too, have a tremendous bearing on the overall appearance of the road and designs for all motorway bridges in Britain have been approved by the Royal Fine Art Commission.

4.24 Landscaping for the driver

The considerations examined above have been chiefly directed towards fitting the road into the landscape. A second factor which is equally important is the provision of features to interest the people using the road. On long stretches of high-speed road, the alignment should, if possible, be directed towards some distant object by which the driver can measure his progress. Topographical features such as a hill or mountain peak are ideally suited for this purpose, but use can be made of more local features such as a church spire, a tall building, or even a factory chimney.

Breaks in any roadside screening should be provided at frequent intervals, but in this connection, it should be remembered that whilst a 50-ft gap is suitable for the pedestrian or cyclist, a vehicle travelling at 70 m.p.h. will traverse this distance in less than half a second and a break of several hundred feet will be necessary to maintain the view for a length of time sufficient for it to be appreciated. Trees are better if placed in groups at intervals along the road rather than forming a continuous avenue with a distracting flicker.

In conclusion, it is worth noting that the art of road landscaping is receiving increasingly more attention in this country, and for a more complete discussion of many of the topics raised above, reference should be made to a recent publication by the British Road Federation.[22]

REFERENCES

1. HIGHWAY RESEARCH BOARD, 'Highway Capacity Manual 1965', *Highway Research Board Special Report 87* (Washington, D.C.: National Academy of Sciences—National Research Council, 1965)
2. MINISTRY OF TRANSPORT, SCOTTISH DEVELOPMENT DEPARTMENT, THE WELSH OFFICE, *Advisory Manual on the Layout of Roads in Rural Areas* (London: H.M.S.O., 1968).
3. AMERICAN ASSOCIATION OF STATE HIGHWAY OFFICIALS, *Geometric Design Standards for the National System of Interstate and Defense Highways* (Washington, D.C.: American Association of State Highway Officials, 1963)
4. BRITISH STANDARDS INSTITUTION, 'Pre-Cast Concrete Kerbs, Channels, Edgings and Quadrants', *B.S. 340: 1963* (London: British Standards Institution, 1963)
5. ROAD RESEARCH LABORATORY, *Research on Road Safety* (London: H.M.S.O., 1963, p. 515)
6. LEEMING, J. J. and BLACK, A. N., 'Road Curvature and Superelevation: a Final Report on Experiments on Comfort and Driving Practice', *Proc. Instn. munic. Engrs.* (London: vol. 76, 1949–50, pp. 522–39)
7. SHORTT, W. H., 'A Practical Method for the Improvement of Existing Railway Curves', *Min. Proc. Instn. civ. Engrs.* (London: vol. 176, 1908–9, pp. 97–118)
8. SMIRNOFF, M. V., 'Analytical Method of Determining the Length of Transition Spiral', *Trans. Amer. Soc. civ. Engrs.* (New York: vol. 116, 1951, pp. 155–85)

9. AMERICAN ASSOCIATION OF STATE HIGHWAY OFFICIALS, *A Policy on Geometric Design of Rural Highways* (Washington, D.C.: American Association of State Highway Officials, 1954)
10. CRAM, I. A., 'Standards for Design of Rural Roads', *J. Instn. Highw. Engrs.* (London: vol. 8, 1961, pp. 271–93)
11. BIRD, G. and MILLER, R. A., 'Studies in Road Friction—II. An Analysis of the Factors Affecting Measurement', *Department of Scientific and Industrial Research and Ministry of Transport, Road Research Technical Paper No. 2* (London: H.M.S.O., 1937)
12. CRAWFORD, A., 'The Overtaking Driver', *Ergonomics* (London: vol. 6, 1963, pp. 153–70)
13. SPENCER, W. H., 'Rural Motorway Design Standards for Current Motorways Plan', *Highway and Bridges and Engineering Works* (New Malden, Surrey: vol. 31, 4 December 1963, pp. 14–20)
14. AMERICAN ASSOCIATION OF STATE HIGHWAY OFFICIALS, *Geometric Design Standards for Highways other than Freeways* (Washington, D.C.: American Association of State Highway Officials, 1962)
15. MINISTRY OF TRANSPORT, SCOTTISH DEVELOPMENT DEPARTMENT and WELSH OFFICE, *Traffic Signs Manual, Chapter 5: Road Markings* (London: H.M.S.O., 1966)
16. MINISTRY OF TRANSPORT, 'Standard Highway Loadings', *Ministry of Transport Memorandum No. 771* (London: H.M.S.O., 1961)
17. BRITISH STANDARDS INSTITUTION, 'Girder Bridges. Part 3: Loads and Stresses. Section A: Loads', *B.S. 153: Part 3A: 1954* (London: British Standards Institution, 1954)
18. MINISTRY OF TRANSPORT, SCOTTISH DEVELOPMENT DEPARTMENT AND WELSH OFFICE, *Roads in Urban Areas* (London: H.M.S.O., 1966)
19. SPENCER, W. H., 'The Co-ordination of Horizontal Alignment of High-Speed Roads', *Instn. civ. Engrs., Road Engineering Division Paper No. 27* (London: Instn. civ. Engrs., 1948)
20. WILLIAMS, SIR OWEN and WILLIAMS, O. T., 'The London–Birmingham Motorway. Luton–Dunchurch: Design and Execution', *Proc. Instn. civ. Engrs.* (London: vol. 15, 1960, pp. 353–86)
21. CROWE, S., *The Landscape of Roads* (London: The Architectural Press, 1960, p. 93)
22. BRITISH ROAD FEDERATION, *Landscaping of Motorways Conference* (London: British Road Federation, 1963)

5

Layout of Road Junctions

- -

Junction layout is perhaps the most important aspect of geometric design, since the overall capacity of any road network is limited by the capacity of its various intersections. Failure to provide the correct type of layout at one particular location may result in congestion and delay to an extent which will impair the efficiency of the road system over a wide area.

5.1 *Types of intersections*

The aim of any junction layout is to provide for the safe movement of traffic, both vehicular and pedestrian, without undue delay and congestion. Various alternative layouts can be adopted and the ultimate choice will be governed by such factors as the nature and volume of the traffic using the junction, the availability of land, and the overall cost. Whatever form is adopted, it is essential that approaching drivers are made fully conversant with the nature of the layout by clear signposting well in advance of the intersection, and in many cases supplementary carriageway markings can be used to guide drivers into the desired paths.

In most road intersections, the crossing takes place at one level, or in American terminology *at grade*. The junction layout may then be arranged to give priority movement along one of the intersecting roads, using legally-enforcable 'Stop' or 'Give Way' signs if necessary, or, alternatively, if both roads carry a reasonably high volume of traffic, signal control or a rotary intersection may be required to avoid the extensive delays which would otherwise occur on the minor road.

When one or both of the roads are expected to carry a large volume of high-speed traffic, a grade separated intersection with the carriageways crossing at different levels is desirable. On such roads, access

80

points should be limited as much as possible and many minor roads carrying purely local traffic can be taken over or pass under the through traffic route without any connecting link. Junctions can then be spaced at 3- to 12-mile intervals in rural areas, but a closer spacing will be required in urban locations. Grade separated intersections at the junction of two motorways are often termed *interchanges*.

T-JUNCTIONS

This is the simplest and probably the most common type of road junction, and is distinguished from a Y-junction by the fact that the angle between the centre-lines of the intersecting roads lies between 75° and 105°.

5.2 Visibility distances

The first essential requirement of the junction layout is that the driver of a vehicle emerging from the minor road has a sufficient visibility distance along the major road in both directions so as to be able to make the turning movement and accelerate up to the speed of the through traffic stream in safety.

Observations of driver behaviour at road junctions have shown that whilst 50% of drivers will accept a gap in the main traffic stream of some 5 to 6 seconds, a few require a 12-second gap or even longer before making the turning or crossing movement. *Roads in Rural Areas*[1] recommends that visibility distances corresponding to the design speed of the road as shown in Table 5.1 should be provided. These

TABLE 5.1 *Minimum visibility distances at intersections*[1]

Design speed (m.p.h.)	Visibility distance (ft)
70	700
60	700
50	600
40	500

distances are approximately equal to an 8-second gap in the approaching stream of traffic at the design speed. This visibility should apply between points 3 ft 6 in above the road surface over the areas defined by:

1. A line 36 ft long along the centre-line of the minor road from the

continuation of the line of the nearer edge of the major road carriageway.

2. A line of length given in Table 5.1 measured both to the left and to the right along the nearer edge of the major road carriageway from its intersection with the centre-line of the minor road.

3. The straight lines joining the terminations of the above lines.

Unless it is obvious to a driver that he is approaching a major road, a 'Give Way' sign should be provided on the minor road.

5.3 Kerb radii and acceleration lanes

The second consideration of junction design is that the emerging vehicle should be able to merge into the through traffic stream as quickly as possible. This requires the use of a kerb radius not less than 35 ft, and preferably of the order of 60 ft, so that the left-turning movement can be carried out at a reasonable speed without the vehicle swinging across the main carriageway.[2] Similarly, a large radius kerb enables vehicles turning left into the minor road to do so without a drastic reduction in speed. Observations have shown that a comfortable cornering speed (in miles per hour) is approximately twice the square root of the kerb radius (in feet) for speeds up to about 35 m.p.h.

To facilitate these merging and diverging movements even further, acceleration and deceleration lanes should be provided wherever possible at junctions. Memorandum No. 575,[3] issued in 1943, suggested the use of 200-ft long acceleration and deceleration lanes tapering uniformly over their length from a maximum width of 8 ft, but observations at junctions with such lanes have shown that in practice they are used by less than 20% of drivers and should be at least twice this length to enable vehicles to reach the speed of through traffic.[4] Acceleration lanes 500 to 800 ft long (depending on the gradient) and 12 ft wide have been provided on the motorways, and detailed recommendations for intersections along all-purpose roads are given in Roads in Rural Areas.[1]

5.4 Single carriageway layout

A study of accidents at three-way junctions on single carriageway roads has shown that the relative accident rate is reduced by providing a fast oblique exit from the main road rather than requiring drivers to undertake a square turning movement.[5] However, to provide the driver emerging from the minor road and turning right with a view along the major road to his left, the layout should be such that this emerging manœuvre is not made at too oblique an angle.

These considerations, together with those outlined in the previous sections, lead to a typical layout for a T-junction on a 24-ft single carriageway road as shown in Figure 5.1. As a slight variation on this

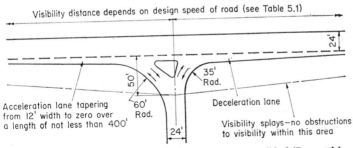

FIGURE 5.1 T-junction on 24-ft single carriageway: modified 'Bennett' layout

layout, Summerfield[4] has proposed that at a three-way junction the right turn from the minor road should be made into an acceleration bay on the far side of the major road, but this suggestion has received little support.

The layout shown in Figure 5.1 has yet to find favour with a large number of highway engineers who fear uncertainties on the part of drivers wishing to turn right off the major road into the minor road. As a result, a smaller, conventional, 'Keep Left' island is often preferred, or otherwise the island is omitted altogether. This view is in keeping with American practice which advocates channelization along he lines shown in Figure 5.2.[6]

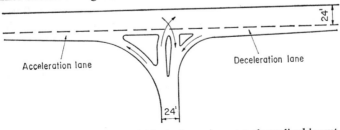

FIGURE 5.2 T-junction on 24-ft single carriageway: channelized layout

5.5 Dual carriageway layout

A T-junction on a high-speed dual carriageway road is potentially dangerous since vehicles turning right off the major road decelerate in the fast traffic lane. In addition, when several vehicles are turning right at the same time and are waiting for a gap in the oncoming traffic stream, the waiting space within the shelter of the central reserve will become filled and a queue will extend backwards into the fast through traffic lane. These difficulties can be overcome by locally widening the

D

central reserve to at least 30 ft and forming a deceleration lane 12 ft wide by some 300 ft long within the width of the reserve (Figure 5.3).

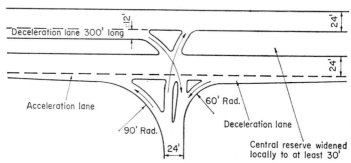

FIGURE 5.3 T-junction on dual carriageway

The widened central reserve at the same time provides waiting space for vehicles turning right into the major road.

On three-lane single carriageways, a similar hazard occurs with vehicles waiting to turn right into a minor road standing in the centre lane facing oncoming traffic. Because of the dangers of a head-on collision, it is advisable to introduce a short length of dual carriageway in the vicinity of the intersection and lay out the junction accordingly.

Such an arrangement has an added advantage when the traffic volume on the major road has reached the design capacity of 1,500 p.c.u. per hour (see page 37), since with a 30% commercial vehicle composition this corresponds to a two-way total of about 900 vehicles per hour or, on the average, one vehicle every four seconds. Although all vehicles travel in groups and approximate to a Poisson distribution as regards the rate of arrival at the junction, there would still be some difficulty for a driver emerging from the minor road and turning right in finding acceptable gaps coinciding in both traffic streams.

OTHER INTERSECTIONS AT GRADE

5.5 Y-junctions

The basic considerations of visibility, kerb radii, acceleration and deceleration lanes, and channelization apply equally to Y-junctions as to T-junctions, and use can be made of the oblique angle of the right-hand splay to provide for fast traffic movements round the left shoulder on a two-lane single carriageway junction (Figure 5.4). The only marked change in layout occurs with a left-hand splayed junction where the design should be such as to prevent drivers turning right into the major

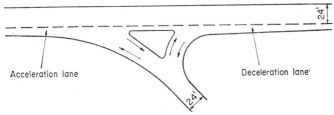

FIGURE 5.4 Right-hand splay Y-junction on 24-ft single carriageway

road from doing so at an oblique angle, and the carriageway adjacent
to the right shoulder should thus be one-directional (Figure 5.5).

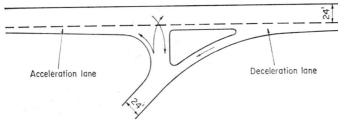

FIGURE 5.5 Left-hand splay Y-junction on 24-ft single carriageway

5.6 Four-way junctions

A straight cross-over layout for the minor road at a four-way junction
has the potential danger that a driver travelling along this road may
not be aware that he is approaching a major road on account of the unbroken alignment of the road ahead. For this reason, it is suggested
that a staggered crossing should be introduced with a minimum spacing
of 120 ft between the two approaches.[1] Each leg of the minor road
then forms a T- or Y-junction at its intersection with the major road
and can be laid out in accordance with the previous sections.

Studies of accident records at staggered crossroads on single carriageway roads have shown that a right–left stagger in which the minor road
vehicle turns firstly to the right and then to the left to continue the
route is inherently safer than a left–right stagger.[7] This is because the
latter involves in the first instance a left-turn movement which can be
made at a relatively high speed and which is followed almost immediately by rapid deceleration and possible stopping in the centre of the
road prior to making the right-turn movement. Vehicles turning to the
right are involved in the greatest proportion of accidents at three-way
junctions,[5] and the incidence is even greater in this case since following
and oncoming drivers receive little warning when the turning vehicle
has just emerged from a side road.

5.7 *Rotary intersections*

Where both roads are fairly heavily-trafficked, a junction with priority flow along one road may cause extensive hold-ups on the side road owing to the lack of acceptable gaps in the through traffic stream. The cheapest way of obtaining turning and crossing opportunities for the side stream traffic is to provide signal control, operating on either a

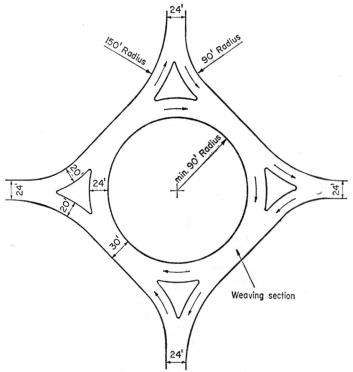

FIGURE 5.6 Rotary intersection

fixed time basis or vehicle-actuated. However, such an installation will naturally impose extensive delays on a proportion of the major road traffic and a preferable layout in these circumstances may be to form a rotary intersection or roundabout.

The principle of a rotary intersection is that all traffic is brought to the same speed (20 to 30 m.p.h. in rural conditions) within the inter-section area and traffic flow is one-directional around the central island. Merging, diverging, and crossing movements take place in the 'weaving' sections between the entry and exit points, which should if possible be spaced at equal distances around the periphery.

A typical layout for a roundabout at the intersection of two single carriageway roads is shown in Figure 5.6. The principal features are:

1. A large diameter central island to allow moderate speeds to be maintained by circulating traffic. The site configuration may suggest a non-circular shape in which case this equivalent radius should be maintained.
2. A relatively sharp entry kerb radius to slow down approaching vehicles to the speed of the circulating traffic.
3. An easier exit kerb radius to allow drivers to accelerate out of the intersection.
4. A throat width of 30 ft around the central island to allow separation between left-turning vehicles and those merging with the circulating traffic.
5. The use of shrubs on the central island to screen the glare of oncoming vehicle headlights. Alternatively, it may be preferable to slope the island to a height of at least 4 ft above the adjacent road level.
6. Where necessary, the provision of crossing points for pedestrians on the approach roads remote from the actual intersection area, and the use of grass verges, shrubs, and possibly guard rails to prevent encroachment on the junction or attempts to cross onto the central island.
7. Adequate lighting and signing of the intersection to warn approaching drivers.

Cram[8] has observed vehicle movements at a rotary intersection in Warwickshire and has concluded that the capacity of a weaving section at a rural roundabout is 2,100 p.c.u. per hour. Further discussion of the capacity of rotary intersections is outside the scope of this book and reference should be made elsewhere for more detailed information,[9] but on the above basis it can be shown that where one or both of the intersecting roads is a dual carriageway working to its design capacity then a rotary intersection would be unsuitable and a grade separated design should be adopted.

GRADE SEPARATED INTERSECTIONS

5.8 *Types of layout*

A grade separated intersection is the only acceptable solution where a heavily-trafficked road is crossed or joined by one carrying more than a light volume of traffic, but the construction of this form of layout has until recently been restricted almost without exception to motorway construction. On these high-speed roads, grade separation has been provided at all intersections regardless of the volume of cross traffic, but connecting slip roads have been constructed only where the volume of turning traffic justifies their inclusion and not generally at closer intervals than three miles.

Where grade separation is employed, right-turn movements on the more heavily-trafficked road are prohibited and drivers wishing to turn right must do so by turning left off the through road into a slip road which allows them to pass under or over their previous alignment.

Various alternative types of layout can be used and the form adopted will depend on a number of factors including the nature and the volume of the traffic on both roads, the topographical features of the inter-section area, the availability of land, and the design speed which it is desired to maintain along the connecting links. A number of typical layouts are shown diagrammatically in Figure 5.7.

Layouts (a) and (b) are typical for the intersection of a motorway with an all-purpose road carrying a moderate volume of traffic. If desired, rotary intersections can be introduced at the slip road junctions on the all-purpose road to assist right-turning movements at these points. Where the all-purpose road crosses over the motorway as shown, the down gradients of the entry slip roads assist vehicles merging with the motorway traffic by providing good visibility and easier acceleration, whilst the exit gradients assist deceleration. If the topography makes it necessary for the motorway to pass over an existing road then particular attention should be given to these points and somewhat longer acceleration and deceleration lanes provided.

The above layouts are not suitable for the junction between a motorway and a heavily-trafficked all-purpose road, since T-junctions at the slip road will cause delay to traffic entering and leaving the motorway whilst rotary intersections will interfere with through traffic flow on the all-purpose road, and in these circumstances a single two-level roundabout is preferable as shown in Figure 5.7(c).

An intersection between two motorways requires free-flowing conditions for all through traffic with connecting links of reasonably large radius for turning vehicles. This is achieved in layouts (d) and (e). The former includes a rotary intersection at a third level, as is proposed for the M.1–M.62 intersection in Yorkshire. The clover leaf interchange avoids three-level construction but requires an enormous area of land and right-turning traffic has a lengthy detour. A third alternative giving more direct link roads and in which all turning movements can be undertaken at speeds of up to 50 m.p.h. is the four-level interchange shown diagrammatically in Figure 5.7(f).

When the two motorways form a T- or Y-junction, as at the Broughton Interchange on the M.6 north of Preston, shown in Figure 5.7(g), a somewhat simpler type of layout based on the above configuration can

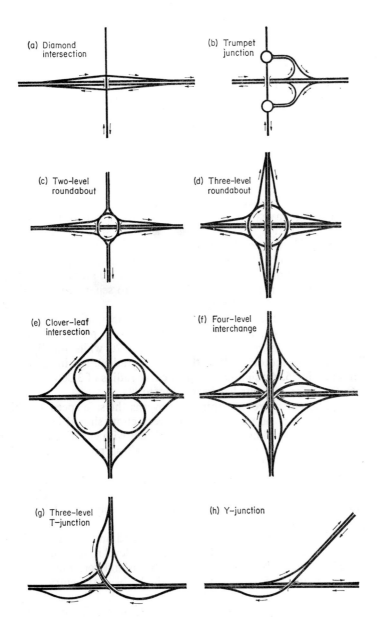

(a) Diamond
intersection

(b) Trumpet
junction

(c) Two-level
roundabout

(d) Three-level
roundabout

(e) Clover-leaf
intersection

(f) Four-level
interchange

(g) Three-level
T-junction

(h) Y-junction

FIGURE 5.7 Grade separated intersections

be adopted, especially when no connections are required between two arms of the junction as in Figure 5.7(h).

5.9 Design details

Acceleration and deceleration lanes form an essential feature of any motorway junction layout. To be fully effective, acceleration lanes must be between 500 ft and 800 ft long, according to the gradient of the lane and the last 300 ft of the slip road, whilst deceleration lanes should be between 400 ft and 700 ft long, depending again on the gradient. On British motorways, these lanes have been constructed with a uniform 12-ft width; the ends tapering to nothing over an additional 150-ft length.

Slip roads and connecting link roads should be one-directional (or of dual carriageway construction for two-way traffic) with a carriageway width of at least 18 ft. The 10-ft wide hard shoulder is now continued alongside the acceleration or deceleration lane and along one side of the slip road as far as the junction with the all-purpose road. On the opposite side of a one-way slip road a 9-ft wide grass verge should be provided; flush marginal strips being used to separate the carriageway from the shoulder and verge.

The length of the slip road is dependent on the gradient and vertical curve radii permitted. The normal gradient for slip roads rising above the motorway is 1 in 25 with a maximum of 1 in 20, whilst for slip roads falling below the motorway level the normal gradient is 1 in 30 and the maximum 1 in 25. A minimum vertical curve radius of 3,000 ft for sags and 6,000 ft. for summits has been adopted.[10]

Horizontal curvature on slip roads governs the safe speed at which vehicles can leave the motorway and every effort should be made to provide as large a radius as possible consistent with ensuring a suitable approach speed to the junction with the all-purpose road. With a trumpet-type layout shown in Figure 5.7(b) a minimum radius of 180 ft is suggested with transitional sections leading onto the tangents. For free-flowing intersections, the minimum curve radius can be related to the design speed (Table 4.1), and should preferably be not less than 1,500 ft.

Raised kerbs are provided at roundabouts and on the entry and exit radii at slip road junctions. For the two- or three-level rotary intersections indicated in Figure 5.7(c) and (d), the central island kerb radius should be not less than 180 ft, whilst those for the kerbs at the entry and exit points to the roundabout should be respectively less than and greater than this value for the reasons stated in Section 5.7. Similarly, the island diameter at a single-level terminal roundabout should not be less than 360 ft, although it should be pointed out that with this type of layout, motorway terminals have been the scenes of frequent accidents and an alternative layout suitable for higher speeds is to be preferred.

REFERENCES

1. MINISTRY OF TRANSPORT, SCOTTISH DEVELOPMENT DEPARTMENT, THE WELSH OFFICE, *Advisory Manual on the Layout of Roads in Rural Areas* (London: H.M.S.O., 1968)
2. CHARLESWORTH, G. and TANNER, J. C., 'Road Junctions in Rural Areas', *Department of Scientific and Industrial Research, Road Research Technical Paper No. 47* (London: H.M.S.O., 1960)
3. MINISTRY OF WAR TRANSPORT, 'Memorandum on the Lay-out and Construction of Roads', *Ministry of War Transport Memorandum No. 575* (London: H.M.S.O., 1943)
4. SUMMERFIELD, K., 'Design of Road Intersections', *Proc. Instn. civ. Engrs.* (London, vol. 5, Part II, 1956, pp. 332–60)
5. TANNER, J. C., 'Accidents at Rural Three-way Junctions', *J. Instn. Highw. Engrs.* (London, vol. 2, No. 11, July 1953, pp. 56–67)
6. HIGHWAY RESEARCH BOARD, 'Channelization—the Design of Highway Intersections at Grade', *Highway Research Board Special Report 74* (Washington, D.C.: National Academy of Sciences—National Research Council, 1962)
7. BENNETT, G. T., 'Road Junctions: Suggestions for Improved Designs', *Public Works, Roads and Transport Congress and Exhibition, 1947, Final Report* (London: The Public Works, Roads and Transport Congress and Exhibition Council, undated, pp. 175–92) also *Proc. Instn. munic. Engrs.* (London: vol. 74, 1947–8, pp. 269–86)
8. CRAM, I. A., 'Standards for Design of Rural Roads', *J. Instn. Highw. Engrs.* (London, vol. 8, 1961, pp. 271–93)
9. ROAD RESEARCH LABORATORY, *Research on Road Traffic* (London: H.M.S.O., 1965, p. 220)
10. BAKER, J. F. A., 'The General Motorway Plan', *Proc. Instn. civ. Engrs.* (London, vol. 15, 1960, pp. 317–32)

6

Highway Location and Setting Out

Having paused to examine in detail the design standards for geometric layout, the sequence of events leading up to the commencement of constructional work can now be continued.

6.1 *Scheme publication*

Once the alignment has been fixed and the decision to go ahead with the scheme has been taken, the proposals must be made known so that objectors are given the opportunity to express their views. Statutory procedures laid down in the Special Roads Act, 1949, and now consolidated in the Highways Act, 1959, require the 'scheme' covering the centre-line location of new motorways to be advertised for a period of three months, during which time objections may be lodged.

Regulations issued by the Ministry of Transport for the scheme require the centre-line of the proposed road to be shown by a continuous black band on a 6 in to 1 mile map, which must be certified up to date within 220 ft of the centre-line on both sides of the road. In addition, copies of the 1 : 2,500 plan and longitudinal section must be available, and if the proposed road is more than 10 miles long, a key plan to a scale of one inch to the mile showing the centre-line is also required.

When objections have been considered—if necessary by means of a public inquiry—and any resulting modifications introduced into the alignment, the scheme is then confirmed and detailed design work can go ahead. Simultaneously with the publication of the scheme, work can proceed on the preparation of the plans and information required for the Orders under Section 3 of the Act covering the alterations and stopping-up of side roads, footpaths, and private accesses necessitated by the new construction works. The amount of work involved in these Orders can be judged from the fact that on a 55-mile section of the M.1 motorway there were 150 alterations of this nature and the reconstruction of about 17 miles of existing road was required.[1] In addition, negotiations must be opened between the District Valuer and all land owners concerned, leading subsequently to any necessary Compulsory Purchase Orders.

6.2 Centre-line location

Following the confirmation of the scheme, the next step in the procedure is to establish the road centre-line in the field so that, if required, further measurements of existing ground levels can be taken and the contract documents prepared.

The usual practice is to locate the intersection points of the tangent sections of the horizontal alignment by scaling their positions on the preliminary survey drawing from one of the traverse stations or from clearly defined topographical features. The deflexion (or intersection) angle at each of these points is then measured and used in curve calculations. When the intersection points are not mutually visible, it may prove easier for subsequent angle measurements if a length of the intermediate tangent is set out in the first place and then extended to fix the intersection points.

The road centre-line is then defined by pegs set at 100-ft centres to form a continuous running chainage from the start of the contract. Additional pegs are used to mark the curve tangent points and also to indicate the points of change from transition curve to circular arc. Before constructional work commences, it is essential that sufficient reference pegs are set outside the limits of future construction so that the centre-line can be easily relocated at any time.

SETTING OUT OF HORIZONTAL CIRCULAR ARCS

6.3 Degree of curve

Horizontal curves have, up to this point, been defined in terms of their radius R ft. However, for setting out calculations it is easier to use an alternative definition of curvature, namely the degree of curve D, which is the angle in degrees subtended at the centre of the curve by a circular arc of length 100 ft. From Figure 6.1 it is obvious that $100 = \pi R D / 180$ or

$$D = 5729 \cdot 6 / R \qquad (6.1)$$

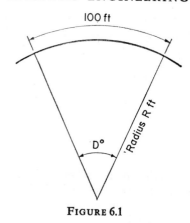

FIGURE 6.1

6.4 *Setting out by theodolite and steel tape*

The setting out procedure can most easily be explained by reference to Figure 6.2. If the two tangents intersect to give a deflexion angle Δ,

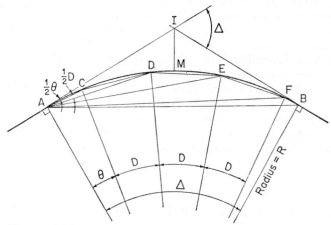

FIGURE 6.2 Setting-out horizontal curve using theodolite and tape

then the tangent distance $AI = IB = R \tan \frac{1}{2}\Delta$. The tangent points can thus be fixed by measuring the distance $R \tan \frac{1}{2}\Delta$ along each tangent from I, or, alternatively, the forward chainage may be carried through to I and that of A obtained by subtracting the calculated tangent distance. It should be noted that the chainage of B is given by the chainage of A plus the length of the arc AB, which is equal to $100\Delta/D$, and that this is *not* the same as the forward chainage of I plus $R \tan \frac{1}{2}\Delta$, since the curve length is necessarily shorter than the sum of the two tangent distances.

The chainage of A is unlikely to be an exact hundred feet, and therefore the first point to be located on the curve at C will be some distance less than a hundred feet from A. Suppose that the arc AC subtends an angle θ at the centre of the circle. Then, by geometry, the angle between the tangent at A and the chord AC will be $\frac{1}{2}\theta$. C can thus be fixed by setting up a theodolite at A, sighting forward to I, turning off an angle $\frac{1}{2}\theta$, and measuring along this line the chord length AC which corresponds to the known arc length AC.

Successive points on the curve at D, E, and F have to be set out at 100-ft intervals and each 100-ft arc will subtend an angle D at the centre of the circle or $\frac{1}{2}D$ at point A on the circumference. Point D can therefore be fixed by turning off the angle $(\frac{1}{2}\theta + \frac{1}{2}D)$ from the tangent at A and measuring the chord length CD, corresponding to 100 ft of arc, by pivoting the tape about C until D lies on the line of sight of the theodolite. Subsequent points can be set out in a similar manner and a check on the overall accuracy of the work can be obtained by closing onto B and comparing the measured chainage with that previously calculated. On long curves, an additional check on the accuracy of the work at an intermediate stage is sometimes advisable, and this can be done by setting out the mid-point M and measuring the external distance MI which should be equal to $R(\sec \frac{1}{2}\Delta - 1)$.

The difference between the arc and chord lengths is dependent on the curve radius and is given by $(R\theta - 2R \sin \frac{1}{2}\theta)$, where R is the radius of the curve and θ is the angle subtended at the centre by an arc of length a. Expressing $\sin \frac{1}{2}\theta$ as the power series $(\theta/2 - \theta^3/48 + \theta^5/3840 - \ldots)$ Lnd neglecting terms containing θ^5 and higher powers, the difference reduces to $R\theta^3/24 = L^3/24R$, since $L = R\theta$. Table 6.1 shows the chord

TABLE 6.1 *Chord lengths for 100-ft arcs of various curvatures*

Degree of curve	Radius (ft)	Chord length (ft)
2°	2,865	99·995
4°	1,432	99·98
6°	955	99·955
8°	716	99·92
10°	573	99·87

lengths corresponding to 100-ft lengths of arc for various curves. The difference is small for large-radius curves of the type used in modern highway design, but a cumulative error will be introduced on sharper curves if the effect is ignored.

The above procedure can be illustrated by a specific example:

The centre-line of a road describes a right-hand curve, curvature 3° 20' through a deflexion angle of 28° 05' 12". The forward chainage of the intersection point is 87 + 23·7 ft. Draw up a table of data to enable the curve to be set out at 100-ft running chainages.

$$D = 3° 20', \text{ and therefore } R = 1718·9 \text{ ft}$$

The tangent distance AI $= R \tan \frac{1}{2}\Delta = 430·0$ ft and hence the chainage of A $= (87 + 23·7) - 430·0 = 82 + 93·7$ ft. The curve length AB $= 100\Delta/D = 842·6$ ft and hence the chainage of B $= 91 + 36·3$ ft.

The first point to be set out on the curve is at chainage 83 + 00 for which the chord length will be 6·3 ft. Subsequent chord lengths corresponding to 100-ft arcs on a 3° 20' curve will be for all practical purposes of length 100 ft, whilst the final chord length to check on point B should be 36·3 ft.

Arcs of length 100 ft will subtend at A an angle equal to

$$\tfrac{1}{2}D = 1° 40' 00''$$

whilst the angles subtended by the first and last chords will be, by proportion, 0° 6' 18" and 0° 36' 18" respectively.

The tabulated data are thus:

Instrument station	Point sighted	Deflexion angle for chord	Horizontal angle on theodolite	Chord length (ft)
A (82 + 93·7)	I	—	0° 00' 00"	—
	83 + 00	0° 06' 18"	0° 06' 18"	6·3
	84 + 00	1° 40' 00"	1° 46' 18"	100·0
	85 + 00	1° 40' 00"	3° 26' 28"	100·0
	...	...	...	...
	90 + 00	1° 40' 00"	11° 46' 18"	100·0
	91 + 00	1° 40' 00"	13° 26' 18"	100·0
	B (91 + 36·3)	0° 36' 18"	14° 02' 36"	36·3

As an arithmetical check, the angle setting when the theodolite is sighting B should be $\frac{1}{2}\Delta = 14° 02' 36''$.

The curve in the above example was right-handed (i.e. curving to the right in the direction of forward chainage). With a left-hand curve, the theodolite at A would be turned anti-clockwise from the initial sighting along the tangent, and the tabulated angles would therefore have to be subtracted from 360° to obtain the correct settings.

6.5 Setting out with two theodolites

As an alternative to using one theodolite and a tape, circular curves can be set out with two theodolites. The procedure is similar to that already described, except that theodolites are set up at points A and B, and whilst A takes a bearing from AI, B sights initially onto A (Figure 6.3). C is then located at the intersection of the two lines of sight by turning

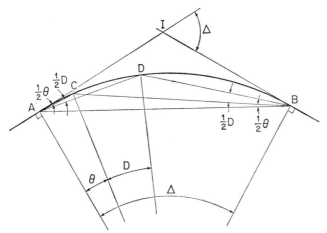

FIGURE 6.3 Setting-out horizontal curve using two theodolites

each theodolite through an angle $\frac{1}{2}\theta$. Similarly, other points on the curve are successively located by setting both theodolites to read $(\frac{1}{2}\theta + \frac{1}{2}D)$, $(\frac{1}{2}\theta + D)$, and $(\frac{1}{2}\theta + \frac{3}{2}D)$ in turn.

The method may be useful when the topography is such as to make accurate taping difficult, but it suffers from the disadvantage that co-ordination must be established between three rather than two people. The major objection to the method, however, lies in the inherent inaccuracy on large-radius curves where the strength of fix is poor. This can be illustrated by reference to Figure 6.4.

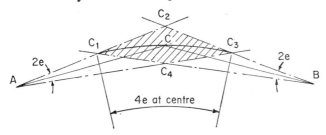

FIGURE 6.4 'Strength of fix' using two theodolites

If the theodolites are such that a particular angle can be set to an accuracy of $\pm e$ seconds, then the location of point C could lie anywhere in the shaded area $C_1C_2C_3C_4$. The maximum lateral error C_2C_4 depends on the distance AC, and even when $e = 10$ seconds and AC = 1,000 ft this error will only be of the order $\pm\frac{1}{2}$ in. However, the longitudinal error C_1C_3 will be much greater and may result in large inaccuracies in the setting out work.

C_1CC_3 is in fact an arc of the circular curve and therefore subtends an angle $4e$ at the centre. Hence the arc length C_1C_3 is $100(4e/3600D)$ ft. For the $3° 20'$ curve used in the previous example, with $e = 10$ seconds, $C_1C_3 = 4$ inches, which corresponds to a chainage error of ± 2 in in the fixing of point C. For a larger radius curve as is commonly found on modern highways, say $D = 0° 40'$, the chainage error would be as much as ± 10 in. Although this is unimportant as regards existing ground levels, a serious error would be introduced in any subsequent setting out work, for example if the peg was referenced and later used to set finished road level on a steep gradient.

Other methods of setting out include one in which offsets are calculated from the tangents or from the chord joining the tangent points, but this is applicable only to curves of relatively short radius, and is not practicable for the relocation of a centre-line when the road is in a cutting or on an embankment.

6.6 Practical difficulties in setting out

Various problems are encountered in setting out work which prevent the straightforward approach described in the two previous sections from being applied directly. Two difficulties occur most frequently in practice and are therefore worthy of special consideration.

In some circumstances, the intersection point I may be inaccessible, possibly being located in a dense wood or obscured by buildings, so that direct measurement of the deflexion angle and forward chainage is prevented. The problem can be overcome by linking the two tangents with a line such as XY (Figure 6.5) and measuring the forward chainage of X, the deflexion angles at X and Y, and the distance XY. The unknown distance XI can then be calculated by applying the sine rule to triangle XIY and, as previously, the tangent distance AI is given by

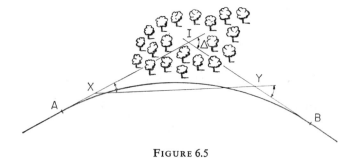

FIGURE 6.5

R tan $\frac{1}{2}\Delta$, where Δ is now the sum of the deflexion angles measured at X and Y. The distance AX can thus be obtained by subtraction and A located by measuring along the tangent from X. In a similar manner, B can be fixed from Y and the setting out procedure continued as before.

A second difficulty encountered in setting out work arises when topographical features prevent the whole of the curve being visible from tangent point A. This is particularly true of long curves and may occur when the road passes through a wood, when the lines of sight are obstructed by buildings, or when the road crosses a ridge.

Suppose in the example given on page 96 that the maximum sighting distance from A is limited to 350 ft. The setting out could be carried out from A as far as point F (chainage 86 + 00), but further points along the curve would not be visible. If the theodolite is transferred to

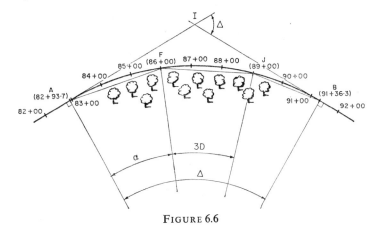

FIGURE 6.6

F (Figure 6.6) and backsighted on A, then the line of sight must be turned through an angle $(180° + \frac{1}{2}\alpha)$ to sight forward along the tangent at F, where α is the angle subtended at the centre by the arc AF. In this case $\alpha = \theta + 3D$. Subsequent points along the curve at 100-ft intervals can thus be set out from F by turning the line of sight from the tangent by an amount $\frac{1}{2}D$ successively, in each case measuring the chord length from the preceding peg, until point J (chainage 89 + 00) has been reached.

This again marks the limit of visibility, and the procedure must be repeated with the instrument moved forward to J, the only difference being that the angle subtended by the arc FJ is now simply $3D$. Finally the accuracy of the setting out can be checked with a closing sight and measurement to tangent point B.

The tabulated data for the setting out work would thus be as shown overleaf.

Instrument station	Point sighted	Deflexion angle for chord	Horizontal angle on theodolite	Chord length (ft)
A (82 + 93·7)	I	—	0° 00′ 00″	—
	83 + 00	0° 06′ 18″	0° 06′ 18″	6·3
	84 + 00	1° 40′ 00″	1° 46′ 18″	100·0
	85 + 00	1° 40′ 00″	3° 26′ 18″	100·0
	F (86 + 00)	1° 40′ 00″	5° 06′ 18″	100·0
F (86 + 00)	A	—	0° 00′ 00″	—
	87 + 00	1° 40′ 00″	186° 46′ 18″	100·0
	88 + 00	1° 40′ 00″	188° 26′ 18″	100·0
	J (89 + 00)	1° 40′ 00″	190° 06′ 18″	100·0
J (89 + 00)	F	—	0° 00′ 00″	—
	90 + 00	1° 40′ 00″	186° 40′ 00″	100·0
	91 + 00	1° 40′ 00″	188° 20′ 00″	100·0
	B (91 + 36·3)	0° 36′ 18″	188° 56′ 18″	36·3

SETTING OUT CIRCULAR ARCS WITH TRANSITION CURVES

6.7 Alternative forms for transition curves

It has been shown in an earlier chapter that the ideal form of transition curve is such that the radius of curvature varies inversely as the length along the curve measured from the origin (see page 62). Only one curve, the clothoid, meets this requirement exactly but there are two other curves, the lemniscate and the cubic parabola, which follow an

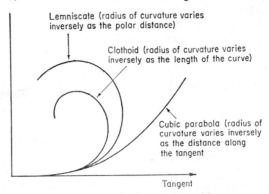

FIGURE 6.7 Alternative forms of transition curves

almost identical path when the deviation from the tangent is small, as is invariably the case with highway transition curves.

The three curves are shown for comparison in Figure 6.7. Various arguments have been advanced in support of one form of curve in preference to the others, but in point of fact these discussions are purely academic, since whichever basic form is taken in the first instance, certain approximations are made in the course of calculations to enable simpler mathematical relationships between the various parameters to be obtained, and exactly the same formulae are ultimately derived from all three approaches. The resulting formulae, therefore, show properties which taken individually are exact for one or other of these curves over its whole length but which taken *en bloc* can only be used for polar deviation angles up to about 5°.

6.8 Basic relationships for transition curves

The basic formulae used in the setting out of transition curves can be derived by reference to Figures 6.8 and 6.9. By convention, the points

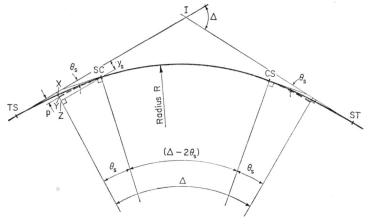

FIGURE 6.8 Setting-out horizontal curve with transitions

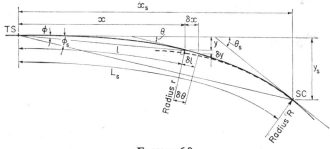

FIGURE 6.9

marking the change from tangent to spiral and spiral to circular arc are denoted TS and SC respectively.

The transition curves are accommodated by setting in the circular arc by a distance p, termed the *shift*, and then running the transition from the TS point, where the radius is infinite, to the SC point where the radius is equal to that of the circular arc (Figure 6.8). The equation of the transition curve (see page 62) is

$$1/r = l/RL_s \qquad (6.2)$$

where r is the radius at a point distance l from the TS point, R the radius of the circular arc, and L is the overall length of the transition curve.

(i) If θ is the angle turned through at a distance l along the transition curve (Figure 6.9) then

$$\delta l = r(\delta\theta)$$

or
$$d\theta/dl = l/RL_s$$

Hence by integration, $\theta = l^2/2RL_s$ and at the end of the transition curve the total angle turned through

$$\theta_s = L_s/2R \text{ radians} = L_sD/200 \text{ degrees} \qquad (6.3)$$

(ii) If the shift is measured at a point X along the transition curve (Figure 6.8), then the distance between X and the SC point is approximately $R\theta_s$, which from above $= \frac{1}{2}L_s$. In other words, the transition curve is located an equal distance either side of the point X. Hence the tangent distance measured from the intersection point I to the TS point is (approximately)

$$\tfrac{1}{2}L_s + (R + p) \tan \tfrac{1}{2}\Delta \qquad (6.4)$$

(iii) The shift p is equal to the offset of SC from the tangent minus the distance YZ (Figure 6.8), i.e.

$$p = y_s - L_s^2/8R \text{ (approximately)}$$

Referring again to Figure 6.9, at any point along the curve

$$\delta y = \delta l \sin \theta \quad \text{and} \quad \delta x = \delta l \cos \theta$$

and by integration it can be shown that

$$y = \frac{l^3}{6RL_s}\left(1 - \frac{\theta^2}{14} + \frac{\theta^4}{440} - \cdots\right)$$

and
$$x = l\left(1 - \frac{\theta^2}{10} + \frac{\theta^4}{216} - \cdots\right)$$

where θ is measured in radians.

Since θ is small, at the end of the transition curve $y_s = L_s^2/6R$ (approximately) and therefore

$$p = L_s^2/6R - L_s^2/8R = L_s^2/24R \qquad (6.5)$$

(iv) For small angles of deviation from the tangent, the coordinates of any point distance l along the transition curve are $x = l, y = l^3/6RL_s$. Hence the polar deviation angle ϕ is given by:

$$\tan \phi = y/x = l^2/6RL_s$$

and therefore $\phi = l^2/6RL_s$ radians $= l^2 D/600L_s$ degrees.

At the end of the transition curve, the polar deviation angle is given by

$$\phi_s = L_s/6R \text{ radians} = L_s D/600 \text{ degrees} \qquad (6.6)$$

A comparison of Equations 6.3 and 6.6 shows that $\phi_s = \theta_s/3$, which incidentally is an exact property of the lemniscate for all values of θ, both large and small.

6.9 Setting out procedure

The setting out of horizontal curves with transitions follows closely the procedure used to set out simple circular arcs. In the first place the deflexion angle must be measured in the field, following which, having decided on acceptable values for L_s and R (or D) at the design stage, the shift can be calculated using Equation 6.5 and substituted in Equation 6.4 to determine the tangent distance. The TS and ST points can then be located on the two tangents, and the chainages of the SC, CS, and ST points calculated by adding L_s, $L_s + 100(\Delta - 2\theta_s)/D$, and $2L_s + 100(\Delta - 2\theta_s)/D$ respectively to the forward chainage of the TS point.

Points along the entry transition curve, TS to SC, can then be set out from the TS point by turning off from the tangent the angle $\phi = l^2 D/600L_s$ degrees and measuring the distance l along the curve. It should be noted that these polar deviation angles are calculated separately for each point on the curve and are not added to the previous reading as when setting out circular arcs. Distances can be measured from the preceding peg, however. Points are set out at 100-ft running chainages along the transition and finally the SC point is fixed by turning off the angle $\phi_s = L_s D/600$ degrees. As a check, the offset from the tangent should be $L_s^2/6R$ at the SC point.

The exit transition, CS to ST, is then set out in a similar manner, working backwards from the ST point to the CS point and again checking the offset from the tangent. The SC and CS points now form the tangent points for the intermediate circular arc, the setting out of which follows the procedure already established. Before a start can be made, however, it is necessary to relate the direction of the tangent at the SC point to that of the initial line of sight. Referring once more to Figure 6.9, it can be seen that if a backsight is taken from the SC point to the TS point, then rotation of the line of sight through an angle

$180° + (\theta_s - \phi_s)$ will align the telescope along the tangent at the SC point. Now since $\phi_s = \frac{1}{3}\theta_s$, the required angular movement is

$$(180° + \tfrac{2}{3}\theta_s) = (180 + L_s D/300) \text{ degrees}$$

If the deflexion angle corresponding to the first point along the circular arc is added to this reading, the telescope will be correctly oriented towards this point and setting out can continue as before.

The procedure can again be illustrated by an example. Using the same data as on page 96 ($\Delta = 28° 05' 12''$, $D = 3° 20'$, forward chainage of $I = 87 + 23\cdot7$ ft) but including 200-ft long transition curves, the calculations are as follows:

$$\text{The shift} \quad p = L_s^2/24R = 0\cdot97 \text{ ft}$$

Hence the tangent distance $= \frac{1}{2}L_s + (R + p) \tan \frac{1}{2}\Delta$

$$= 100 + 1719\cdot9 \tan 14° 02' 36''$$
$$= 530\cdot2 \text{ ft}$$

The angle turned through along each transition $\theta_s = L_s D/200$ degrees, and for $L_s = 200$ ft, $\theta_s = 3° 20'$.

The length of circular arc $= 100(\Delta - 2\theta_s)/D = 642\cdot6$ ft

The chainages are thus: TS   81 + 93·5

                    SC   83 + 93·5

                    CS   90 + 36·1

                    ST   92 + 36·1

On the entry transition, two intermediate points have to be set out at chainages 82 + 00 and 83 + 00 for which $l = 6\cdot5$ ft and 106·5 ft, $\phi = 0° 00' 04''$ and $0° 18' 54''$ respectively. Similarly on the exit transition there are two intermediate points at chainages 91 + 00 and 92 + 00 for which $l = 136\cdot1$ ft and 36·1 ft, $\phi = 0° 30' 52''$ and $0° 02' 10''$ respectively.

The first point on the circular arc is at chainage 84 + 00, corresponding to a chord length of 6·5 ft and a deflexion angle of 06′ 30″ at the SC point. Hence from the backsight onto the TS point, the line of sight must be turned through the clockwise angle

$$(180° + 2° 13' 20'' + 06' 30'') = 182° 19' 50''$$

to sight towards this point. For subsequent points, the added deflexion angle is $\frac{1}{2}D = 1° 40' 00''$ until the final sighting onto the CS point, for which the deflexion angle is $0° 36' 06''$.

The tabulated data are as shown in table on facing page.

6.10 Setting out tables

It will be appreciated that the calculation of setting out data for transition curves is a somewhat lengthy procedure and various sets of tables have been produced from time to time in order to reduce the amount of work involved. Probably the best known tables are those of Criswell[2] which give the values of shift, transition angle, tangential offsets, and other data for various combinations of transition curve length and degree of curve. The transition curve lengths tabulated have actually been derived from nominal design speeds in the range 20–100 m.p.h., using Shortt's formula with $C = 1$ or 2 (see page 63), but the data can be abstracted for any transition curve, irrespective of how the length is determined, by choosing the appropriate combination of degree of curve and transition length.

Instrument station	Point sighted	Deflexion angle for chord	Horizontal angle on theodolite	Chord length (ft)
TS (81 + 93·5)	I	—	0° 00′ 00″	—
	82 + 00	—	0° 00′ 04″	6·5
	83 + 00	—	0° 18′ 54″	100·0
	SC (83 + 93·5)	—	1° 06′ 40″	93·5
ST (92 + 36·1)	I	—	360° 00′ 00″	—
	92 + 00	—	359° 57′ 50″	36·1
	91 + 00	—	359° 29′ 08″	100·0
	CS (90 + 36·1)	—	358° 53′ 20″	63·9
SC (83 + 93·5)	TS	—	0° 00′ 00″	—
	84 + 00	0° 06′ 30″	182° 19′ 50″	6·5
	85 + 00	1° 40′ 00″	183° 59′ 50″	100·0
	...	...	...	...
	89 + 00	1° 40′ 00″	190° 39′ 50″	100·0
	90 + 00	1° 40′ 00″	192° 19′ 50″	100·0
	CS (90 + 36·1)	0° 36′ 06″	192° 55′ 56″	36·1

Note: All chord lengths are measured from the preceding peg

6.11 Use of the osculating circle

Circumstances may occasionally arise when it is necessary to set out the transition curve in the reverse direction from the SC (or CS) point to the TS (or ST) point and this may be achieved by using the principle of the osculating circle. The net angular deflexion from the tangent at the SC point to any point along the transition curve is equal to the osculating circle deflexion calculated for the distance from the SC point to the point concerned minus the polar deviation angle corresponding to that same distance; the radius of the osculating circle being, in this particular case, equal to that of the circular arc.[2]

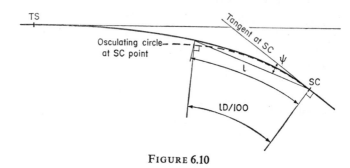

FIGURE 6.10

Thus to set out a point at a distance l from the SC point, the net angular deflexion from the tangent is

$$\psi = lD/200 - l^2D/600L_s \text{ degrees} \quad \text{(Figure 6.10)}$$

$$= \frac{lD}{200}\left((1 - \frac{l}{3L_s}\right) \text{ degrees} \tag{6.7}$$

SETTING OUT VERTICAL CURVES

6.12 Vertical curve calculations

Although the profiles for vertical alignment are not set out in the field until the contract has been awarded and constructional work is under-way, it is necessary to complete the design at an early stage so that finished road levels can be calculated and subsequently used in the design of bridges, drainage schemes, and other ancillary works.

Vertical curves have already been referred to in Sections 4.17–19 dealing with design standards for visibility and curvature. As previously stated, the curves are usually parabolic in shape and extend for an equal distance either side of the vertical intersection point (V.I.P.). The vertical distance between the tangent and the curve is thus given by the relationship $y = kx^2$ (Figure 6.11), where k is a constant. When

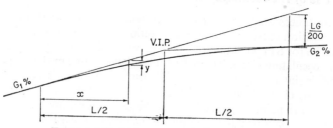

FIGURE 6.11 Setting-out parabolic vertical curve

$x = L$, $y = LG/200$ where G is the algebraic difference between the grades $(G_1 - G_2)$, and thus $y = Gx^2/200L$ or, more conveniently,

$$y = \frac{GL}{200}\left(\frac{x}{L}\right)^2 \qquad (6.8)$$

For a particular vertical curve, the gradients and the V.I.P. level will have been determined by the design considerations affecting the overall road profile whilst L will have been chosen to satisfy visibility requirements or other alternative design criteria. The substitution of these values into Equation 6.8 enables levels to be calculated at points along the vertical curve, as in the following example.

A parabolic vertical curve 1,200 ft long is to be constructed between a rising gradient of 2·5% and a falling gradient of 1%. The V.I.P. is at chainage 57 + 00 ft and has a reduced level of 152·50 ft. Tabulate the levels along the curve at 100-ft running chainages.

The curve extends from chainage 51 + 00 to chainage 63 + 00, and the reduced levels at these points are 152·50 − 15·00 = 137·50 and 152·50 − 6·00 = 146·50. $L = 1,200$, $G_1 = +2·5$, $G_2 = -1$, hence $G = 3·5$.

Equation 6·8 thus gives $y = 21(x/L)^2$ and the reduced levels over the length of the curve are as follows:

Chainage (ft)	x (ft)	y (ft)	R.L. on tangent (ft)	R.L. on curve (ft)
51 + 00	0	0	137·50	137·50
52 + 00	100	0·15	140·00	139·85
53 + 00	200	0·58	142·50	141·92
54 + 00	300	1·31	145·00	143·69
55 + 00	400	2·23	147·50	145·27
56 + 00	500	3·65	150·00	146·35
57 + 00	600	5·25	152·50	147·25
58 + 00	700	7·15	155·00	147·85
59 + 00	800	9·33	157·50	148·27
60 + 00	900	11·81	160·00	148·19
61 + 00	1,000	14·58	162·50	147·92
62 + 00	1,100	17·65	165·00	147·35
63 + 00	1,200	21·00	167·50	146·50

The final line of the table gives a check on the previously calculated level at chainage 63 + 00.

In the above example, the curve level has been obtained throughout by subtracting y from the rising tangent level. When large values are involved this may lead to some inaccuracy in the second decimal place and for this reason it is often preferable to treat each half of the curve separately, using the same basic equation but applying it only for $x \leqslant \frac{1}{2}L$. The tabulated data will appear thus:

Chainage (ft)	x (ft)	y (ft)	R.L. on tangent (f)	R.L. on curve (ft)
51 + 00	0	0	137·50	137·50
52 + 00	100	0·15	140·00	139·85
...	...	...	...	...
56 + 00	500	3·65	150·00	146·35
57 + 00	600	5·25	152·50	147·25
58 + 00	500	3·65	151·50	147·85
59 + 00	400	2·23	150·50	148·27
60 + 00	300	1·31	149·50	148·19
61 + 00	200	0·58	148·50	147·92
62 + 00	100	0·15	147·50	147·35
63 + 00	0	0	146·50	146·50

6.13 Computer application to vertical curve design

Much of the routine calculation work entailed in vertical curve design can be carried out more speedily and effectively with the aid of a digital computer using a relatively simple programme.

A recent paper given to the Institution of Highway Engineers has described a programme used for such calculations on the 21-mile long Durham Motorway.[3] With this programme, data consisting of the vertical intersection point chainages and levels taken from the profile drawing are fed into the computer together with specified minimum values for sag and summit radii and curve length (Figure 6.12). These minimum values are used unless a special length or radius is nominated for a particular curve.

The computer calculates the vertical alignment of the road at nominated intervals of chainage and also at any intermediate chainages specified, prints out the levels at these points, plots a longitudinal section to a vertical scale 10 ft to 1 in, and tabulates the calculated gradients between intersection points together with the lengths and radii of all vertical curves (Figure 6.13). In addition, cards are punched giving intersection point data for use with a subsequent programme which calculates the finished levels on a road cross-section.

One advantage of computer application to curve design is that in working up the profile graphically the engineer need not now bother about locating vertical intersection points at 'round' chainages and levels, or choosing grades which will make calculations a little easier. The gradients are simply drawn in on the profile as seems best and the intersection points scaled off to give the programme data, so providing in reality a more flexible method of design.

Special chainages

Job No	Special chainage	Special chainage	Special chainage	Special chainage	Special chainage	Special chainage	Special chainage	Special chainage	Special chainage	Special chainage	Special chainage	Special chainage	Special chainage

Header card

Job No	Min. curve length	Min. sag radius	Min. summit radius	Interval

Intersection points

Job No	Chainage	Level	Length of curve	Radius of curve

Notes

Interval: Maximum 100·00'. For 50' write 05000

Job No: Any combination of 3 letters or figures ~ E.G. A19

Chainage: Ten digits to two places of decimals. E.G. chainage 300 write 000030000

Level: Five digits in the form xxx·xx E.G. a level of 67·26 A.O.D. is written 06726

Length of curve: As chainage

Radius: Eight digits given to nearest foot: E.G. radius of 60,000 ft is written 00060000

Special chainage: Fill in chainage of any odd point required. If more than 7 are required consult programme write-up. (need not be used)

Header card: If minima are not required leave blank. Interval essential.

FIGURE 6.12 Data presentation for vertical alignment[a]

14,100.00   251.32
14,200.00   253.09
14,300.00   255.18
14,325.00   255.76   E.V.C.   2.3333 PC grade   Next I.P.   15,600.00   285.50
14,325.00   255.75   B.V.C.   Radius   67,788 ft   Length   2,550.00 ft
14,400.00   257.46
14,500.00   259.60
14,600.00   261.61
14,700.00   263.46
14,800.00   265.17
14,900.00   266.73
15,000.00   268.14
15,100.00   269.40
15,200.00   270.52
15,300.00   271.49
15,400.00   272.31
15,500.00   272.99
15,600.00   273.51
15,700.00   273.88
15,800.00   274.12
15,900.00   274.20
16,000.00   274.14
16,100.00   273.93
16,200.00   273.57
16,300.00   273.06
16,400.00   272.41
16,500.00   271.61
16,600.00   270.65
16,700.00   269.57
16,800.00   268.32
16,875.00   267.29   E.V.C.   1.4284-PC grade   Next I.P.   19,050.00   236.22
16,900.00   266.93
17,000.00   265.50
17,100.00   264.07
17,200.00   262.65
17,300.00   261.22
17,400.00   259.79
17,500.00   258.36
17,600.00   256.93
17,700.00   255.50
17,800.00   254.08
17,900.00   252.65
18,000.00   251.22
18,100.00   249.79
18,200.00   248.36
18,300.00   246.93
18,400.00   245.50
18,500.00   244.08
18,550.00   243.36   B.V.C.   Radius   54,529 ft   Length   1,000.00 ft
18,600.00   242.67
18,700.00   241.43
18,800.00   240.36
18,900.00   239.48
19,000.00   238.79
19,100.00   238.27
19,200.00   237.95
19,300.00   237.81
19,400.00   237.84
19,500.00   238.07
19,550.00   238.25   E.V.C.   .4055 PC grade   Next I.P.   25,900.00   264.00
19,600.00   238.45
19,700.00   238.86
19,800.00   239.26
19,900.00   239.67
20,000.00   240.07
20,100.00   240.48

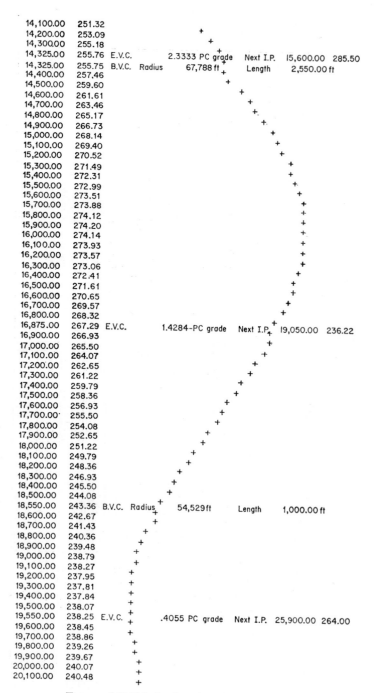

FIGURE 6.13 Tabulated vertical alignment details[3]

SETTING OUT SLOPE STAKES

6.14 Slope stake location

Slope stakes are used to mark the tops of cuttings and the toes of embankments and must be set out in advance of the constructional work so as to give the contractor guidance in the removal of topsoil and in the subsequent excavation and filling work.

At a particular cross-section, the slope stake positions will depend on the formation width, the cutting or embankment side slopes, and the level differences between the existing ground and the future formation level (Figure 6.14). If cross-sections have already been drawn at 100-ft

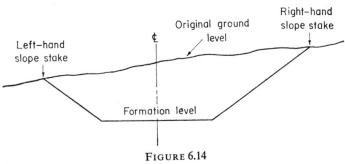

FIGURE 6.14

intervals for earthwork calculation purposes, then the slope stake positions can be scaled from these sections and the stakes set out by offsetting the required distances from the centre-line.

Alternatively, where a digital computer is being used to determine earthwork quantities (see page 114), the slope stake coordinates are required at an intermediate stage in the calculations and can therefore be printed out and tabulated with the other results, thus enabling the slope stakes to be located directly in the field.

REFERENCES

1. WILLIAMS, SIR OWEN and WILLIAMS, O. T., 'The London–Birmingham Motorway. Luton–Dunchurch: Design and Execution', *Proc. Instn. civ. Engrs.* (London: vol. 15, 1960, pp. 353–86)
2. CRISWELL, H., *Highway Spirals, Superelevation and Vertical Curves* (London: Carriers Publishing Co. Ltd, 1958, 3rd edition)
3. COTTON, W. H. B. and PETRIE, J. M., 'Digital Computers and their Use in a County Highways Department', *J. Instn. Highw. Engrs.* (London: vol. 11, 1964, pp. 72–88)

7

Earthwork Calculations

Earth-moving operations form a substantial part of any rural highway project and probably represent the largest variable factor in constructional costs. In this chapter it is proposed to examine the various methods used for earthwork calculations, both at the preliminary planning stage and later for final payment to the contractor.

EARTHWORK VOLUMES

7.1 Preliminary earthwork calculations

The first estimate of earthworks is required following the reconnaissance survey (see page 41) when alternative routes are under consideration. An examination of the proposed longitudinal sections will give a fair indication of the relative amounts of earthworks involved, although an accurate comparison is not possible on account of the uncertainty concerning existing ground levels, which at that stage have to be interpolated from widely spaced contours on the 6-in Ordnance Survey sheets or from infrequent spot heights obtained during a ground survey. Moreover, the absence of detailed information with regard to soil types, rock levels, and ground-water conditions makes true comparison of costs even more difficult.

Once the preliminary survey has been carried out, however, and the alignment fixed with a reasonable degree of certainty, a better estimate of earthworks can be made. In many instances it will still be sufficient to work off the longitudinal profile (plotted to scales of 1 : 2,500 horizontally and 1 : 250 vertically), assuming a constant depth of cut or fill across the section, but on some occasions it may be preferable to draw

Cross-sect. interval	Job ref	WL1	WL2	WL3	WL4	WL5	WR1	WR2	WR3	WR4	WR5
1 2	6 7	9 10 11	15 16	20 21	25 26	30 31	35 36	40 41	45 46	50 51	55 56 60
1		1									
1		1		•	•		•		•	•	•
1		1	•		•		•	•		•	•
1		1		•	•		•	•	•	•	•

Job ref	DC	DL1	DL2	DL3	DL4	DR1	DR2	DR3	DR4	P if punch required
7 9 10 11	14 15	18 19	22 23	26 27	30 31	34 35	38 39	42 43	46 47	
1 2						•			•	
1 2		•		•	•	•	•	•	•	
1 2	•		•	•	•	•	•	•	•	
1 2		•	•	•	•	•	•	•	•	

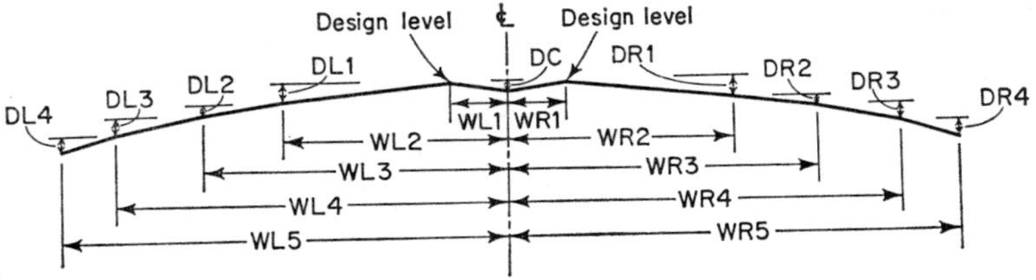

Notes

The widths are expressed in five digits in the form xx·xx
24' 9" is written 02475

The differences in level are in the four digit form xx·xx. A crossfall of $6\frac{1}{2}$ in is written 0054.

From the design level outwards, all the D values give drop in level. If a rise in level is needed at any point put a minus sign over the second decimal place.

FIGURE 7.1 Data for eleven-point motorway cross-section[2]

cross-sections to a 1 : 250 natural scale and measure the areas by planimeter. In either case, side slopes appropriate to the type of material
anticipated in the cuttings and embankments must be chosen (see
Table 8.1). Earthwork volumes are then calculated from cross-
sectional areas at the 100-ft running chainage points using the end areas
formula

$$V = \tfrac{1}{2}L(A_1 + A_2) \qquad (7.1)$$

where A_1 and A_2 are the cross-sectional areas distance L apart.

7.2 Calculation from cross-sectional levels

Whilst the above methods of calculation are sufficiently accurate for
planning purposes, a more precise measurement is eventually required
on which payment to the contractor can be based. Since it is physically
impossible to record every undulation in ground level, the established
method of measurement is by cross-sectioning at 100-ft intervals, or
closer if warranted by the irregular nature of the ground, but there are
a number of variations of procedure. It is therefore important that the
contract documents should state clearly the method of calculation
which is to be employed so as to avoid arguments at a later date.

The traditional procedure is to plot cross-sections at 100-ft centres to
a 1 : 250 natural scale, using spot levels taken along the centre-line and
at offsets of 50, 100, and 150 ft to either side, or wherever there is a
marked change of slope, following the location survey. Alternatively,
if aerial survey methods have been used to produce 1 : 500 scale plans
of the whole road alignment, contoured at 1-ft or 2-ft intervals to an
accuracy of ± 4 in in plan and elevation, the original ground levels can
be taken directly from these plans. In plotting the cross-sections, allowance should be made for the initial stripping of 6–12 in of topsoil over
the full width of the section between the slope stakes, and also for the
placing of a 4–8-in layer of soil on the side slopes of cuttings and embankments. The areas are then measured by planimeter and the volumes
calculated by applying the end areas formula. When working out areas
by planimeter it is necessary to take account of shrinkage of the paper,
and for this reason any photocopy prints of the cross-sections should be
made on true-to-scale printing paper.

7.3 Computer application to earthworks

Since the plotting of cross-sections is a tedious and laborious procedure, considerable use is now being made of computer programmes
for earthwork calculations.[1, 2] With these programmes, data relating to
the finished road levels and the original ground profiles at each cross-
section are fed into the computer together with other data specifying

FIGURE 7.2 Superelevation data for cross-section level programme[a]

Job ref	Chainage at which application starts	Length of application	Length over which super. held	Max. change in level L	Max. change in level R	L	R

(Column positions: 9, 10 … 15 … 19, 20 … 23, 24 … 29, 30 … 33, 34 … 37, 38, 39)

If more than 4 horizontal curves are to be considered consult write-up for interleaving

Job ref: Any 3 characters

Chainage: In form xxxxxxx·xx write 6350 as 000063·5000

Length of application: To nearest foot. For a maximum rate of application of 0·5% make this length 300 times maximum change in level

Length over which super.held: Normally length of circular arc to nearest foot. 600ft write 00600

Maximum change in level left (L) and right (R): This is the distance moved vertically by the outer channels from the straight road condition to the superelevated, expressed in form xx·xx feet

L, R: For left-hand side dropping put D in col. 38, otherwise L for lifting. For right-hand side dropping put D in col. 39 otherwise L for lifting

116 HIGHWAY ENGINEERING

such factors as constructional thickness, depth of topsoil, and side slopes of cuttings and embankments. The computer uses this information to calculate the area of cut or fill at each cross-section and tabulates the total volumes of cut and fill together with the adjusted earthwork balance up to each section. In addition, slope stake coordinates, which are computed at an intermediate stage of the calculations, may be printed out and used, if desired, in setting out these stakes during the constructional survey.

An example of computer application to earthwork calculations can be seen with reference to the design of the 21-mile long Durham Motorway.[2] Figure 7.1 shows the data presentation for an eleven-point motorway cross-section used on tangent sections of the alignment. Offsets are expressed with respect to the road centre-line and levels are related to the edges of the carriageway adjacent to the central reserve which are the pivoting points for the application of superelevation (see page 64). By providing the computer with the 'design levels' at the required intervals of chainage (which, incidentally, can be obtained directly from a previous computer programme—see page 108) together with data relating to the application of superelevation as indicated in Figure 7.2, the cross-section levels can be tabulated at each interval of chainage and data cards punched out for use with the next part of the programme. Part of a typical print-out is given in Table 7.1. If necessary, the standard

TABLE 7.1 *Typical print-out of cross-section levels*[a]

Chainage	52.50	42.50	42.40	32.50	6.50	C.L.	6.50	32.50	42.40	42.50	52.50	Comment
15,100.00	268.09	268.59	268.42	268.75	269.40	269.07	269.40	268.75	268.42	268.59	268.09	VC
15,200.00	269.21	269.71	269.54	269.87	270.52	270.19	270.52	269.87	269.54	269.71	269.21	VC
15,300.00	270.18	270.68	270.51	270.84	271.49	271.16	271.49	270.84	270.51	270.68	270.18	VC
15,400.00	271.00	271.50	271.33	271.66	272.31	271.98	272.31	271.66	271.33	271.50	271.00	VC
15,500.00	271.68	272.18	272.01	272.34	272.99	272.66	272.99	272.34	272.01	272.18	271.68	VC
15,600.00	272.20	272.70	272.53	272.86	273.51	273.18	273.51	272.86	272.53	272.70	272.20	VC
15,700.00	272.57	273.07	272.90	273.23	273.88	273.55	273.88	273.23	272.90	273.07	272.57	VC
15,800.00	272.81	273.31	273.14	273.47	274.12	273.79	274.12	273.47	273.14	273.31	272.81	VC
15,900.00	272.89	273.39	273.22	273.55	274.20	273.87	274.20	273.55	273.22	273.39	272.89	VC
16,000.00	272.83	273.33	273.16	273.49	274.14	273.81	274.14	273.49	273.16	273.33	272.83	VC
16,100.00	272.62	273.12	272.95	273.28	273.93	273.60	273.93	273.28	272.95	273.12	272.62	VC
16,200.00	272.26	272.76	272.59	272.92	273.57	273.24	273.57	272.92	272.59	272.76	272.26	VC

road cross-section cards can be modified to take account of such factors as the addition of acceleration and deceleration lanes and the local widening of the central reserve.

The next part of the computer programme uses the existing ground and finished road levels to calculate the toe distances for cuttings and embankments, the topsoil areas and volumes, and the side slope lengths and areas. The data for the programme comprise:

1. Existing ground levels defined by distance left or right of the centre-line and height above sea level (Figure 7.3).
2. Finished road levels in the same form, as obtained from the first part of the programme or punched by hand.

Notes:

(1) A maximum of 15 points may be defined at one section on 3 cards numbered 1, 2 and 3 in col. 18

(2) The level at the centre line (distance OOOOO) must be given. The programme can work with this one level only

(3) The points are recorded from left to right across the section through the ℄. The left-most level comes first and the right-most last

(4) The number of points may vary and the ℄ need not be in the same relative position

(5) Distance from ℄ (left and right) and level are in the form xxx·xx

(6) Chainage to nearest foot in form xxx,xxx on every card

Job ref	Chainage	CD No	Distance	Level	Distance	Level	Distance	Level	Distance	Level	Distance	Level	Distance	Level	Distance	Level
1 3 4 5	10	18	21 25	26 30	31 35	36 40	41 45	46 50	51 55	56 60	61 65	66 70				

Put high order zeros in chainage.   Col. 18 must be completed (1, 2 or 3)

FIGURE 7.3 Ground level data for earthworks programme[2]

Header card:

This specifies the constant values in the job and the programme uses these throughout successive cross-sections until a new header card inserted in the pack immediately after the group of cards for the cross-section at which the change is required alters the values.

The first header card normally precedes the ground and road level cards.

Notes:

All the values are defined by five digits in the form xxx·xx; hence a verge widening of 2ft is written 00200, and a side slope of 1 in 3 is written 00300, only the horizontal part of the ratio being given.

Job ref	Zero	Put P in col. 10 if punch rqd.	Height for change in side slope	Height of bank at which widening is to be applied	Normal side slope 1 in ~	Side slope above specified height 1 in ~	Widening to be applied to verges	Addition to back verge level in cut	Natural topsoil depth in feet	Depth of soil on slopes measured vertically (ft)	Average construction depth (ft)	Factor applied to cut moved to fill
1	3	4 5	9 10 11	15 16	20 21	25 26	30 31	35 36	40 41	45 46	50 51	55 56	60
	0	H D R										
	0	H D R										
	0	H D R										
	0	H D R										

FIGURE 7.4 Header card data for earthworks programme[2]

TABLE 7.2 *Typical print-out of toe distances, topsoil volumes, and side slope areas²*

Chainage ft	Left toe distance ft	Right toe distance ft	Topsoil area yd²	Total topsoil area yd²	Topsoil volume yd³	Total topsoil volume yd³	Left slope length yd	Right slope length yd	Total slope length yd	Side slope area yd²	Total slope area yd²
15100	148.76	145.57	1635	1635	273	273	34	33	67	1072	1072
15200	142.40	154.54	3299	4934	550	823	32	36	135	2244	3316
15300	130.85	145.64	3072	8006	512	1335	28	33	196	2013	5329
15400	122.77	134.26	2856	10862	476	1811	25	29	250	1782	7111
15500	100.42	115.22	2396	13258	399	2210	17	22	289	1287	8398
15600	69.86	70.50	1560	14818	260	2470	6	7	302	429	8827
15700	63.77	57.17	1344	16162	224	2694	4	2	308	198	9025
15800	57.02	52.61	1218	17380	203	2897	2		310	66	9091
15900	54.11C	53.25	1193	18573	199	3096	1		311	33	9124
16000C	54.92C	56.29	1236	19809	206	3302	1	1	313	66	9190
16100C	60.14C	60.78	1344	21153	224	3526	3	3	319	198	9388
16200C	64.15C	64.84	1433	22586	239	3765	4	5	328	297	9685

3. Side slopes, which may be specified to vary above and below a nominated height.
4. Any widening to verges to be applied above a nominated height of bank.

5. Any alteration to back of verge level when in cutting.
6. Natural topsoil depth.

3–6 need only be specified once at the beginning of the programme (Figure 7.4), but may be altered by inserting a card with new constants at the appropriate chainage. The results are tabulated as shown in Table 7.2, and, if required, new road and ground cards are punched. The road cards have any verge adjustments incorporated in them and the ground levels are pruned off at the toe distances.

The third part of the programme uses the calculated toe distances together with the existing ground and finished road levels to calculate the cut and fill areas at each cross-section, the cut and fill volumes between each successive pair of cross-sections, the running totals of cut and fill, and the earthwork balance up to each chainage, making an allowance in the latter case to take account of bulking and shrinkage of cut material transferred to fill (see page 127).

The data for the programme are:

1. Natural topsoil depth.
2. Depth of soil to be placed on slopes.
3. Average construction depth.
4. Factor applied to cut transferred to fill.
5. Road and ground levels and toe distances produced by the previous part of the programme.

As before, 1–4 apply throughout unless varied by inserting fresh instructions. Results are tabulated in the form shown in Table 7.3. The adjusted earthwork balance is in this case obtained by multiplying the cut

TABLE 7.3 *Typical print-out of earthwork volumes*[2]

Chainage	Cut area yd^2	Fill area yd^2	Cut volume yd^3	Fill volume yd^3	Total cut volume yd^3	Total fill volume yd^3	Adjusted earthwork balance yd^3	Un- adjusted balance yd^3
15,300		603		10,052		10,052	10052–	10052–
15,400		501		16,698		26,750	26750–	26750–
15,500		287		9,566		36,316	36316–	36316–
15,600		95		3,166		39,482	39482–	39482–
15,700		28		933		40,415	40415–	40415–
15,800	7	1	233	33	233	40,448	40238–	40215–
15,900	11		367		600	40,448	39908–	39848–
16,000	36		1,200		1,800	40,448	38828–	38648–
16,100	67		2,233		4,033	40,448	36818–	36415–
16,200	96		3,200		7,233	40,448	33938–	33215–

volume by 0·9 before subtracting the volume of fill. Finally, the earth-works balance curve can be plotted out by the computer to a suitable vertical scale and used in the preparation of the mass haul diagram (see page 128).

The foregoing method of computation implies the manual preparation of ground level data for each cross-section on punched cards or perforated tape. Whilst this is still necessary when ground survey methods are employed and information has to be transferred from the surveyor's level book, it is now possible with photogrammetric methods of survey to use a read-out device in conjunction with a precise stereoscopic plotting instrument to record the coordinates and height of any point on the stereo model automatically on punched cards or tape. Ground levels relating to a selected alignment can thus be obtained directly from the large-scale photographs used in the preparation of 1 : 500 scale plans in a form acceptable to a particular computer programme, and the whole earthworks calculation can be performed in a manner which requires the minimum of attention from the engineer.

One further advantage of the use of computers which should not be overlooked, particularly by organizations having direct access to a machine, is that several trial vertical profiles can be examined in turn to determine which is the most suitable. Such examination would rarely be possible when traditional methods of calculation are employed on account of length of time involved in each calculation. In addition, it should be noted that the earthwork programmes are designed to operate with a minimum amount of data—for example, a single centre-line level can be used to represent the original ground profile at each cross-section if desired—and therefore the computer can be usefully employed for approximate calculations at the preliminary design stage as well as for those of greater accuracy, the advantage being, of course, that the results are available much more quickly than by other more conventional means.

The cost of carrying out earthwork calculations by digital computer depends on the type of machine used, the machine time involved, and the amount of programming required, but for one particular commercial computer is of the order £6–10 per mile with cross-sections at 100-ft intervals.[1]

7.4 Calculation from slope stake coordinates

When a digital computer is not available for earthwork calculations, it is still possible to avoid drawing out individual cross-sections by simplifying the existing ground profile to a form which allows calculations of cross-sectional area to be made by sliderule or by desk calculator.

The method assumes that the original ground slopes uniformly between the centre-line and each slope stake (Figure 7.5) and makes use

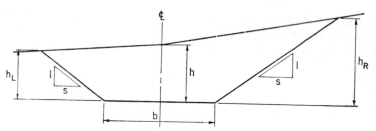

FIGURE 7.5 Three-level section in cutting

of the level differences between these three points and the road formation, which is assumed horizontal at a level representative of the average
value for the cross-section. The cross-sectional area is then given by:

$$A = \tfrac{1}{4}b(h_{\mathrm{L}}' + 2h + h_{\mathrm{R}}) + \tfrac{1}{2}sh(h_{\mathrm{L}} + h_{\mathrm{R}})$$ (7.2)

where b is the width of formation, h_{L} the level difference between the
left-hand slope stake and the formation level, h_{R} the level difference
between the right-hand slope stake and the formation level, h the level
difference between the original ground level along the centre-line and
the formation level, and s the side slope, expressed as 1 (vertically) in
s (horizontally).

Equation 7.2 is derived in Appendix IIa. The volumes between
adjacent pairs of cross-sections can then be obtained as before using
Equation 7.1, making appropriate corrections for the depth of topsoil
to be removed initially and also allowing for subsequent soiling of the
side slopes.

Equation 7.2 is applicable to sections which are wholly in cutting or
wholly on embankment. In many instances the section is in sidelong
ground, being partially in cutting and partially on embankment
(Figure 7.6). The relevant formulae (see Appendix IIb) are in this case:
Area of cut,

$$A_{\mathrm{C}} = \tfrac{1}{4}b\left[\frac{h^2}{(h + h_{\mathrm{L}})} + h + h_{\mathrm{R}}\right] + \tfrac{1}{2}sh\left[\frac{hh_{\mathrm{L}}}{(h + h_{\mathrm{L}})} + h_{\mathrm{R}}\right]$$ (7.3)

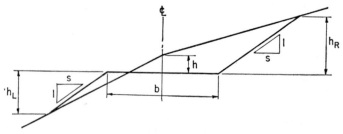

FIGURE 7.6 Three-level section in sidelong ground

Area of fill, $A_F = \frac{1}{4}b\left[\dfrac{h_L{}^2}{(h + h_L)}\right] - \dfrac{shh_L{}^2}{2(h + h_L)}$ (7.4)

7.5 Prismoidal formula

Up to this point, volumes have been calculated from cross-sectional areas by applying the end areas formula (Equation 7.1). If it is assumed that the faces of the earth solid between adjacent cross-sections are planar (Figure 7.7) then the solid so formed is a prismoid and the true

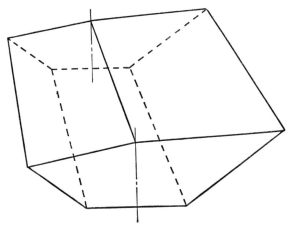

FIGURE 7.7

volume is obtained by using the prismoidal formula:

$$V = \frac{1}{6}L(A_1 + 4M + A_2)$$ (7.5)

where A_1 and A_2 are the cross-sectional areas distance L apart, and M is the area of a section mid-way between the two ends (*Note:* M is not necessarily the mean of A_1 and A_2).

The difference between the two formulae can be illustrated by applying Equations 7.1 and 7.5 in turn to two simple geometrical figures (Figure 7.8). In the first case, a wedge of base area A and length L, the

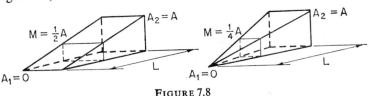

FIGURE 7.8

mid-area is $\frac{1}{2}A$ and both formulae give the volume correctly as $V = \frac{1}{2}AL$. In the second case, a pyramid of base area A and length L, the mid-area

E*

is now $\frac{1}{4}A$ but the end areas formula still gives the volume as $\frac{1}{2}AL$ whilst the prismoidal formula once again gives the correct volume $V = \frac{1}{3}AL$. The end areas formula will in fact overestimate the volume in all cases where the solid is tapering in two directions.

It can be seen that the prismoid depicted in Figure 7.7 is composed of a number of prisms, wedges, and pyramids which together form the total earth volume. For those parts which consist of prisms or wedges either formula will give the correct volume, but for those parts which are pyramids only the prismoidal formula will give the true volume. Fortunately, in general, these comprise only a small fraction of the total volume, and hence the use of the end areas formula leads to only a slight overestimation of the true volume.

The prismoidal formula is in any case difficult to apply where volumes are being determined from cross-sectional levels, either by plotting sections or by computer, although it can be used without a great deal of extra work when volumes are being calculated from slope stake coordinates.

7.6 Prismoidal correction

The prismoidal correction is the difference between the volumes calculated by the end areas and the prismoidal formulae and hence is given by:

$$\text{Prismoidal correction} = \tfrac{1}{2}L(A_1 + A_2) - \tfrac{1}{6}L(A_1 + 4M + A_2)$$
$$= \tfrac{1}{3}L(A_1 - 2M + A_2) \qquad (7.6)$$

It is normally a positive quantity, but for certain unusually shaped earth solids may be negative.

When it is felt desirable to apply the prismoidal formula to earthwork calculations, the usual practice is to use the end areas formula in the first instance and then subtract the prismoidal correction. At first glance, this may seem to offer no reduction in the amount of calculation involved, since both Equations 7.5 and 7.6 require the evaluation of the mid-area M. However, with a three-level section Equation 7.6 can be modified and expressed in a much more usable form in terms of the level differences at the two end cross-sections, giving for both the general case with the section wholly in cutting or on embankment and the particular case in sidelong ground (see Appendices IIc and IId):

$$\text{Prismoidal correction} = \tfrac{1}{12}Ls(h - h')[(h_L - h_L') + (h_R - h_R')] \qquad (7.7)$$

where h_L, h, and h_R are the level differences between the original ground surface and the formation at one end section of the prismoid. h_L', h', h_R' are the corresponding values at the other end section, L the distance between the two sections, and s is the side slope, expressed as 1 in s. Equation 7.7 is thus applied to each pair of cross-sections in turn to determine the prismoidal correction for each 100-ft length.

7.7 Curvature correction

The calculations for volume dealt with so far are strictly applicable only to straight sections of road, since using the end areas or prismoidal formulae requires the end cross-sections to be in parallel planes. When the centre-line of a road describes a circular arc or transition spiral, this basic provision no longer applies. However, it is still convenient to consider the cross-sections as being parallel in order to calculate the volume and then apply a curvature correction where warranted.

Consider three successive cross-sections on a circular arc in cutting (Figure 7.9), where X, Y, and Z are the centre-line pegs and ACE,

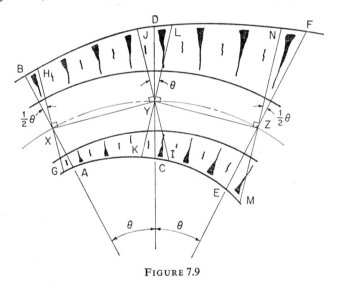

FIGURE 7.9

BDF mark the limits of excavation. Then for the calculation of the volume between cross-sections at X and Y, if the earth solid is assumed to be prismoidal, the actual volume calculated will be that between the parallel planes GXH and IYJ at right angles to the chord XY. Similarly, if the same assumption is made for the volume between the cross-sections at Y and Z, the actual volume calculated will be that between the parallel planes KYL and MZN at right angles to the chord YZ. Hence in the total volume measurement for the cutting, the volume represented in plan by triangle IYK will have been included twice, whilst that represented in plan by triangle JYL will have been omitted altogether.

If these volumes are equal, as would be the case with the original ground surface at a constant level across the section, then the net error will be zero. However, with sloping ground, as is more usually the case, an error equal to the difference in the volumes represented in plan by triangles JYL and IYK will be incurred. It is therefore necessary to correct for such an error at each cross-section along the curve.

If Figure 7.10 represents the cross-section of the cutting at peg Y, then the volume represented in plan by triangle IYK is approximately equal to the area CYQP rotated about axis YQ through an angle θ. Similarly, the volume represented in plan by triangle JYL is equal to the area YDRQ rotated about axis YQ through an angle θ. Hence the net volume difference, or curvature correction, at the section is equal to area YDS rotated about axis YQ through an angle θ, where S is the mirror image of C on the cross-section.

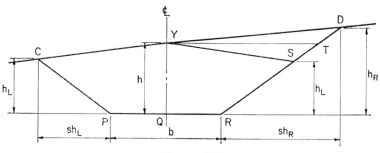

FIGURE 7.10

In the case of the three-level section, this area $= \frac{1}{2}YT.(h_R - h_L)$, where YT is a horizontal line, i.e.

$$A = \frac{1}{2}(\frac{1}{2}b + sh)(h_R - h_L)$$

The volume is equal to the area multiplied by the length of path of the centroid when rotated about axis YQ through an angle θ. The centroid lies at a horizontal distance $\frac{2}{3}[\frac{1}{2}b + \frac{1}{2}(sh_L + sh_R)]$ from the axis, and thus the volume equals

$$\frac{1}{2}(\frac{1}{2}b + sh)(h_R - h_L) \times \frac{2}{3}[\frac{1}{2}b + \frac{1}{2}(sh_L + sh_R)] \times \theta$$

Writing $\theta = L/R$ for a curve of radius R with cross-sections distance L apart, the curvature correction

$$= \frac{L}{12R}(b + 2sh)(h_R - h_L)(b + sh_L + sh_R) \qquad (7.8)$$

The correction is applicable to each cross-section on the horizontal curve, being added or subtracted according to the slope of the original ground surface in relation to the hand of the curve. When the cross-section occurs at a tangent point, then the curvature correction is half the above value, since the area is rotated only through an angle $\frac{1}{2}\theta$.

7.8 *Use of prismoidal and curvature corrections*

The difficulties associated with applying prismoidal corrections to volumes other than those calculated from simplified three-level sections have already been mentioned, and similar difficulty exists with the use of curvature corrections. For this reason it is common practice to ignore these corrections altogether and use only the end areas formula for volume calculations. The total error involved by this approximation is unlikely to exceed 5% and in many instances will be much smaller.

Where corrections can be determined, it is largely a matter of opinion as to whether or not they should be brought into the calculations. On one hand, it can be argued that the approximation of the existing ground surface to a three-level section is in itself introducing too great an inaccuracy to justify the subsequent use of these corrections. Conversely, it can be pointed out that errors incurred by ground surface irregularities should compensate each other, whilst those introduced by omitting prismoidal and curvature corrections are cumulative, although on longer contracts the latter would compensate to some extent.

Whichever system is adopted, the important point is that the contract documents should state explicitly the method of measurement to be used so that disputes over payment can be avoided when final measurement is being carried out.

7.9 *Bulking and shrinkage of materials*

Some materials such as rock and chalk increase in volume when excavated and subsequently compacted to form an embankment, whilst others such as gravel, sandy soils, and clays show a decrease in volume as a result of more thorough compaction. These phenomena are termed *bulking* and *shrinkage*.

Standard practice is to base payment on the volume of voids formed by the removal of excavated material without allowance for bulking and shrinkage;[3, 4] thus avoiding the necessity to take account of these factors. When considering the balancing of earthworks between cuttings and embankments, however, allowance must be made for bulking and shrinkage by adjusting the excavated volumes in accordance with the nature of the material to be handled. In practice, trials or experience of the material are necessary to determine the appropriate factor to be used, since this varies considerably from one material to another, but typical values are 1·3 for rock and 0·9 for sands and clays.

MASS HAUL DIAGRAM

7.10 Haulage of material

The cost of any earth-moving operation depends not only on the volume and nature of the materials to be handled but also on the distance which these materials have to be carried from the point of excavation to the point of tipping and compaction. In road schemes, the earthworks are usually planned so that, where suitable, material excavated from a cutting can be used to form an embankment further along the road. As this may entail carting (or hauling) the material over a considerable distance, the cost of haulage must be taken into account either by inserting an appropriate item in the Bill of Quantities or, alternatively, by the contractor making allowance for haulage in the rates quoted for the item(s) covering excavation in cutting and forming of embankments.

Current practice on most road construction contracts is to use the latter arrangement. This avoids the necessity to agree haulage distances and simplifies the final measurement of earthworks, particularly when some of the excavated material is unsuitable for use in embankments. In this case, it is left to the contractor to estimate the amount of haulage involved and adjust his prices accordingly, and this can best be determined by constructing a mass haul or earthworks balance diagram.

7.11 Nature of the mass haul diagram

The mass haul diagram is related to the longitudinal profile of the road and shows the net cumulative volume, adjusted for bulking and shrinkage, up to any chainage along the centre-line. Excavated volumes in cutting are considered positive whilst volumes of embankments are negative. The diagram (Figure 7.11) has certain characteristics which may be listed as follows:

1. If at any chainage the diagram is above the base line, then the net volume up to that section is positive; that is, a surplus of cut. Below the base line denotes a deficit of fill.
2. A rising gradient on the diagram means that the road is in cutting at that section. A falling gradient denotes embankment.
3. A maximum point occurs at the end of a cutting and a minimum point occurs at the end of an embankment.
4. The vertical distance between any two points on the diagram is a measure of the net volume of earthworks between these sections.
5. Any horizontal line on the diagram, including the base line, cuts the diagram at sections between which earthworks are balanced.
6. The length of any such balance line represents the maximum haulage distance between the sections.

Horizontal balance lines such as ABC can be inserted on the diagram by the contractor to assist in planning his earthworks programme. This will be governed to some extent by site conditions and by the availability of bridges to cross physical barriers such as rivers and railways and also by the desirability to carry out scraper excavation and transportation on a falling gradient. Depending on the actual cost of excavation, hauling, and compacting, a situation may eventually be reached when it is not economical to transport excavated material from

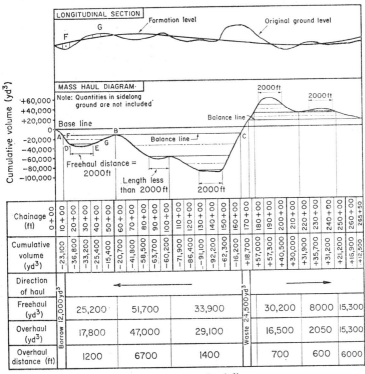

FIGURE 7.11 Mass haul diagram

one point on the contract to another some distance away, since it would be cheaper to run the material from a cutting into a nearby spoil heap and excavate a corresponding amount of material from a borrow pit close to the site of the embankment. Thus the most economical arrangement of balance lines may be as shown in Figure 7.11 with some 12,000 cu yd of material being imported to form part of the embankment at the start of the contract whilst some 24,500 cu yd of excavated material is run to waste between chainages 161 + 00 and 168 + 00.

A convenient method of disposing of surplus material is to build embankments to an overall greater width, or with flatter side slopes, than actually required by the contract. Similarly, a cutting may sometimes be widened to provide additional filling material.

7.12 Freehaul and overhaul

On certain road contracts, the Bill of Quantities may be drawn up so that the items relating to general excavation and compaction of material include haulage only within a specified distance, termed the *freehaul distance*. Haulage over and above this distance is paid for under an additional item, the unit for which is cu yd per 100 ft, and the extra distance involved is termed the *overhaul distance*. The amounts of material involved under these items are termed the *freehaul* and *overhaul* respectively, and these volumes can be ascertained by reference to the mass haul diagram.

If in Figure 7.11, lines such as DE are drawn of length equal to the freehaul distance, say 2,000 ft, then the volumes of material on which overhaul payments are required are given by the vertical distances between these freehaul lines and the corresponding balance lines. The overhaul distances are measured between the respective centres of gravity of the material in cutting and in embankment minus the freehaul distance, for example FG − DE = FD + EG. (For most practical purposes, FG can be considered to bisect the vertical distance between DE and the balance line AB, although this is not strictly correct.) Similarly, other freehaul lines of length equal to, or less than, 2,000 ft can be drawn on the diagram, the freehaul, overhaul, and overhaul distances obtained, and the data tabulated below the diagram. The cost of the earth-moving operations can then be calculated by applying the appropriate rates to these quantities.

REFERENCES

1. ELLIOTT BROTHERS (LONDON) LTD, 'Cut and Fill: a Program for the Elliott 402F Digital Computer', *Cement and Concrete Association Publication DC11/60* (London: Cement and Concrete Association, 1960)
2. COTTON, W. H. B. and PETRIE, J. M., 'Digital Computers and their Use in a County Highways Department', *J. Instn. Highw. Engrs.* (London: vol. 11, 1964, pp. 72–88)
3. INSTITUTION OF CIVIL ENGINEERS, *Standard Method of Measurement of Civil Engineering Quantities* (London: Instn. civ. Engrs., 1953)
4. MINISTRY OF TRANSPORT, *Notes on the Third Edition of the Specification for Road and Bridge Works and on the Preparation of Bills of Quantities* (London: H.M.S.O., 1963)

8

Earthwork Formation

Road construction consists essentially of two distinct phases; firstly the earthworks and secondly the construction of the overlying pavement which forms the actual running surface of the road. The earthworks are concerned with the preparation of the natural soil or imported filling material to the correct levels, gradients, and crossfalls, and ideally the longitudinal profile of the road should be so arranged that all the material excavated from cuttings, if suitable, can be used in forming embankments. The upper surface of the earthworks is termed the *formation*, and the soil lying immediately below this level is referred to as the *subgrade*.

The engineering problems associated with earthworks can be subdivided into those which are present during construction and those which are related to the subsequent opening of the road to traffic. The former may be grouped under the general heading of stability and settlement problems, whilst the latter are concerned with the ability of the subgrade to withstand the wheel loads transmitted through the road pavement.

8.1 *Stability and settlement problems*

These problems arise during the formation of embankments and cuttings and can be handled by the application of soil mechanics principles, using information given by the soil survey (see page 49). Detailed discussion of many of these topics falls outside the scope of this book, but it is considered appropriate to mention the chief problems encountered and explain briefly the various methods which may be adopted to overcome constructional difficulties.

One of the most important considerations at the design stage is the choice of suitable side slopes for cuttings and embankments. With non-cohesive soils, the maximum side slopes are governed only by the natural angle of repose of the material, but a slip-circle analysis[1] is necessary with cohesive soils to take account of the overall height of the bank. Typical side slopes for various materials are shown in Table 8.1. Slopes of 1 in 2 and flatter can be formed and maintained by mechanical plant travelling up the slope, and for this reason it is often preferable to use a maximum side slope of 1 in 2 rather than that determined purely by stability considerations. At bridge sites, the side slopes are often increased to 1 in 1½ and revetted, if necessary, to reduce the span or decrease the length of the wing walls.

Where the subsoil underlying an embankment consists of unstable material such as peat or soft clay, special precautions must be taken to prevent damage to the finished road surface as a result of the super-imposed load of the embankment causing consolidation of this under-lying layer. If this material exists as a shallow deposit up to about 10 ft

TABLE 8.1 *Typical side slopes for cuttings and embankments*

Material	Cuttings	Embankments
Igneous rocks and hard sedimentary rocks	1 in ¼	1 in 1–1½
Slate, shales, marls, chalk, and softer sedimentary rocks	1 in ½–¾	1 in 1½
Gravel	1 in 1	1 in 1½
Sand	1 in 1½–2	1 in 1½–2
Clay	1 in 2	1 in 2–4

in depth then the most satisfactory treatment is to excavate it completely and replace it by selected fill. Where the layer is of greater thickness, complete excavation would in most cases be uneconomical and other methods of treatment must be considered.

One approach is to excavate the peat to a depth of 8–10 ft, leaving the lower part to be displaced by the weight of the embankment itself. This displacement process can be accelerated by providing a surcharge load of about 5 ft of filling material above the embankment formation level. When the underlying subsoil is sufficiently stiff to resist displacement in this manner, but is still liable to give rise to considerable settlement, the process may be assisted by using explosives, termed 'bog blasting', or by jetting.

In the jetting procedure, the embankment is built across the com-pressible subsoil and pipes of ¾–1 in diameter are sunk to just above the bottom of the soft layer. The pipes are then withdrawn slowly as water is pumped into the material at pressures of up to 250 lb/sq in. The increase in moisture content reduces the strength of the soft material so allowing its displacement by the overlying fill. In some cases, jetting has been used effectively in conjunction with bog blasting.

A further alternative form of construction over peat incorporates a lightweight raft of brushwood or logs placed directly on top of the compressible subsoil. These fascine mattresses serve to spread the weight of the road, so reducing differential settlement, and at the same time prevent fill material from penetrating and sinking into the underlying layer. Fascines have been used with considerable success for both main and secondary roads in Holland, and also in the Highlands of Scotland. Various methods of road construction over peat have been reviewed by Tresidder.[2]

When the nature of the subsoil material is such that the cost of full or partial excavation cannot be justified but consolidation is still probable, or if the embankment itself consists of clay compacted at a moisture

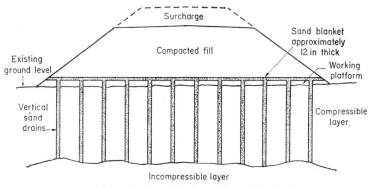

FIGURE 8.1 Vertical sand drains under road embankment

content close to its plastic limit and hence in a near-saturated condition, consolidation may be allowed for by delaying the construction of the road pavement for a year or more after forming the embankment. This is of particular importance in the vicinity of underpasses where differential settlement is likely to occur.

If such a delay is not possible under the specific contractual conditions, the rate of consolidation can be increased by surcharge loading the embankment or by the use of vertical sand drains. These are sand-filled boreholes, usually 8–24 in diameter, and are formed at 6–20-ft centres in the compressible layer, connecting to a horizontal sand blanket at ground level (Figure 8.1). Sand drains decrease the length of the drainage path which the water has to travel as it is squeezed out of the soil and so enable the pore water pressure to be dissipated more quickly. Approximately 3,300 sand drains, 15 in diameter and driven at 10-ft centres to a depth of between 15 and 30 ft, were used to stabilize the soft, alluvial deposits of sandy or clayey silts underlying the northern embankment to the Thelwall Bridge (M.6) over the river Mersey. Experience has shown, however, that vertical sand drains do not increase the rate of settlement of embankments constructed over peat.[3]

8.2 *Factors affecting subgrade strength*

The strength of the subgrade determines the thickness of the pavement layer which is required to transmit the wheel loads to the subgrade. To give an economical thickness of pavement, the subgrade strength should be made as high as possible. This can be achieved by:

1. Removing poor material from the floor of cuttings and replacing with selected fill, and rejecting poor material for forming embankments or using only in the lower layers.
2. Providing adequate subsoil drainage.
3. Avoiding frost damage to the subgrade.
4. Ensuring thorough compaction of the subgrade to a high dry density.

The implications of 2, 3, and 4 will be considered in turn.

SUBSOIL DRAINAGE

8.3 *Seepage and moisture movement*

Increases in moisture content reduce the strength and bearing capacity of a soil and must therefore be minimized as much as possible. In addition, changes in the moisture content of clay soils may give rise to corresponding volume changes such that swelling of the soil takes place with increase in moisture content and shrinkage with decrease in moisture content.

Changes in soil moisture content can take place in various ways, the most usual of which are indicated diagrammatically in Figure 8.2. To counteract such possible changes, a subsoil drainage system should be provided on those sections of the road where necessary. These drains are best located in parallel trenches running either side of the paved

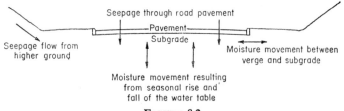

FIGURE 8.2

carriageway as shown in Figure 8.3. A herring-bone system of drains is undesirable, except where the subgrade is excessively wet, since the formation under the carriageways must be disturbed during installation and difficulties may occur in maintenance. Surface water run-off from the carriageway should be prevented from entering the subsoil drains by

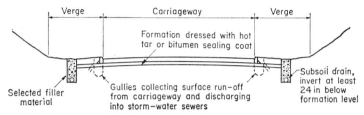

FIGURE 8.3 Subsoil drainage system

collecting into gullies which discharge into a separate surface water sewer (see page 267).

Subsoil drains are usually not less than 6 in diameter and may be formed with either salt-glazed ware or concrete pipes laid with open joints, or may be porous or perforated concrete pipes. Agricultural land drains are sometimes used for under-carriageway-formation drains.

(i) *Seepage from high ground*
Seepage from high ground occurs when a layer of permeable soil overlies an impermeable layer. If the depth to this layer is less than 4 ft below formation level, the subsoil drain should be constructed as a cut-off drain with the trench taken down to the impermeable surface (Figure 8.4). In this case, the pipe should be bedded on impervious

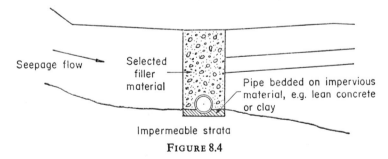

FIGURE 8.4

material such as clay or lean concrete to prevent water from collecting underneath the pipe and eventually causing deterioration of the subgrade. Where the impermeable stratum is at a lower level and the seepage zone is deep, then it is generally not practicable to intercept all the seepage water and the intercepting subsoil drain is positioned so as to keep the seepage water at least 4 ft below formation level. In cases where an impermeable layer outcrops across the line of a road, as on a gradient, additional transverse cut-off drains may be necessary to intercept seepage water under the road itself.

(ii) *Seepage through road pavement*
It is difficult to achieve a completely impermeable road surface since the joints between concrete road slabs tend to deteriorate after a time and so allow ingress of water, in addition to which the action of successive freezing and thawing will eventually cause the deterioration and cracking of most surfacing materials. Means must therefore be found of preventing such moisture from penetrating into the subgrade and so causing further deterioration of the pavement. Perhaps the most satisfactory solution, and one which has the added advantage of protecting the subgrade during construction, is to apply a hot tar or bitumen sealing coat to the formation as soon as it has been prepared. *Road Note No. 17*[4] specifies tars and cut-back bitumens which are suitable for this purpose and also indicates acceptable rates of spread. Where subsoil drains are provided, this sealing coat or surface dressing should extend as far as the drainage trench and in any case for at least 3 ft beyond the edges of the carriageway so that water percolating through the road surface is carried to a point where it will not affect the soil beneath the road.

(iii) *Suction from water table*
Where roads are in cutting or at ground level, it is important to prevent the water table from rising too close to formation level, since moisture movements associated with capillary action can cause changes in subgrade moisture content. It is usually considered that a stable subgrade can be maintained if the water table is kept at least 4–5 ft below formation level, and subsoil drains running along the carriageway at the appropriate depth will achieve this. An estimate of the capacity requirements of these drains may be obtained by measuring the depth of the water table at a number of points transversely across the road whilst ground water is being pumped from open trenches dug out along the line of the proposed subsoil drains. Such tests should normally be carried out in winter when the water table is standing at its highest level.

(iv) *Moisture movement between verge and subgrade*
Further changes in the moisture content of the road pavement and subgrade materials may take place as a result of the transfer of moisture to and from the soil in the road verges. The verges will normally have a higher moisture content than the subgrade in winter and a lower one in summer, and therefore moisture will be transferred to the subgrade in winter and *vice versa* in summer. With clay subgrades, this will result in

swelling and shrinkage of the subgrade along the carriageway edges with consequent differential rise and fall with respect to the road crown, and in spells of prolonged drought may give rise to longitudinal cracking along the road surface. A subsoil drain situated between the verge and the carriageway will prevent this transfer of moisture, but on those sections of road where subsoil drainage is not otherwise required, as on embankments, then the use of surfaced or paved shoulders alongside the carriageway, as on the more recent motorways, removes the point of weakness from the edge of the carriageway to the outside of the shoulder where its effect is much less critical.

8.4 Trench backfill material

Experience has shown that the grading of the material used to backfill the drainage trench should be carefully selected in accordance with that of the surrounding soil so that the filler offers little resistance to the flow of water but resists the passage of silt. Laboratory tests made by the U.S. Corps of Engineers[5] have indicated that the proper grading of the backfill (filter) material should be such that the 15% size of the backfill is at least 5 times the 15% size but not more than 5 times the 85% size of the adjacent soil. The former requirement ensures that the backfill is more permeable than the soil, whilst the latter provides for sufficient fine material in the backfill to prevent infiltration of the surrounding soil causing clogging of the filter material and the subsoil drain and also possible erosion of the subgrade. For a cohesive soil, the 15% size of the backfill material need not be less than 0·1 mm.

The limit for the coarse particle sizes of the backfill is determined by

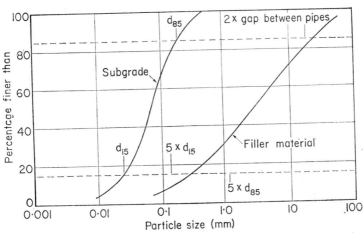

FIGURE 8.5 Relation between particle-size distribution of subgrade and subsoil drain backfill material[5]

the sizes of the holes in perforated pipes or the gaps at the joints of open-jointed pipes. The 85% size of the backfill must be greater than twice this size. A suitable grading curve in accordance with these requirements is shown in Figure 8.5.

FROST DAMAGE TO SUBGRADE

8.5 *Frost heave*

During periods of very low temperatures, frost may penetrate deeply into the subgrade and trouble may be experienced with certain types of

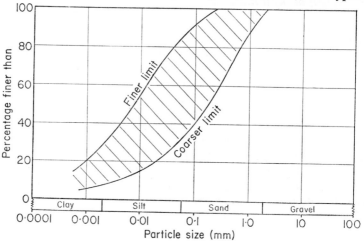

FIGURE 8.6 Particle-size limits within which soils are likely to be frost-susceptible under British climatic conditions

soils as a result of moisture freezing in the soil pores. Associated with this freezing process are suction forces which tend to draw moisture upwards through the soil into the freezing zone. If the particle-size distribution of the soil is such that there are sufficient small pores in an ice-free condition, then considerable migration of water takes place and horizontal layers or lenses of ice are formed in the upper layers of the soil. These lenses vary in thickness from $\frac{1}{32}$ in to over 1 in and result in a corresponding displacement of the road surface—a phenomenon known as *frost heave*. During periods of thaw, thawing will normally take place from the formation downwards, so causing water to be trapped in the subgrade above a frozen zone of soil. This will result in a loss of subgrade strength and bearing capacity, and may necessitate the road being closed to prevent serious damage occurring to the road pavement.

The soils which are particularly liable to cause frost heave are those containing an appreciable amount of small-sized particles (at least 15% finer than 0·02 mm) but not having sufficient fine particles to reduce the soil permeability to the extent that water is unable to enter the frozen soil zone at the required rate, as is the case with most medium and heavy clays. Investigations carried out in southern England by the Road Research Laboratory over a period of ten years suggest particle-size limits for frost-susceptible soils as shown in Figure 8.6.

The formation of ice lenses can be reduced by ensuring that the level of the water table is well below formation, since the suction exerted by the growth of these lenses must be sufficient to draw moisture upwards through the soil. The likelihood of frost damage may be further reduced by providing sufficient constructional thickness of pavement above formation level to prevent frost penetration to this depth. It has usually been considered in this country that 18 in of pavement is sufficient for this purpose, but experience in the winter 1962–3 has shown that frost may penetrate to a depth of 24 in or more in exceptionally prolonged cold spells. On main roads, this thickness is often required in any case from traffic loading considerations, but on secondary roads, particularly those constructed on chalk subgrades which are also very frost-susceptible but which would otherwise need only perhaps 8 in of pavement, the financial aspect often precludes construction to a safe thickness and occasional frost damage must be tolerated.

COMPACTION OF SOIL

8.6 *Theory of soil compaction*

Loose soil consists of particles of soil and water together with air voids. Compaction of the soil reduces the proportion of air voids and hence subsequent changes in moisture content are less likely to occur. If compaction is not carried out thoroughly during construction, then traffic using the road at a future date will cause further compaction to take place with consequent distortion and damage to the road pavement.

When a sample of soil is compacted in the laboratory in a standard manner at various moisture contents, then the dry density produced by the compaction process is related to the soil moisture content in a manner such as Figure 8.7. At low moisture contents, the soil is stiff and difficult to work, and therefore the compacted soil still contains an appreciable proportion of air voids and hence has a low dry density. With increasing moisture content, the same amount of effort is able to produce a greater degree of compaction and a correspondingly greater dry density until a point is reached where the voids in the soil are almost completely filled with water. From this point, further increases in

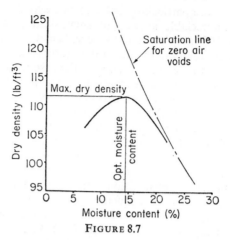

FIGURE 8.7

moisture content result in soil particles being displaced by water, and the dry density thus decreases again as the soil approaches the saturation line for zero air voids, which is given by the relationship:

$$\gamma_D = \frac{G\gamma_W}{1 + mG} \quad \text{(see Appendix III)} \tag{8.1}$$

where γ_D is the dry density of the soil, γ_W the density of water, and G the specific gravity of the soil particles.

$$m \text{ is the moisture content of the soil} = \frac{\text{wt. of water}}{\text{wt. of soil particles}}$$

The maximum dry density for a given amount of compaction occurs at a certain moisture content which is termed the *optimum moisture*

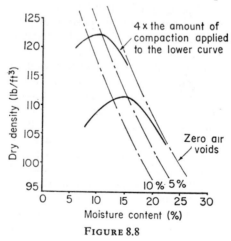

FIGURE 8.8

content. If the amount of compactive effort is increased, a different compaction curve is produced having a higher value of maximum dry density and a lower optimum moisture content (Figure 8.8). The maximum dry densities occur along a line which corresponds approximately to the theoretical curve for 5% air voids,

$$\gamma_D = 0.95 \frac{G\gamma_W}{1 + mG} \tag{8.2}$$

8.7 Standard compaction tests

To enable a comparison to be made between various types of soil, the amount of compaction has been standardized for laboratory testing. B.S. 1377: 1961[6] gives the procedures for two standard tests which are termed the B.S. Standard Compaction Test and the B.S. Heavy Compaction Test respectively.

In the former test, a sample of soil is air dried and passed through a ¾-in B.S. sieve, after which it is mixed with a small amount of water and compacted in three equal layers into a mould 4 in diameter and 4·6 in high (volume $\frac{1}{30}$ cu ft) using a 2-in diameter rammer weighing 5½ lb and falling through a height of 12 in. 25 blows are given to each layer of soil, after which a 2-in high surcharge collar is removed and the soil is trimmed off level with the top of the mould. The mould is then weighed to determine the bulk density of the soil and the moisture content is found by taking a sample of compacted soil from the interior of the mould. The dry density is then calculated from the formula:

$$\gamma_D = \frac{\gamma_B}{1 + m} \tag{8.3}$$

where γ_B is the bulk density of the soil.

The procedure is repeated at increasing moisture contents over the range 3–15% in steps of about 1·5% for sandy soils and 9–26% in steps of about 3% for cohesive soils, using a fresh sample of soil for each test, and the dry density–moisture content curve is drawn. If the specific gravity of the soil particles is known then the theoretical curve for zero air voids serves as a guide for drawing the compaction curve at the higher moisture contents. This test was first developed by Proctor in 1933 in California and is sometimes referred to as the Proctor or A.A.S.H.O. (American Association of State Highway Officials) Test.

The B.S. Heavy Compaction Test (otherwise known as the Modified A.A.S.H.O. Test) is similar, but uses a 10-lb rammer falling through a height of 18 in and the soil sample is compacted in five equal layers instead of in three. Since the compactive effort is approximately 4½ times that of the Standard Compaction Test, a higher maximum dry density and a lower optimum moisture content is produced, the difference between the two tests being more marked with clay and silty soils rather than with sands and gravels.

8.8 Field compaction plant

A variety of different types of compaction plant are available for compacting soil in the field, and these may be broadly classified into three groups in which the compactive effort is applied to the soil by rolling, ramming, and vibration respectively.

The most usual types of rollers in this country are the smooth-wheeled roller (Plate 8.1) and the pneumatic-tyred roller (Plate 8.2). Smooth-wheeled rollers are self-propelled and may be either the conventional three-wheel type or the tandem type, with a total dead weight of up to 20 tons. The distribution of weight between the rolls can be adjusted by a sliding weight or by ballasting the wheels with water.

Pneumatic-tyred rollers are usually the multiple-wheel type, consisting of a platform or box mounted between two axles. The rear axle has one more wheel than the front axle, and the wheels are so arranged that they track between each other to give full coverage at each pass. The roller is loaded with kentledge (or ballasted with water in the case of the box type) to increase the effective weight. The earlier types of roller were up to 12 tons gross weight, with tyre pressures in the range 30–40 lb/sq in, but in recent years much larger rollers have been developed to enable the compaction specification requirements to be more easily achieved. One such roller is 45 tons gross weight and has four closely spaced wheels mounted on a single axle with tyre pressures of 140 lb/sq in.

A third type of roller rarely used in this country is the sheepsfoot roller which consists of a hollow cylindrical steel drum with projecting feet which may be club-foot or taper-foot in shape. The roller may be ballasted with water or wet sand and is towed by a tractor. A typical size of roller is 5 tons gross weight with an 8 ft long by 3 ft 6 in diameter roll. The sheepsfoot roller compacts a layer of soil from the bottom upwards in contrast with the smooth-wheeled and pneumatic-tyred rollers which compact from the surface downwards.

A more recent introduction into the range of compaction plant is the grid roller which gives a kneading action to the soil in addition to static compression and is thus a variation of the smooth-wheeled roller.

In the second group of compacting plant, energy is applied to the soil by ramming, the most common appliances being the frog rammer and the small power rammer (Plate 8.3). The former may weigh up to 1 ton and have a base diameter of 3 ft whilst the latter normally weighs between 70 lb and 3 cwt. Rammers have a low output compared with rollers, but are useful in confined spaces such as when backfilling trenches.

Vibratory compactors may be either plate or roller type (Plates 8.4 and 8.5), the larger machines often being self-propelled units (Plate 8.6).

The smaller vibratory units are particularly useful for compacting confined areas to which access would be difficult for the larger types of compaction plant, as for instance behind bridge abutments (Plate 8.7).

8.9 Comparative performance of compaction plant

In order to assess the relative merits of these various types of compaction plant with different types of soil, the Road Research Laboratory has carried out several series of full-scale tests under controlled conditions. For the earlier tests[7, 8] five different soil types typical of British conditions were used—a heavy clay, a silty clay, a sandy clay, a sand, and a gravel–sand–clay (hoggin)—and each was prepared to a 9-in loose thickness resting on top of a 2-ft base of compacted soil in order to simulate field conditions. The dry density of each soil was determined after a progressively increasing number of passes of the plant under test, this procedure being repeated over a range of moisture contents and continuing in each case until refusal or 64 passes. The relationships between dry density, moisture content, and the number of passes were then examined.

A similar procedure was adopted for a later series of tests with different sizes of pneumatic-tyred rollers,[9] except that in some of these tests the soils were prepared to a 12-in loose thickness, since preliminary tests had shown that the heavier rollers could compact layers of this thickness satisfactorily. Three of the soil types used, heavy clay, well-graded sand, and gravel–sand–clay, were almost identical with the corresponding soils of the earlier tests, but the fourth soil, a sandy clay, was intermediate between the silty clay and sandy clay used previously. Subsequent series of tests have since been carried out with heavier types of vibrating rollers and vibrating-plate compactors[10, 11] and more recently with vibrating sheepsfoot rollers[12] (Plate 8.8).

All the tests showed a relationship between dry density and moisture content similar to that obtained in laboratory compaction tests with a maximum dry density occurring at a certain optimum moisture content, both values varying according to the type of compaction plant used and the number of passes employed. Figure 8.9 shows a number of typical curves for the silty clay. However, the tests further showed that there was no correlation between the relative performance of the various items of plant throughout the full range of soils tested, nor between any single item of plant and either of the laboratory compaction tests (Table 8.2). It therefore follows that these laboratory tests cannot be used to predict plant performance in the field and that their principal value lies in the classification and selection of suitable fill material. It should also be noted that the term 'optimum moisture content' is meaningless unless related to a particular item of compaction plant and a stated number of passes.

The dry density–moisture content curve for a particular soil compacted by a particular type of plant can thus be established only by carrying out full-scale compaction trials in advance of actual construction. These trials will show the maximum dry density which can be achieved by a given number of passes of that type of plant and the corresponding optimum moisture content. This moisture content may, however, not be the most suitable for constructional purposes, since if it differs greatly from the natural moisture content of the excavated material then the soil will require either mechanical aeration or spraying with water to obtain this optimum value. Under normal British conditions, especially in winter, it will rarely be practicable to reduce the

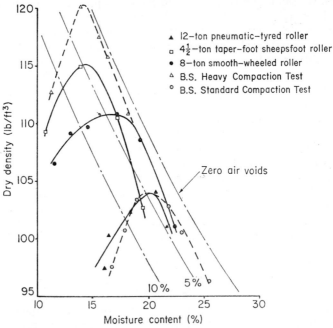

FIGURE 8.9 Effect of moisture content on the dry density of silty clay fully-compacted in 9-in loose layers by different types of plant[7]

moisture content of cohesive soils by aeration without causing undue delays in construction. Furthermore, since subsequent changes in moisture content of cohesive soils result in corresponding volume changes, the ideal moisture content at which the soil should be compacted is that which will not change significantly during the life of the road. This 'equilibrium moisture content' can be calculated from a knowledge of the suction properties of the soil, but in practice it is usual to assume it to be the same as the natural moisture content of the soil

BLE 8.2 *Comparison of maximum dry densities (lb/cu ft) and optimum moisture contents obtained for different soils in laboratory tests and when fully compacted by various types of compaction plant*[7, 8]

type	Heavy clay		Silty clay		Sandy clay		Sand		Gravel–sand–clay	
	Max. dry dens.	Opt. m.c.	Max. dry dens.	Opt. m.c.	Max. dry dens.	Opt. m.c.	Max. dry dens.	Opt. m.c.	Max. dry dens.	Opt. m.c.
Standard Compaction Test	97	26	104	21	115	14	121	11	129	9
Heavy Compaction Test	113	17	120	14	128	11	130	9	138	7
on smooth-wheeled roller	96	21	110	17	114	16	131	9	137	7
on smooth-wheeled roller	104	20	111	16	116	14	132	9	138	7
on pneumatic-tyred roller	98	25	105	20	108	18	127	11	126	7
on club-foot sheepsfoot roller	107	16	116	13	119	12	*	*	130	6
on taper-foot sheepsfoot roller	107	15	115	14	120	12	*	*	128	5
cwt frog rammer	106	17	110	15	116	13	128	10	136	7
wt frog rammer	110	18	116	12	121	11	129	8	137	6
wt vibrating roller	*	*	*	*	*	*	124	11	123	8
on vibrating roller	96	21	110	17	†	†	133	7	139	6
wt vibrating-plate compactor	*	*	*	*	*	*	128	10	127	9
on vibrating-plate compactor	98	17	†	†	117	15	128	9	137	7

* plant unsuitable   † plant not tested

measured 3–4 ft below the surface, that is at a depth largely unaffected by seasonal changes. It is therefore suggested that a soil should be compacted at or near to this natural moisture content, and thus a more critical assessment of the relative performance of the various types of compaction plant can be made by examining the dry densities achieved at a moisture content which is typical for each soil type under average British conditions rather than at a number of different optimum moisture contents appropriate to each type of compaction plant. Such a comparison is made in Table 8.3.

It can be seen at once that neither form of sheepsfoot roller is suitable for British conditions as a result of the low optimum moisture contents for this type of plant in comparison with the average natural moisture contents of soils in this country. These types of rollers are, however, very useful for compacting all materials except sand in more arid climates where soils have lower natural moisture contents.

Most of the other types of plant tested could achieve a satisfactory

TABLE 8.3 *Comparison of maximum dry densities (lb/cu ft) obtained for different soils when fully compacted by various types of compaction plant at moisture contents which are typical for soils in Great Britain*[7,8,9]

Soil type	Heavy clay	Silty clay	Sandy clay	Sand	Gravel–sand–clay
Average natural moisture content in Great Britain (%)	25	21	17	9	7
Theoretical maximum dry density at this moisture content	102	107	116	136	140
2¾-ton smooth-wheeled roller	91	103	113	131	137
8-ton smooth-wheeled roller	96	105	112	132	138
12-ton pneumatic-tyred roller	98	103	108	125	126
20-ton pneumatic-tyred roller	†	†	†	128	133
45-ton pneumatic-tyred roller	†	†	†	131	138
5-ton club-foot sheepsfoot roller	*	*	*	*	129
4½-ton taper-foot sheepsfoot roller	*	*	*	*	*
12-cwt frog rammer	95	98	111	126	136
2-cwt power rammer	98	103	110	128	133
4-cwt vibrating roller	*	*	*	122	122
2½-ton vibrating roller	*	103	†	131	138
4-cwt vibrating-plate compactor	*	*	*	126	120
2-ton vibrating-plate compactor	*	†	109	128	137

* plant unsuitable   † plant not tested

state of compaction throughout the range of soils tested, but some, in particular certain items of vibratory equipment, proved to be suitable only for the more granular soils. In general, the heavier items of plant were capable of achieving higher dry densities.

8.10 Choice of compaction plant

Table 8.3 shows that most types of compaction plant, apart from sheeps foot rollers, are capable of compacting soils at moisture contents typical of British conditions to a high percentage of the theoretical dry densities corresponding to zero air voids. Apart from those circumstances which limit the type of plant by their size and location, the choice is largely determined by considerations of output and operating costs. The output depends on the width and thickness of the compacted layer, the vehicle speed, and the number of passes required to achieve the required dry density (or percentage air voids). Operating costs are dependent on the capital or hiring charges for the plant, including a tractor where the equipment has to be towed, the operator's wages, and the cost of fuel

Lewis[13] has made a comparison of the cost per cubic yard of com pacted soil for various types of plant, the number of passes required being that to achieve a state of compaction corresponding to 10% air voids at the average natural moisture contents for soils in the British Isles (Table 8.4). These figures have been based on the assumption of 50 minutes' operating time per hour with no allowance for maintenance work or for delays due to bad weather, and the costs should therefore be considered as being a guide to relative performance rather than absolute operating costs. In addition, the right-hand column of Table 8.4 lists the soil types and conditions for which each type of plant is suitable.

From this information, the following general observations can be made:

1. Smooth-wheeled rollers, grid rollers, and pneumatic-tyred rollers are suitable for most soil types and are cheap to operate, especially the heavier items of plant. The highest output of any of the types of compaction plant listed can be achieved with the 45-ton pneumatic-tyred roller.

2. Power rammers and frog rammers will compact all types of soil, but because of the low output and high operating costs their use is restricted to reinstatement of trenches and other confined areas.

3. The smaller types of vibrating rollers and vibrating-plate compactors have also a low output and their use is restricted to granular soils. The heavier items of vibratory equipment are suitable for most soil types, except that vibrating rollers will not compact uniformly graded sand and vibrating-plate compactors are unsuitable for heavy clay soils. The operating costs of these heavier types of vibratory plant are somewhat higher than smooth-wheeled, grid, or pneumatic-tyred rollers and the output is considerably lower.

8.11 Control of field compaction

As has already been stated, the moisture content at which compaction should be allowed to proceed should be close to the natural moisture content of the excavated material. The exact range of moisture content specified is normally left to the discretion of the engineer, but when decided, this will determine whether any given material is acceptable for use in embankments or must be run to spoil.

Normally the maximum allowable moisture content of plastic soils is 2% above the plastic limit for that material. For non-plastic material, the current Ministry of Transport Specification[14] requires that compaction work for embankments should be carried out only when the moisture content of the material is within 1% wetter to 2% drier than the moisture content of samples in cuttings or in borrow pits which are at least 1 ft above the level of the water table, or, alternatively, when the

F

TABLE 8.4 *Average possible outputs of plant and costs per cubic yard of compacted soil*[13]

Type of plant	Approximate hourly cost of operating plant, including hire, wages of operator and fuel (s d)	Average output of plant							Soil types and conditions for which the plant is suitable
		Width compacted by plant (in)	Speed of rolling (ft/min)	Number of passes required	Area compacted per hour (sq yd)	Depth of compacted layer (in)	Output of compacted soil per hour (cu yd)	Cost per cubic yard of compacted soil (pence)	
2¼-ton smooth-wheeled roller	14 6	51	180	8	530	5	74	2·4	Most soil types under moisture conditions of the British Isles
8-ton smooth-wheeled roller	20 0	70	180	4	1,460	6	243	1·0	All soil types except soft wet clay and uniformly graded sand
13½-ton grid roller with 80-hp track-laying tractor	65 0	62	440	7	1,800	8	400	2·0	All types of soil over wide range of moisture conditions by adjustment of ballast
13½-ton grid roller with 150-hp wheeled tractor	80 0	62	880	8	3,160	8	700	1·4	See remarks above, but with the qualification that this combination is not suitable for uniformly graded sand or soils in very wet conditions
12-ton pneumatic-tyred roller	45 0	82	200	4	1,900	5	264	2·0	Most types of soil under moisture conditions of British Isles, and particularly wet cohesive materials
20-ton pneumatic-tyred roller	60 0	84	200	4	1,940	6	323	2·2	Most types of soil over wide range of moisture

Machine			Area in sq ft	Blows per min	Blows					Suitable soils
2-cwt power rammer	8	6	0·49 (Area in sq ft)	60 Blows per min	6 Blows	27	6	4·5	23	Reinstatement of trenches and compaction in confined areas of all soil types
12-cwt frog rammer	13	6	4·6 (Area in sq ft)	50 Blows per min	12 Blows	106	12	35	4·6	Reinstatement of large trenches of all soil types
4-cwt vibrating roller	6	6	24	30 (Hand propelled)	8	42	3	3·5	22	Granular soils only
6¾-cwt vibrating roller	8	6	28	60	12	65	6	11	9·4	Granular soils only
19½-cwt tandem vibrating roller	11	0	32	67	4	248	6	41	3·2	Granular soils only with the exception of uniformly graded sand
3¼-ton towed vibrating roller	35	0	72	120	6	670	10	185	2·3	All soil types
3¾-ton tandem vibrating roller	18	0	39	65	4	293	7	57	3·8	All soil types except uniformly graded sands
4-cwt vibrating-plate compactor	10	6	15	28	3	65	6	11	12	Granular soils only
13-cwt vibrating-plate compactor	12	6	24	53	4	148	8	33	4·6	Most soil types
14-cwt vibrating-plate compactor	12	6	24	42	2	233	6	39	3·8	Most soil types except heavy clay
1½-ton vibrating-plate compactor	17	0	30	25	2	174	12	58	3·5	Most soil types
2-ton vibrating-plate compactor	17	0	34	27	2	213	12	71	2·9	Most soil types except heavy clay
40-hp track-laying tractor	35	0	30	350	6	810	6	135	3·1	Most soil types when no normal compaction plant is available
80-hp track-laying tractor	55	0	40	440	6	1,360	6	227	2·9	Most soil types when no normal compaction plant is available

moisture content lies within the range of the optimum moisture conten and 3% below the optimum as determined by the B.S. Standard Com paction Test. These requirements have proved very difficult to operat in practice, however, on account of the wide range of moisture conten experienced under British climatic conditions and many engineers fee that this part of the Specification should be rewritten in a more workabl form.

In addition to specifying the range of moisture content to be used fo compacting the soil, a further stipulation must be made regarding th dry density to be achieved. Alternatively, the dry density may be con trolled by specifying the maximum air void content for the compacte soil. The former method of control, termed the relative compactio method, usually requires the soil to be compacted to a dry density c 90% or 95% of the maximum dry density determined in one of the B.S laboratory compaction tests. This method has a number of definite di advantages which may be summarized as follows:

1. A laboratory compaction test must be carried out on each varia tion of soil type, since the maximum dry density obtained in th laboratory compaction test is dependent on the type of materia and the grading. This imposes an additional burden on site con trol staff and also means that the results of the control testing ma be further delayed.

2. No account is taken of the actual moisture content of the soil i relation to dry density specified and the saturation curve for zer air voids. If the soil moisture content is considerably in excess c the laboratory optimum moisture content, as for soil A on Figur 8.10, then it would be impossible ever to achieve 95% relativ compaction. Conversely, if the soil is very dry, as soil B on Figur 8.10, then the required relative compaction could be achieved wit

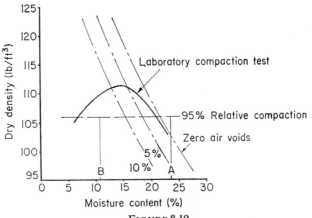

FIGURE 8.10

the soil still having more than 15% air voids. This would be most undesirable, particularly with cohesive soils which would undoubtedly take up moisture and swell at some subsequent time.

A more satisfactory method of controlling compaction is the second approach which stipulates the maximum permissible air void content of the compacted soil. This is in fact a much more logical approach to the problem, since the object of soil compaction is essentially to reduce the air voids and so prevent subsequent changes in moisture content. Specifications[14] often require the material to be compacted so that at least 9 out of every 10 consecutive samples have a dry density corresponding to not more than 10% air voids in the main body of the embankment and not more than 5% air voids in the top 2 ft, although these figures must, in practice, depend on the type and grading of the fill material and should be based on the results of laboratory strength and compressibility tests and on full-scale field compaction trials carried out at the commencement of the contract. The air void content of the compacted material is calculated from measurements of bulk density and moisture content using the formula:

$$\gamma_B = \frac{G\gamma_W(1+m)}{1+mG}\left(\frac{100-a}{100}\right) \tag{8.4}$$

where a is the air void content (%) and the other symbols are as previously defined.

To enable this calculation to be performed, the specific gravity of the soil particles G must be known. In the absence of such data, it may be assumed as 2·60 for clean sands and gravels, 2·65 for clay sands and clay gravels, 2·70 for sandy or silty clays, and 2·75 for heavy clays. In any case, as large an error as ±0.05 in the assumed specific gravity would only result in an error of $\pm1–1.5$ in the calculation of the percentage air voids.[13]

8.12 Field measurement of density and moisture content

Control of field compaction by either of the two methods previously outlined requires frequent determination of the density and moisture content of the compacted soil, and also measurements of the moisture content of the excavated soil to assess its suitability as filling material. B.S. 1377[6] gives a number of standard methods of measuring field dry density, the two most commonly used being the sand-replacement method (Test 12A or 12B) and the core-cutter method (Test 12D). Both these methods are outlined briefly below; in each case the bulk density of the soil is determined by finding the weight of material occupying a known volume and, by measuring the moisture content of a representative sample, the dry density can then be calculated.

(i) *Sand-replacement method*

A hole approximately 4 in diameter (8 in diameter for coarse-grained soils) is excavated to the depth of the layer to be tested and the material removed is weighed. The volume of the hole is then determined by running in dry, closely-graded sand (passing No. 25 but retained on No. 52 B.S. sieve) of known bulk density from a suitable container, the volume of sand used being found by weighing the sand-filled container before and after the test. The test may be performed on all types of soils, but is liable to give too high a value for the bulk density of wet granular materials as a result of the surrounding soil flowing into the sample hole during excavation.

(ii) *Core-cutter method*

This method is useful for soft, cohesive soils which are free from stones. A 4-in internal diameter cutter of known weight and volume is driven into the soil and then dug out. The soil sample is trimmed flush with the ends of the cutter and weighed to determine the bulk density.

Measurements of moisture content may be made by the standard oven drying method (B.S. 1377, Test 1A), or more rapid determinations may be made using the sand-bath method (B.S. 1377, Test 1B). Alternatively, only slightly less accurate measurements of moisture content can be made within the space of a few minutes using either the *Speedy* moisture tester, in which the gas pressure developed by the reaction between the moisture contained in a known weight of wet soil and calcium carbide gives a direct reading of moisture content on a pressure gauge, or an *Inframatic* type of balance, which gives a direct reading of moisture content on a calibrated scale as 10 g of wet soil in the balance pan are dried quickly under a powerful lamp. In both of the last two methods, the moisture content is given on a wet weight basis rather than the more usual dry weight definition.

With any of the standard methods for field dry density, it is necessary to make a number of measurements over a comparatively small area in order to obtain a representative average value, since considerable variations occur as a result of testing errors. It has been suggested that between 5 and 10 measurements per 1,000 cu yd of fill constitute a reasonable number as regards the amount of testing time involved, but recent work indicates that about 40 dry density and moisture content measurements per 1,000 cu yd of fill are necessary to obtain a mean value with an accuracy not poorer than ± 2 for the percentage air voids at the 90% confidence limits.[15] Clearly this number of tests would be impracticable using the standard methods of measurement, but efforts are at present being made to develop methods which can be carried out with greater rapidity.

One possible approach is based on the fact that the scattering and absorption of gamma radiation is a function of the bulk density of the material.[16] Briefly, a radioactive source (caesium 137) contained in the end of a stainless-steel probe is inserted in the soil to a depth of up to 6 in and a Geiger–Muller tube which detects gamma radiation is placed on the surface about 8 in from the probe to measure the rate of transmission of radiation through the material. Alternatively, in soils containing large stones which make it difficult to insert the probe without causing undue disturbance, both the source and detector may be placed on the surface separated by lead shielding and the back-scatter method used, although this method suffers from the disadvantage that measurements are largely confined to the upper 2 in of soil.

Since this equipment records the bulk density, it is necessary to determine also the moisture content of the material before the dry density can be calculated. This may also be done with nuclear techniques using a radium/beryllium source of fast neutrons placed on the ground surface alongside a boron trifluoride counter which records the number of slow neutrons scattered back after collisions have occurred between the fast neutrons and nuclei of hydrogen present in the soil moisture. This measurement is also made on a unit volume basis and therefore the difference of the two readings gives the dry density of the soil.

The two pieces of equipment are normally combined together to form a compact portable unit. Readings of density and moisture are taken in turn and the bulk density and moisture content are read off calibration charts provided with the equipment. In theory, the calibrations should be independent of the type of material, but investigations carried out by the Road Research Laboratory with a number of types of commercial apparatus, have indicated that the calibrations are affected to some extent in this way.[17] This difficulty, together with the restriction of measurements with a surface source to the top few inches of material, has prevented the widespread acceptance of this equipment for compaction control at present, although it might be useful in supplementing the results obtained by other methods on a comparative basis.

CONSTRUCTIONAL METHODS

8.13 Excavating plant

The most common types of excavating plant used on roadworks are the general purpose excavator and the tractor-scraper unit. The former can be adapted to act as a dragline, a face shovel, or a drag shovel by fitting different types of jib equipment, whilst the latter may have either a track-laying or a wheeled tractor and is used both for excavating and transporting the material.

Draglines operate from the top surface of the material to be excavated, digging below this level, whereas face shovels work from the bottom of the excavation digging upwards. Face shovels will deal with a wide variety of materials, including hard rock shattered by blasting, but draglines are not suitable for quite such hard material and their output is slightly lower. The latter are useful, however, in certain circumstances on account of their longer reach and where access to the bottom of the excavation is difficult. The drag shovel is used for excavating narrow trenches, particularly in harder materials which are unsuitable for a dragline, the digging action in this case being downwards and towards the machine. With all three forms of excavator, vehicles are required to transport material away from the excavation and these may be ordinary tipping lorries or special rubber-tyred dump trucks with capacities up to 40 cu yd which are not suitable for operating over public roads.

The smaller face shovels with a bucket capacity of $\frac{3}{8}$ cu yd have an output ranging from 25 cu yd per hour with wet sticky clay to 85 cu yd per hour with light sandy soils, whilst the large machines with 4 cu yd buckets can excavate between 350 and 580 cu yd per hour, depending on the material being handled. Corresponding figures for intermediate size machines are 70–165 cu yd per hour with $\frac{3}{4}$ cu yd buckets and 145–285 cu yd per hour with $1\frac{1}{2}$ cu yd buckets.[18] These figures are based on average operating conditions with the boom swinging through 90° to the attendant lorry or dump truck and no allowance is made for delays. Dragline outputs are approximately 20% less than the above figures.

Tractor-scraper units are particularly suitable for the excavation of cuttings and the forming of embankments on road schemes, where the material is usually sufficiently soft to be handled without the need to resort to blasting. On short hauls, up to a maximum distance of about $\frac{1}{4}$ mile, scrapers drawn by track-laying or crawler tractors are generally employed, but on longer hauls where the haulage and return journeys comprise a large part of the cycle time the faster but less powerful wheeled tractor units are normally used. With wheeled tractors, the assistance of a pusher tractor during loading operations is essential and pusher tractors are now frequently used to advantage with crawler tractor units.

Scraper capacities range up to 40 cu yd or more and the output depends not only on the horsepower and capacity of the unit but also on the haulage distance and the type of terrain. Typical output figures for a 20 cu yd scraper vary from 50 to 200 cu yd per hour according to the time of the hauling cycle. During a haul the tractor unit should operate in the highest possible gear and to maintain efficiency haul routes should be kept in good order by suitable plant such as graders, bulldozers, and rollers. Where possible, loading and hauling of material should take place on a downward gradient and waiting time prior to loading should be eliminated by matching scrapers with pushers in the correct ratio for the particular job.

In considering the output from all types of excavating plant, allowance must be made for the increase in volume of a material when loose compared with that in its natural state. This 'swell' is of the order 25–40% for sands and clays but rather more than this for hard rock shattered by blasting, and the figures given above should be reduced accordingly to take account of this factor. Allowance should also be made for loss of working time due to breakdown, minor items of maintenance, and other unavoidable causes, and an efficiency factor of 85%, which corresponds to approximately 50 minutes' working time per hour, is commonly adopted.

The choice of excavating plant for a particular contract is largely determined by economic considerations. On large schemes, such factors as the type and volume of material to be handled, the nature of the excavation (deep or shallow) and the length of hauls are important, and if suitable equipment is not already available plant may be bought specially for the job or hired for the duration of the contract. Such an arrangement may not be economical on a small scheme, however, and in this case other considerations such as the type of plant available at the contractor's depot, the transporting distances involved, and the contractor's other commitments may be over-riding factors in the choice of excavation plant.

8.14 *Excavation of cuttings*

For payment purposes, excavated material is subdivided into two classes —solid rock and common excavation. Solid rock is defined so as to include all material which would be very difficult to loosen with normal excavating machinery without some preliminary blasting or drilling, and includes boulders and detached pieces of rock exceeding 6 cu ft in size in general excavation and 3 cu ft in trenches. Common excavation means excavation in any materials which are not solid rock as defined above.

Before commencing the main excavation operation, the topsoil should be removed over the width of the earthworks between the slope stakes and stockpiled in separate heaps. The excavation of cuttings should be carried out in two stages, and at all times the work should be arranged so that the excavated surface has a sufficient crossfall to shed water and prevent ponding. In the longitudinal section, excavation should proceed from the lowest point of the cutting to prevent water from being trapped during the course of the work. In the first stage, the area between the extremities of the carriageway(s), including any hard shoulders, should be excavated to a level 12 in above formation level, during which time constructional traffic may continue to use the surface so formed.

F*

Secondly, when required, this excess of material should be trimmed off in a single operation down to formation level and constructional plant, other than that required to complete this operation, must then be restricted to avoid damage to the subgrade. Within 24 hours of this preparation of the formation, the surface should be dressed with hot tar or bitumen unless the formation is to be covered with a sealed pavement layer within that time. This sealing coat should be blinded with $\frac{3}{16}$-in gravel, crushed rock, or slag at the rate of 200 sq yd per ton to prevent it being picked up by constructional traffic, which must of course be limited in type and size to prevent damage to the subgrade.[4]

When unsuitable material is encountered at subgrade level it should be excavated and run to spoil. Unsuitable material includes material forming swamps, marshes or bogs, peat, slurry, mud, and highly organic silt or clay. The resultant excavation should be backfilled with suitably compacted material deposited in layers not exceeding 9 in loose thickness. Where this backfill has to be deposited below standing water, compaction may be omitted provided that free-draining material such as clean gravel is used.

8.15 *Forming of embankments*

As for cuttings, topsoil should first be removed from the areas to be used for embankments. Provided that the underlying subsoil forms a suitable foundation, the embankment should then be built up in a series of layers across the full width of the earthworks. These layers should normally not exceed 9 in loose thickness, but where compaction trials indicate that thicker layers can be satisfactorily compacted then layers up to 15 in loose thickness may be used. Each layer should be compacted so as to achieve the specified dry density or percentage air voids in at least 9 out of every 10 consecutive samples, particular attention being paid to the compaction of the filling material behind bridge abutments and at the edges of the embankment. The type of compaction plant used should be chosen with regard to the types of materials to be handled and the amount of earthworks involved. In some cases it may be possible to use constructional traffic (rubber-tyred trucks, track-laying machines, or scrapers) to compact the soil, but there is a danger that these vehicles will tend to follow previously established tracks and so give non-uniform compaction across the embankment. End- or side-tipping of material to form the embankment is undesirable since the material cannot be properly compacted when tipped in this manner.

Where possible, all suitable excavated material should be used to form embankments. Unsuitable material includes peat, running silt, highly organic clay or silt, material in a frozen condition, clay with a liquid limit exceeding 80% and/or a plasticity index exceeding 55%, and material whose moisture content is outside the range specified for compaction. In many cases imported filling material will be required and often waste material such as slag, burnt colliery shale, quarry waste, or pulverized fuel ash (fly ash) may be available locally. The latter is the waste product of combustion from electricity generating stations and is a lightweight, free-draining material with a compacted dry density of about 85 lb/cu ft. It has been used with considerable success in embankments[19] but should be compacted at a moisture content not normally exceeding 25%.

Where materials of differing quality are to be used in the embankment, the material with the highest bearing capacity should be placed in the topmost 2 ft below formation level. Isolated boulders of size in the range $\frac{1}{2}$–3 cu ft may be incorporated in embankments not composed of rock-fill provided that these are placed more than 2 ft below formation level.

The construction of embankments should be carried out in two stages. Firstly, the area between the extremities of the carriageway(s) including any central reserve and hard shoulders should be brought up to a level 6 in above formation level, during which time constructional traffic may continue to use the surface so formed. Secondly, when it is necessary to complete the formation, this excess of material should be trimmed off in a single operation, and the use by constructional plant must then be curtailed. The formation should be sealed within a period of 24 hours as in cuttings. At all times during construction, sufficient crossfall should be provided to enable the surface to shed water and prevent ponding.

Where unsuitable foundation material is encountered at the site of the embankment then this should be treated by one of the methods described earlier in this chapter. If excavation is decided upon, then this material should be replaced by suitable backfill deposited and compacted as in the body of the embankment, except that where this backfill has to be deposited in standing water, compaction may be omitted provided that free-draining material such as clean gravel is used. Further recommendations on constructional methods and procedure are given in CP 2003.[20]

1. TAYLOR, D. W., *Fundamentals of Soil Mechanics* (New York: Wiley; London: Chapman and Hall, 1948, p. 431)
2. TRESIDDER, J. O., 'A Review of Existing Methods of Road Construction over Peat', *Department of Scientific and Industrial Research, Road Research Technical Paper No. 40* (London: H.M.S.O., 1958)
3. LAKE, J. R., 'Recent Investigations in Scotland on the Design and Construction of Roads', *J. Instn. Highw. Engrs.* (London: vol. 11, 1964, pp. 155–65)

4. ROAD RESEARCH LABORATORY, 'The Protection of Subgrades and Granular Sub-Bases and Bases', *Ministry of Transport Road Research Road Note No. 17* (London: H.M.S.O., 1968 (2nd edition))

5. U.S. WATERWAYS EXPERIMENT STATION, 'Investigation of Filter Requirements for Underdrains', *U.S. War Department: Corps of Engineers: Technical Memorandum No. 183-1* (Vicksburg, Mississippi: U.S. Waterways Experiment Station, 1941)

6. BRITISH STANDARDS INSTITUTION, 'Methods of Testing Soils for Civil Engineering Purposes', *B.S. 1377: 1961* (London: British Standards Institution, 1961)

7. WILLIAMS, F. H. P. and MACLEAN, D. J., 'The Compaction of Soil: a Study of the Performance of Plant', *Department of Scientific and Industrial Research, Road Research Technical Paper No. 17* (London: H.M.S.O., 1950)

8. LEWIS, W. A., 'Further Studies in the Compaction of Soil and the Performance of Compaction Plant', *Department of Scientific and Industrial Research, Road Research Technical Paper No. 33* (London: H.M.S.O., 1954)

9. LEWIS, W. A., 'Investigation of the Performance of Pneumatic-Tyred Rollers in the Compaction of Soil', *Department of Scientific and Industrial Research, Road Research Technical Paper No. 45* (London: H.M.S.O., 1959)

10. LEWIS, W. A., 'Recent Research into the Compaction of Soil by Vibratory Compaction Equipment', *Proc. 5th int. Conf. Soil Mech., Paris, 1961* (Paris: Dunod, vol. 2, 1961, pp. 261-8)

11. DEPARTMENT OF SCIENTIFIC AND INDUSTRIAL RESEARCH, *Road Research 1961* (London: H.M.S.O., 1962, p. 69)

12. DEPARTMENT OF SCIENTIFIC AND INDUSTRIAL RESEARCH, *Road Research 1962* (London: H.M.S.O., 1963, p. 82)

13. LEWIS, W. A., 'Compaction of Soils and Road Bases', *J. Instn. Highw. Engrs.* (London: vol. 9, 1962, pp. 181-202)

14. MINISTRY OF TRANSPORT, *Specification for Road and Bridge Works* (London: H.M.S.O., 1963 (3rd edition))

15. DEPARTMENT OF SCIENTIFIC AND INDUSTRIAL RESEARCH, *Road Research 1963* (London: H.M.S.O., 1964, p. 101)

16. MEIGH, A. C. and SKIPP, B. P., 'Gamma-Ray and Neutron Methods of Measuring Soil Density and Moisture', *Geotechnique* (London: vol. 10, 1960, pp. 110-26)

17. LEWIS, W. A., 'Nuclear Apparatus for Density and Moisture Measurement: Study of Factors Affecting Accuracy', *Roads and Road Construction* (London: vol. 43, 1965, pp. 37-43)

18. HAMMOND, R., *Earthmoving and Excavating Plant* (London: C.R. Books Ltd, 1964, p. 29)

19. RAYMOND, S., 'Pulverised Fuel Ash as an Embankment Material', *Proc. Instn. civ. Engrs.* (London: vol. 19, 1961, pp. 515-36)

20. THE COUNCIL FOR CODES OF PRACTICE, 'Earthworks', *British Standard Code of Practice CP 2003, 1959* (London: British Standards Institution, 1959)

9

Soil Stabilization

- -

The highway engineer is continually faced with the problem of increasing the strength and stability of the natural soil in order to improve its load-bearing properties. The measures discussed in the previous chapter are largely directed towards this purpose, but these soil characteristics may sometimes be further improved by applying, in addition, one of a number of procedures known collectively as soil stabilization techniques.

All these procedures have in common the fact that material is added to the natural soil to produce a stronger and more stable material. In some cases deficient particle sizes are added to give a more satisfactory grading—a process known as mechanical stabilization—whilst in other instances cement, lime, bitumen, or various chemicals are used to bind the particles of soil together and so increase its strength. When the soil has been treated in this manner, it ceases to be part of the subgrade and becomes instead part (or in some cases the whole) of the pavement structure.

MECHANICAL STABILIZATION

9.1 Grading requirements

The shear strength of a soil is derived from both the cohesion and the internal friction characteristics of the material. Cohesion is a property associated mainly with the clay fraction of the soil, whilst internal friction is chiefly a characteristic of sands and gravels. A combination of these two properties can be found in a suitably graded material such as hoggin, which occurs naturally in parts of southern England. Over-

159

seas, similar gravel–sand–clay deposits can be found in a number of countries, for example in the eastern states of the U.S.A.[1]

When the natural soil contains only a narrow range of particle sizes, then the addition of particle sizes which are lacking produces a better graded material which is inherently stronger and more stable than the natural soil. Further, the use of a well-graded material ensures that it is possible to compact to a high dry density with a low proportion of air voids, and so lessens the risk of a subsequent increase in moisture content. The practice of adding broken stone or gravel to cohesive soils has, of course, been used for hundreds of years since the time when such measures formed the sole basis of road construction and maintenance.

Fuller and Thompson[2] have suggested that concreting aggregates should be graded in accordance with the relationship:

$$\text{Percentage passing any sieve} = 100\left(\frac{\text{Sieve aperture size}}{\text{Maximum particle size}}\right)^{\frac{1}{2}} \quad (9.1)$$

so as to achieve a high density. A similar requirement can be applied to mechanically stabilized soils, except that the proportion passing the No. 200 sieve should be somewhat greater than is given by this formula to obtain sufficient cohesion. However, in practice, it is not necessary to use such a carefully controlled distribution of particle sizes and a reasonably wide range of grading can be tolerated. Table 9.1 gives a

TABLE 9.1 *Grading of material for mechanical stabilization*[3]

B.S sieve size	Percentage passing		
	Nominal maximum size		
	3 in	1½ in	¾ in
3 in	100	—	—
1½ in	80–100	100	—
¾ in	60–80	80–100	100
⅜ in	45–65	55–80	80–100
3/16 in	30–50	40–60	50–75
No. 7	—	30–50	35–60
No. 25	10–30	15–30	15–35
No. 200	5–15	5–15	5–15

Note 1: Not less than 10% should be retained between each pair of successive sieves specified for use, excepting the largest pair

Note 2: The material passing the No. 36 sieve shall have the following characteristics (B.S. 1377):

Liquid limit not exceeding 25%

Plasticity index not exceeding 6%

range of grading limits for material of three maximum sizes, with the additional specification that not less than 10% of material should be retained between each of the stated sieves, excepting the largest pair.[3] This ensures that no fraction can be entirely absent from a material which may otherwise satisfy the grading limits on each individual sieve.

STABILIZATION WITH CEMENT

9.2 Suitable soil characteristics

Soil–cement stabilization is a method of construction in which cement is mixed with pulverized soil to form a material which when compacted and allowed to harden possesses appreciable strength and considerable resistance to weathering. This form of construction was first used in Great Britain as long ago as 1917, but has only been employed to any appreciable extent in this country since 1945. By far the greatest proportion of soil–cement construction has been carried out in the U.S.A. from 1935 onwards, and by 1955 over 110 million square yards had been completed. Considerable amounts have also been used in South Africa and in Germany.

Most soil types are suitable for soil–cement excepting those containing an appreciable amount of active organic matter and also coarse-grained soils with material exceeding 2 in size which is likely to damage the machines pulverizing the soil and mixing in the cement. Mixing may also prove difficult with heavy clay soils, but field experience has shown that satisfactory results can be obtained when the liquid limit is not greater than 45% and the plastic limit is not greater than 20%.

Active organic matter prevents the cement from hydrating and can exist at depths of up to five feet below the surface according to the type of soil profile. *Road Research Technical Paper No. 61*[4] describes research into the occurrence and properties of organic matter in soils as regards its interference with the hardening of cement-stabilized soils and also outlines a test which has been developed for detecting the presence of deleterious organic matter. The test consists of the measurement of the pH of a soil–cement paste 1 hour after it has been mixed with water; the inability to reach a pH of 12·1 indicating that the soil is unsuitable for stabilization.

The current M.O.T. Specification[5] requires that material used for cement stabilization should be well-graded with a grading finer than the limits given in Table 9.2 and a coefficient of uniformity (the ratio of the aperture size through which 60% of the material passes to the aperture size through which 10% passes) of not less than 10, although in certain cases material with a grading curve slightly outside these limits may be

TABLE 9.2 *Grading of material for cement stabilization*[5]

B.S. sieve size	Percentage passing not less than
2 in	100
1½ in	95
¾ in	45
⅜ in	35
3/16 in	30
No. 7	25
No. 25	12
No. 52	5
No. 200	0

Note 1: The material shall be well-graded with a coefficient of uniformity (ratio 60% size to 10% size) of not less than 10
Note 2: The material passing the No. 36 sieve shall have the following characteristics (B.S. 1377):
Liquid limit not exceeding 45%
Plastic limit not exceeding 20%

acceptable provided that all other requirements are satisfied (Clause 818).

9.3 *Strength requirements and site control*

In Great Britain the cement content is expressed as a percentage of the weight of dry soil. The proportion of cement required is normally between 5 and 15%, depending on the type of soil, and is determined by the strength requirements of the mix. An unconfined compressive strength of not less than 250 lb/sq in at 7 days has often been specified, but the most recent M.O.T. Specification[5] requires that the average 7-day crushing strength for each batch of five test specimens should be not less than 400 lb/sq in for cylindrical samples with a height/diameter ratio of 2 : 1 or 500 lb/sq in for cubical specimens. In addition, the stabilized material should have such a uniformity that the root mean square value of the coefficient of variation of crushing strength of five successive batches of five test specimens does not exceed 40%.

Cylindrical specimens should be prepared in accordance with B.S. 1924,[6] using 4 in × 2 in internal diameter moulds for fine-grained soils (not less than 80% passing a No. 7 B.S. sieve), 8 in × 4 in internal diameter moulds for medium-grained soils (not less than 80% passing a ¾-in B.S. sieve), and 12 in × 6 in internal diameter moulds for coarse-grained soils (not less than 80% passing a 1½-in B.S. sieve). When making the initial laboratory tests to determine the required cement content, it is important that the specimens are prepared at the same moisture content and compacted to the same density as will be achieved in the actual stabilized layer, since strength is a function of these factors as well as cement content. The moisture content to be used in the field should be determined from preliminary compaction trials and will normally be the optimum moisture content for a given number of passes of the type of compaction plant employed. As the required cement content is not known at this stage, a proportion of 10% cement can be used in these preliminary trials without significantly affecting the optimum moisture content and maximum dry density achieved.

Where preliminary compaction trials are not possible, then the moisture content used for compacting granular soils should be the optimum moisture content as determined by the B.S. Heavy Compaction Test on the stabilized soil (see page 141), whilst for cohesive soils the moisture content should be 2% less than the plastic limit of the fresh soil–cement mixture. In either case, laboratory specimens should be prepared to a dry density corresponding to 5% air voids, and this same value should be aimed at when compacting the stabilized layer in the field.

Regular site control testing of the cement-stabilized material should be carried out to ensure that the compacted material is capable of achieving the specified strength requirements. Clause 3011 of the M.O.T. Specification requires five samples of the mixed material to be taken at random immediately prior to compaction for each 1,000 sq yd of compacted layer. From each of these samples, a cylindrical or cubical test specimen should be prepared in accordance with B.S. 1924, each specimen being compacted to within 2 lb/cu ft of the average density of the compacted layer as measured by sand-replacement tests (see page 152), within the period 4–24 hours after completion of the compaction work. These specimens should be tested for unconfined compressive strength at an age of 7 days, after curing in the prescribed manner, and from these results the average strength of each batch and the root mean square value of the coefficient of variation of five successive batches can be determined.

9.4 *Stabilized P.F.A.*

When pulverized fuel ash (P.F.A.) is being used to form an embankment (see page 157), the upper layers of the material can be strengthened by the addition of cement. Laboratory investigations and controlled site experiments have indicated that a cement content of about 10% will produce a 7-day unconfined compressive strength exceeding 250 lb/sq in.[7]

Specimens for laboratory testing should again be prepared at the same moisture content and be compacted to the same dry density as is achieved in the actual construction work. Field measurements have shown that even with the most suitable types of compaction plant (vibrating rollers and pneumatic-tyred rollers) the compacted density of the stabilized layer is usually only 90–95% of that achieved in the B.S. Standard Compaction Test.

OTHER STABILIZING AGENTS

9.5 *Lime stabilization*

As an alternative to cement, hydrated lime can be mixed with certain soils to produce a stronger and more workable material.

In recent laboratory investigations[8] covering a variety of soil types ranging from heavy clay to a sandy gravel, it was found that the addition of up to 10% lime produced an increase in the unconfined compressive strength of the soils. This increase was most marked for those soils containing an appreciable amount of clayey material, but was generally much smaller than that obtained by adding a similar quantity of cement, except with the heavy clay for which the two stabilizers produced similar results. Further, with plastic soils, the addition of lime increased the plastic limit of the soil so that the material appeared drier and more friable, and was thus more easily broken up and mixed with the stabilizer.

With all the soils tested, strength increased with age, as with soil–cement, and it is suggested that this gain of strength results from a reaction between the lime and the clay fractions of soil which includes both chemical and physical effects. Compounds analogous to those formed during the hydration of Portland cement are produced and these give rise to the continued increase in strength over a considerable period of time. The action of lime differs from that of cement, however, in that with the latter only water is necessary to allow the hydration process to proceed.

Other investigations in the same series showed that this rate of gain of strength was greatly accelerated at a temperature of 45°C and this no doubt contributes towards the successful use of lime-stabilized material for road construction in parts of Africa and in the southern states of the U.S.A. In Zambia, 3% of hydrated lime has been used extensively to stabilize the clayey gravels which are widely available,[9] the points in favour of lime stabilization being the clayey nature of the local soils, the warm climate, and the fact that locally-produced lime is much cheaper than imported cement.

The potentialities of lime stabilization in Great Britain appear limited, since there is little difference in the price of lime and cement and the latter invariably gives a stronger material. However, it is thought that lime may be used advantageously in the construction of low-cost roads on farms and other lightly trafficked roads; one particular point in favour being that compaction need not be carried out immediately after mixing.

9.6 Stabilization with bitumen

A number of bituminous materials including cut-back bitumens, bitumen emulsions, and road tars, have been used effectively as soil stabilizing agents.[1] These materials increase the strength of the soil by binding the particles together and also act as waterproofing agents, preventing the absorption of water and so maintaining the strength of the stabilized material. Between 2 and 4% of bitumen is sufficient to give a substantial reduction in the amount of water absorbed, but larger amounts of up to 10% may be required to stabilize heavy cohesive soils.

Apart from the 'sand-mix' process which was widely used for airfield construction during the war and subsequently for a number of lightly trafficked roads, bituminous stabilization has not been used extensively in Great Britain. This is because most soils in countries with temperate climates have relatively high natural moisture contents, so that the addition of a fluid stabilizer would cause most cohesive soils to become plastic and therefore difficult to compact. With sands, however, excess water can be squeezed out by rolling and sand-mix construction is possible. In this process, 4–10% of cut-back bitumen is mixed with the wet sand to which 1 to 2% of hydrated lime has been added to assist coating (see also page 214).

In hot, dry climates overseas, soils often have a low moisture content and the use of a fluid stabilizer will not only assist in obtaining the optimum moisture content for compaction purposes, but in so doing may also contribute towards water economy. In these conditions, a wide range of soils including clays may be stabilized provided that the processing plant can pulverize the soil and mix in the stabilizer, although the process is most suitable for well-graded granular materials.

Where the soil and climatic conditions are suitable to permit the construction of unsurfaced earth roads, then the stability of these roads during the rainy season may be improved by simply spraying the surface with oil or cut-back bitumen at the rate of approximately 1 gallon per sq yd. This sprayed material penetrates into the soil to a depth of up to 1 in and so forms a stabilized crust. Oiled-earth roads are very popular in the U.S.A. and in the Middle East, where crude oil is both cheap and plentiful, and this form of stabilization has been used extensively in the construction of secondary roads. Because of the slippery nature of these roads when wet it is advisable to apply a light dressing of sand to the sprayed surface.

9.7 Chemical stabilizing agents

Considerable interest has been shown recently in the use of chemicals other than cement, lime, or bitumen for improving the strength of soil and increasing the resistance to softening by water. These chemicals are too numerous to mention in detail, but among them are various resinous compounds which waterproof the soil and calcium chloride which, because of its deliquescent nature, retains moisture in soil and so assists the compaction of mechanically stabilized material in hot climates. Some of these admixtures, including those mentioned above, are normally used by themselves, whilst other chemicals have been used as secondary additives to the more conventional stabilizing materials, for example, pulverized fuel ash in conjunction with hydrated lime.

Sherwood[10] has reviewed the use of a number of these chemicals and concluded that few are likely to find a use in this country because of the high cost compared with cement, lime, and bitumen, although there is scope for developing stabilizers which will deal effectively with highly organic soils and heavy clay.

CONSTRUCTIONAL METHODS

The stabilized soil may be prepared either by mix-in-place methods, in which the soil is treated without actually removing it from its natural position, or by mixing the material in a travelling or centralized mixing plant and subsequently spreading and compacting it in layers to form the required thickness. Either method may be used for preparing a single layer not exceeding 6 in compacted thickness, but where the overall thickness of the stabilized layer exceeds 6 in then the material should be compacted in two or more layers each within the range 3–6 in compacted thickness; in which case the mix-in-place process can only be used for the bottom layer.

9.8 Mix-in-place methods

Construction may be carried out under this heading using either multi-pass or single-pass machines, except that only the latter should be used with plastic soils. In both cases, the first stage of construction consists of thoroughly pulverizing the soil to the required depth to form a fine tilth so that at least 80%, exclusive of stones, will pass a $\frac{3}{16}$-in B.S. sieve.

With multi-pass construction, pulverization is best carried out by a rotary soil mixer but in the absence of special machines, ordinary agricultural plant such as cultivators and disc-harrows can be used, though less efficiently. In either case, it is advisable to use a ripper or plough for the initial breaking up of the soil to locate any boulders, and so avoid damage to the tines of the pulverizing machines. The depth of pulverization should be such as to allow subsequent compaction to the required thickness, for instance 8 in for a compacted layer 6 in thick.

On completion of pulverization, the surface should be graded to the correct crossfall or camber and the moisture content of the soil measured. If this is more than 3% below that required for compaction purposes, then a water sprayer should be used to make the necessary adjustment. The water should be evenly distributed over the surface and care must be taken never to allow the sprayer to remain stationary over one spot. Following the addition of water, the soil must again be mixed to obtain uniformity throughout the pulverized layer. Wet granular soils can be aerated by making additional passes of the soil mixer with the hood raised so that loose soil is flung into the air. After adjusting the moisture content, regrading of the surface will be necessary, and a light rolling may be advisable at this stage.

The stabilizer is next added to the soil. Where powder stabilizers such as cement or lime are being used, these may be distributed by a mechanical spreader (Plate 9.1) or bags may be 'spotted' at the required intervals. Liquid stabilizers are applied through spraybars and in this case the operation may be combined with adjustment of the moisture content. The stabilizer and pulverized soil must then be intimately mixed together (Plate 9.2), making several passes of the soil mixer as required until the material is uniform in colour and texture to the required depth. After this, the moisture content of the stabilized soil should again be measured and any final adjustment made, followed by a thorough mixing and a final grading of the surface. Compaction of the stabilized soil should commence immediately after this final grading.

Initial compaction should be carried out with a light smooth-wheeled roller, say 2–3 tons, followed by a heavier 8–10-ton smooth-wheeled roller. The surface may be finished if desired with further passes of the light roller to smooth out small irregularities between successive passes of the heavier plant. Alternatively pneumatic-tyred or vibrating rollers, dropping-weight compactors, or vibrating-plate compactors may be used. Compaction should be started at the edge of the road, working towards the centre where the road cross-section is cambered or towards the higher side where a straight crossfall is used, and should continue until an average dry density corresponding to 5% air voids has been attained for the full depth of the compacted layer. Immediately after the compaction is completed, those stabilized materials such as soil–cement which require curing for a period of at least 7 days should be covered with impermeable plastic sheeting or a 3-in layer of damp sand or else the surface of the stabilized layer should be sprayed with a quick-breaking bitumen emulsion at the rate 6–8 sq yd per gallon.

Single-pass construction follows the same general procedure as the multi-pass method, except that the complete sequence of operations, apart from the initial breaking up of heavy soils and final rolling, is performed by a single pass of a train of tractor-drawn equipment consisting of a pulverizer unit followed by a compactor unit (Plate 9.3). The first unit consists of a high-speed pulverizing rotor and carries a hopper spreader for powder stabilizers and also a spraybar which is fed from a water tanker running ahead of or alongside the train. The second unit is comprised of a mixing rotor and a number of dropping-weight compactors.

Single-pass machines have the advantage that, apart from any initial breaking up of the soil, the soil is completely processed within a few minutes and interference by the weather between the various stages is eliminated. On the other hand, multi-pass methods allow greater flexibility of operation and delays arising from plant breakdowns can be reduced on large contracts by duplicating the important items of equipment. In addition, special equipment is not absolutely essential—an important factor in overseas countries.

9.9 Travelling plant method

In this method of construction the surface is prepared to the required levels and crossfall after which the soil requiring treatment is bladed by a special type of grader into a continuous heap or windrow, some prior pulverization being required with certain types of soil. If powder stabilizers are being used, these are normally spread uniformly along the top of the windrow and the material is picked up by the travelling mixer moving forward continuously at a slow speed. The soil and stabilizer are fed at a controlled rate into a pug-mill where water is added and mixed with the soil. From the pug-mill, the stabilized material is discharged onto the formation where it is subsequently spread, compacted, and cured as for the mix-in-place methods. The procedure with fluid stabilizers is similar, except that in this case the stabilizer is added to the soil in the pug-mill along with any necessary mixing water.

Travel-mixers may be similar to the Barber–Greene type of asphalt mixer in which the material is fed from the windrow to the pug-mill by means of a bucket elevator discharging into a hopper or a modified motor grader may be employed with the mixer housed in the space normally occupied by the blade. In the latter case, the windrow is guided into the mixer as the machine moves forward and no elevator is required.

9.10 Stationary plant method

The use of stationary plant for mixing the stabilized soil is a convenient method to adopt when imported rather than the natural soil is being processed, particularly when materials from two different sources have to be blended together. The mixing plant can be sited close to the borrow pit or at some convenient point which is centrally placed for the construction work. Ordinary drum-type concrete mixers are unsuitable for mixing soils containing an appreciable amount of fine material as this tends to stick in the mixer drum, and therefore paddle or pan mixers, either batch or continuous type, should be employed for this work.

The chief advantage of this method over the other forms of construction is that the stabilized material is of more uniform quality and is laid to a definite thickness on a prepared formation. The method is an expensive one, however, when *in situ* material has to be processed, and the output is generally lower than for other forms of treatment.

REFERENCES

1. CLARE, K. E., 'The Use of Stabilized Soil for Road Construction in the U.S.A.', *Department of Scientific and Industrial Research, Road Research Technical Paper No. 29* (London: H.M.S.O., 1954)
2. FULLER, W. B. and THOMPSON, S. E., 'The Laws of Proportioning Concrete', *Trans. Amer. Soc. civ. Engrs.* (New York: vol. 59, 1907, pp. 67–143)
3. ROAD RESEARCH LABORATORY, *Soil Mechanics for Road Engineers* (London: H.M.S.O., 1952, p. 226)
4. SHERWOOD, P. T., 'The Effect of Soil Organic Matter on the Setting of Soil–Cement Mixtures', *Department of Scientific and Industrial Research, Road Research Technical Paper No. 61* (London: H.M.S.O., 1962)
5. MINISTRY OF TRANSPORT, *Specification for Road and Bridge Works* (London: H.M.S.O., 1963 (3rd edition))
6. BRITISH STANDARDS INSTITUTION, 'Methods of Test for Stabilized Soils', *B.S. 1924: 1957* (London: British Standards Institution, 1957)
7. RAYMOND, S. and SMITH, P. H., 'The Use of Stabilized P.F.A. in Road Construction', *P.F.A. for Stabilization and Grouting* (London: Central Electricity Generating Board, 1964, pp. 1–10), also *Civil Engineering and Public Works Review* (London: vol. 59, 1964, pp. 70–2, 238–40, and 361–3)
8. DUMBLETON, M. J., 'Investigations to Assess the Potentialities of Lime for Soil Stabilization in the United Kingdom', *Department of Scientific and Industrial Research, Road Research Technical Paper No. 64* (London: H.M.S.O., 1962)
9. CARTMELL, H. S. and BERGH, A. O., 'Lime Stabilization of Soils for Use as Road Foundations in Northern Rhodesia', *Department of Scientific and Industrial Research, Road Research Overseas Bulletin No. 9* (Harmondsworth: Road Research Laboratory, 1958)
10. SHERWOOD, P. T., 'Soil Stabilization by the Use of Chemical Admixtures', *Roads and Road Construction* (London: vol. 39, 1961, pp. 102–10)

10

Introduction to Pavement Design

- -

The basic requirement of a road is that it should provide a uniform, skid-resistant running surface which has a long life and needs little maintenance. The cost of fulfilling this requirement varies in each individual case and depends not only on the volume and type of traffic using the road but also on the soil and climatic conditions.

10.1 *Earth roads*

The cheapest form of road to construct, though not necessarily to maintain, is one in which the natural soil is used as the running surface. Until little more than a hundred years ago this type of road formed the majority of the highways in this country and at the present time there are many hundreds of miles of earth roads in overseas countries, particularly in those parts of Africa and Asia where the natural sand–clay deposits form suitably stable material. Under such conditions, earth roads may be impassable for part of the year as a result of seasonal storms, but, because of the generally dry climate and the fact that most are only lightly trafficked, they are economically justified in many cases. There is, however, a tendency for corrugations to form transversely across the road or for longitudinal rutting to take place, and dust is always a problem in dry weather.[1]

In Great Britain and other countries with temperate climates, earth roads are totally unsuitable for modern traffic requirements, since most soils become unstable with increased moisture content although they may have possessed satisfactory load-bearing properties when initially compacted. Means must therefore be found to protect the soil from large changes in moisture content and at the same time reduce the intensity of loading on the subgrade. This is usually achieved by placing layers of imported material on top of the subgrade to form the road pavement, although a cheaper method suitable for light traffic and often used overseas is simply to surface dress or stabilize the natural soil (see Chapter 9).

10.2 Types of road pavement

The modern road pavement is usually composed of several layers of material of differing quality; the strongest material being placed uppermost and forming the actual running surface. This layer is termed the *surfacing* and may be subdivided into a wearing course and a base course, whilst the other layers are termed the *base* and *sub-base* (Figure 10.1). It is not necessary for all three layers to be used; often the sub-

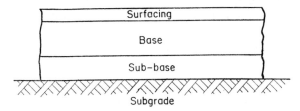

FIGURE 10.1 Structural elements of a road pavement

base is omitted, and in certain circumstances the base may be left out also.

The more common forms of construction employ a bituminous or a concrete surfacing and are referred to as flexible and rigid pavements respectively. Flexible construction uses a relatively thin layer of tar- or bitumen-bound surfacing material with a thicker base of crushed stone, bituminous-bound material, or lean concrete, beneath which there is often a sub-base of granular material or stabilized soil.

Rigid pavements have a concrete slab surfacing, 5–12 in thick, usually resting on a thinner base of granular material. A sub-base is not normally required in this type of construction.

Typical examples of flexible and rigid construction are shown in Figures 10.2 and 10.3, and the design procedure and constructional details for the two types are discussed in Chapters 11 and 12 respectively.

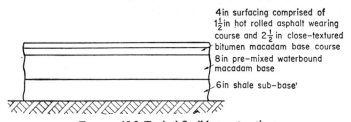

4in surfacing comprised of 1½in hot rolled asphalt wearing course and 2½ in close-textured bitumen macadam base course
8in pre-mixed waterbound macadam base
6in shale sub-base'

FIGURE 10.2 Typical flexible construction

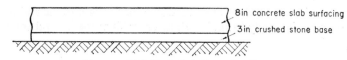

8in concrete slab surfacing

3in crushed stone base

FIGURE 10.3 Typical rigid construction

10.3 *Scope of pavement design*

The requirements which the pavement should fulfil can be set out as follows:

1. The pavement should be of sufficient thickness to spread the surface loading to a pressure intensity which the subgrade is capable of withstanding.
2. The pavement itself should be sufficiently strong to carry the stresses imposed upon it.
3. Where necessary, the pavement should be of sufficient thickness to prevent damage to a frost-susceptible subgrade.
4. The pavement should be composed of frost-resistant material.
5. The pavement surfacing should be impervious to the penetration of surface water, which would weaken both the pavement and the subgrade.
6. The pavement surfacing should have a skid-resistant texture.

Whilst pavement design in its widest sense must be considered to include all these factors, the term is usually restricted to cover the procedure for determining the thickness of the various layers in order to satisfy (1) and (2). The overall thickness of the pavement may have to be increased above that determined from this design procedure in order to satisfy (3). Requirements (4), (5), and (6) can be achieved by the choice of suitable materials, and are dealt with in subsequent chapters.

The design procedures for both flexible and rigid pavements which are used at present in this and in many other countries are largely based on the actual performance of existing pavement structures rather than on strictly theoretical considerations. However, it is important to consider the theoretical approaches to pavement design, since, in the first place, these can lead to a better understanding of the results of full-scale investigations, and, secondly, it is hoped that eventually it will be possible to design road pavements on a somewhat less empirical basis.

10.4 *Loading on pavement*

Before any theoretical design procedure for pavement thickness can be examined, it is necessary to consider the surface loading to which the pavement is subjected.

Except for vehicles with multiple wheels, the wheel spacing is generally sufficiently great for the areas of pavement affected by each wheel not to overlap, and therefore the design should be based on a single wheel load rather than on the total weight of the vehicle. With multiple wheels, the combined effect varies according to the wheel spacing in relation to the pavement thickness and other factors, but can never exceed that for a single wheel carrying the same total load as the multiple wheels. Consideration should be given, however, to the case where vehicles are parked or are passing closely together, when the areas of influence from one wheel of each vehicle may overlap. Sparkes[2] has considered a number of arrangements of vehicles and his results suggest that the maximum stresses in concrete slabs may be increased by up to 50% above those for an isolated wheel load, depending upon the type of subgrade and the position of the loads with respect to the slab edges.

Impact effects are normally ignored, since modern roads should have well-finished surfaces with only small irregularities. In addition, the Maryland and W.A.S.H.O. Road Tests[3, 4] have shown that the stresses produced by fast-moving vehicles are less than for similar stationary vehicles as a result of the mass and elasticity of the road structure preventing the full static deflexion from taking place during the short duration of dynamic loading. This reduction of stress is assumed to counteract any increase from impact.

Pavement failure is generally associated with progressive irreversible deformation of the subgrade as a result of a large number of load applications rather than from one single load. In the present state of knowledge there is no means by which the effect of repetitive loading can be included in the theory, other than by arbitrarily increasing the design static wheel load. Repetition of loads and impact effects are automatically allowed for, of course, in wholly empirical methods.

10.5 Contact pressure

The contact pressure between the wheel and the road surface depends on the tyre inflation pressure and the tyre wall stiffness. In an investigation with aeroplane tyres, Lawton[5] found that the tyre imprint pattern on a rigid plate was approximately elliptical and that the average contact pressure was greater than the inflation pressure with a low tyre pressure but vice versa with the same tyre at a high pressure. The maximum contact pressure was independent of the nature of the supporting material when the tyre was carrying a high percentage of its rated load and was approximately 130% of the average rigid plate contact pressure, the distribution pattern being ellipsoidal along both axes. In order to simplify calculations, however, most theoretical studies have assumed uniform contact pressure distribution over a circular area, with the contact pressure equal to the tyre inflation pressure. The effect of contact pressure on the stress distribution pattern is further discussed on page 177.

STRESS DISTRIBUTION THROUGH PAVEMENT

10.6 *Boussinesq elastic theory*

The simplest approach to pavement design is to consider the pavement and subgrade to form a homogeneous, elastic, isotropic material. Boussinesq first analysed the stress distribution due to the application of a vertical point load P at the surface of such a material, and showed that the vertical stress σ at any point at a depth z below the surface and

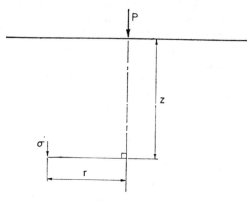

FIGURE 10.4

at a horizontal distance r from the axis of the load (Figure 10.4) is given by:[6]

$$\sigma = \frac{3P}{2\pi z^2}\left[\frac{1}{1 + (r/z)^2}\right]^{5/2} \tag{10.1}$$

For uniform contact pressure distribution p over a circular area, each element of the area can be considered to carry a concentrated load of magnitude $p(\delta A)$ and the vertical stress at any point within the material can be determined by integrating Equation 10.1 over the contact area.

The maximum vertical stress on a horizontal plane at a depth z below the surface occurs beneath the centre of the loaded area and is given by:

$$\sigma_z = \int_{r=0}^{r=a} \frac{3p}{2\pi z^2}\left[\frac{1}{1 + (r/z)^2}\right]^{5/2} \mathrm{d}A$$

where p is the uniform contact pressure at the surface and a the radius of the circular contact area.

This reduces to:

$$\sigma_z = p\left[1 - \frac{z^3}{(a^2 + z^2)^{3/2}}\right] \tag{10.2}$$

The vertical stress at other points within the material can also be calculated in a similar manner and Figure 10.5 shows the 'bulbs' of uniform vertical stress under a uniformly loaded circular area.

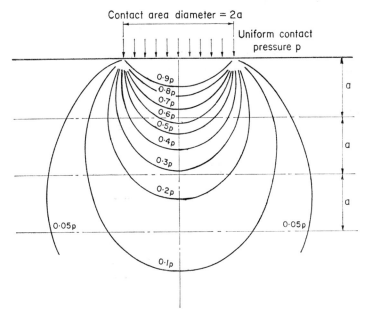

FIGURE 10.5 Bulbs of pressure for homogeneous material under uniform circular load

The horizontal radial stress at a depth z beneath the centre of the loaded area is given by:

$$\sigma_R = \tfrac{1}{2}p \left[1 + 2\nu - \frac{2(1 + \nu)z}{(a^2 + z^2)^{1/2}} + \frac{z^3}{(a^2 + z^2)^{3/2}} \right] \quad (10.3)$$

where ν is Poisson's ratio for the material.

Poisson's ratio is difficult to determine exactly for soils, but it is usual to assume that $\nu = 0.5$, in which case:

$$\sigma_R = \tfrac{1}{2}p \left[2 - \frac{3z}{(a^2 + z^2)^{1/2}} + \frac{z^3}{(a^2 + z^2)^{3/2}} \right] \quad (10.4)$$

The Boussinesq analysis can be applied to pavement design by calculating the maximum shear stress at any depth from the vertical and horizontal stresses, and comparing this with the shear strength of the pavement and subgrade materials. The thickness of the pavement layer can then be chosen so that the shear stress at the depth of the pavement–subgrade interface does not exceed the shear strength of the subgrade.

Alternatively, the surface deflexion at the centre of the loaded area may be used as the limiting factor, as follows:

The vertical elastic strain δ at a depth z beneath the centre of the loaded area is given by:

$$\delta = \frac{1}{E}(\sigma_z - 2\nu\sigma_R) \tag{10.5}$$

where E is the modulus of elasticity of the material.

Hence, if it is assumed that there is an incompressible pavement layer of thickness h on top of a compressible subgrade, then the total vertical displacement at the centre of the loaded area can be obtained by substituting in Equation 10.5 the values for σ_z and σ_R from Equations 10.2 and 10.3 and integrating between the limits $z = h$ and $z = \infty$. This gives:

$$\Delta = \frac{p}{E}\left[(2 - 2\nu^2)(a^2 + h^2)^{1/2} - \frac{(1 + \nu)h^2}{(a^2 + h^2)^{1/2}} + (\nu + 2\nu^2 - 1)h\right]$$

where Δ is the vertical displacement at the centre of the loaded area and E is modulus of elasticity of the subgrade.

When $\nu = 0.5$, this reduces to

$$\Delta = \frac{3pa^2}{2E(a^2 + h^2)^{1/2}} = F_1\frac{pa}{E} \tag{10.6}$$

where

$$F_1 = \frac{3}{2}\left[\frac{1}{1 + (h/a)^2}\right]^{1/2}$$

Thus, by limiting the surface deflexion in Equation 10.6 to an arbitrarily chosen value, say 0·2 in, the required pavement thickness h can be obtained.

Neither of these methods is satisfactory for design purposes, however, since the conception of a pavement layer overlying a subgrade is not in keeping with the original application of the analysis to a homogeneous material. Moreover, the separation of the material into compressible and incompressible parts for the purpose of the displacement analysis is again contrary to the initial assumption of a material with uniform elastic properties.

The modulus of elasticity of a soil subgrade would normally lie between 1,000 and 10,000 lb/sq in, whilst that for a crushed stone base would be between 10,000 and 100,000 lb/sq in and for a concrete slab between 4×10^6 and 6×10^6 lb/sq in. This difference in elastic properties between the various layers of material forming the pavement and the subgrade will give rise to completely different stress and displacement patterns compared with a homogeneous material, and will result in an overestimation of the stresses and displacements in the actual pavement. The analysis can give, therefore, no more than a general guide to pavement performance under different loading conditions, although in addition it forms a useful basis for more precise theoretical calculations.

10.7 Effect of tyre pressure on stress distribution

It is interesting to consider the effect of tyre pressure on the maximum vertical stresses calculated from the Boussinesq theory. Assuming that the tyre inflation and contact pressures are equal, then for a fixed wheel load with tyre pressure p and circular contact area radius a, an increase in tyre pressure to $2p$ will result in a decrease in contact area radius to $a/\sqrt{2}$. The vertical stress σ_z at any depth z beneath the centre of the

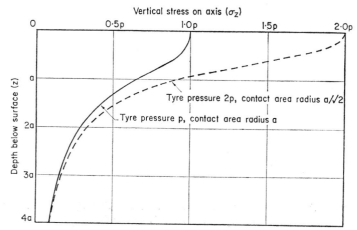

FIGURE 10.6 Effects of tyre pressure on the vertical stress beneath the centre of a uniformly-loaded circular area

loaded area can thus be obtained by substituting $2p$ for p and $a/\sqrt{2}$ for a in Equation 10.2. Hence:

$$\sigma_z = 2p\left[1 - \frac{z^3}{(\tfrac{1}{2}a^2 + z^2)^{3/2}}\right] \qquad (10.7)$$

The vertical stress distributions for tyre pressures p and $2p$ are shown in Figure 10.6. It can be seen that the higher tyre pressure results in much greater stresses in the upper layers of the pavement, but that the difference is insignificant at a depth equal to $3a$.

10.8 Burmister two-layer theory

As a result of the limitations of the Boussinesq analysis when applied to a pavement resting on a subgrade with a widely different modulus of elasticity, Burmister[7] extended the theory to cover a two-layer system consisting of an elastic slab, infinite in the horizontal plane but of finite depth, resting on a second elastic material of lower modulus of elasticity which is infinite in extent both horizontally and vertically. Burmister calculated the vertical displacement at the surface at the centre of the applied load for various ratios of moduli of elasticity for the two layers and for various ratios of the depth of the upper layer to the radius of the applied load, assuming uniform contact pressure over a circular area and a perfectly rough interface between the two layers. The results of these calculations are shown graphically in Figure 10.7.

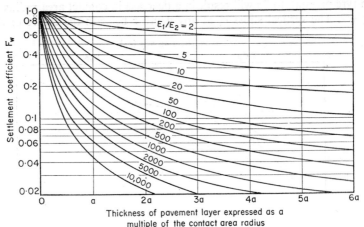

Thickness of pavement layer expressed as a
multiple of the contact area radius

FIGURE 10.7 Influence curves for the settlement coefficient F_W for the two-layer elastic system[7] (Poisson's ratio = 0·5)

where a settlement coefficient F_W is plotted against the thickness of the upper layer h for various ratios of moduli of elasticity. The vertical displacement is given by:

$$\Delta = F_W \frac{1 \cdot 5pa}{E_2} \qquad (10.8)$$

where Δ is the vertical displacement at the surface, p the uniform contact pressure at the surface, a the radius of the applied load, and E_2 the modulus of elasticity of the lower layer.

In the design procedure, the pavement is considered as the upper layer and the subgrade as the lower layer, and the thickness of the pavement is selected so that the vertical displacement at the surface under the wheel is limited to a particular value which Burmister suggested should be 0·2 in for flexible pavements and 0·05 in for rigid pavements.

For example, consider a flexible road pavement which is to be constructed to carry a 4-ton wheel load with a tyre inflation pressure 100 lb/sq in. The moduli of elasticity of the pavement material and subgrade are 10,000 lb/sq in and 2,000 lb/sq in respectively.

PLATE 8.1 Three-wheel smooth-wheeled roller

PLATE 8.2 Pneumatic-tyred roller

PLATE 8.3 Wacker vibro-rammer

PLATE 8.4 Wacker vibro-plate
compactor

PLATE 8.5 3¾-ton towed vibratory roller

PLATE 8.6 3½-ton self-propelled vibrating roller

PLATE 8.7 7¼-cwt hand-steered vibrating roller

PLATE 8.8 5-ton towed vibrating sheepsfoot roller

PLATE 9.1   Howard Unispreader distributing cement for the stabilized sub-base of the Harthill
By-Pass, Scotland

PLATE 9.2   Howard Unimix mixing stabilizer and pulverized soil on the Harthill By-Pass, Scotland

PLATE 9.3 Howard 48 soil stabilization train at work on the sub-base of an airfield runway

PLATE 11.1 Spreading lean concrete base by machine between marginal haunches

PLATE 11.2 Compacting lean concrete by means of a vibrating roller

PLATE 11.3 Transportable asphalt mixing plant: output 40–45 tons per hour. The plant is electrically driven and electro-pneumatically controlled to mix at temperatures of 180–450°F (82–232°C)

PLATE 11.4 Coated macadam mixing plant: output 40–60 tons per hour. Stockpiles of crushed graded material can be seen between the plant and the quarry face

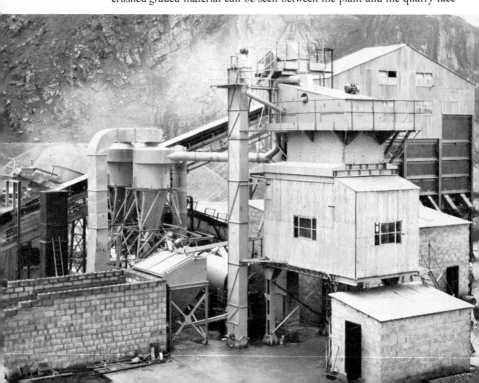

PLATE 11.5   Laying open-textured base course material

PLATE 11.6   Laying dense wearing course material

PLATE 11.7 Applying pre-coated chippings to hot-rolled asphalt wearing course on the Wigan South Link, M.6 motorway

PLATE 11.8   Close-up view of a dense tar surfacing wearing course
on close-textured base course material

PLATE 11.9   Contractor's laboratory for testing bituminous materials

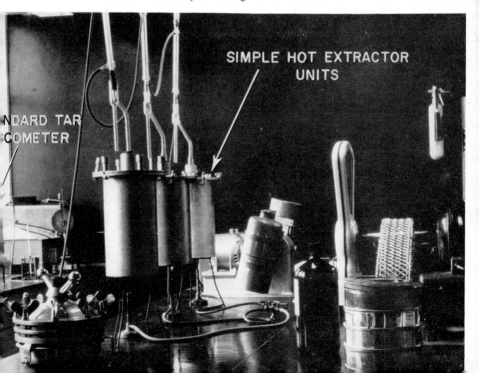

PLATE 11.10 Use of bulk tank sprayer for surface dressing operations

Assuming a uniform contact pressure p equal to the tyre inflation pressure and a circular contact area radius a,

$$P = 8{,}960 = p(\pi a^2) = 314 \cdot 2a^2$$

Hence $a = 5 \cdot 33$ in.

Limiting the vertical displacement Δ to $0 \cdot 2$ in, from Equation 10.8

$$\Delta = 0 \cdot 2 = F_W \frac{1 \cdot 5pa}{E_2}$$

Since $E_2 = 2{,}000$ lb/sq in,

$$F_W = \frac{0 \cdot 2(2{,}000)}{1 \cdot 5(533)} = 0 \cdot 50$$

From Figure 10.7 for $F_W = 0 \cdot 50$ and $E_1/E_2 = 5$, the required pavement thickness $h = 1 \cdot 5a = 8$ in.

In further work Burmister[8] extended the analysis to calculate the displacement at the centre of the loaded area with a three-layer system.

10.9 Stresses in layered pavements

Using the two-layer and three-layer analysis developed by Burmister,[8] Fox,[9] and Acum and Fox[10] have calculated the vertical, horizontal, and shear stresses for certain specific cases of layered pavements. These provide a more rational basis for pavement design since the stresses can be contained within certain limits, whereas with Burmister's design

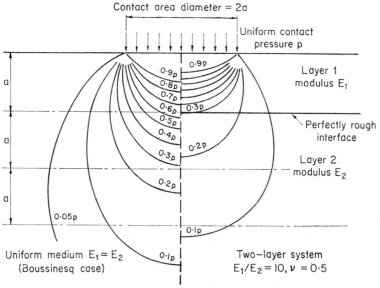

FIGURE 10.8 Comparison between the vertical stress distribution in a uniform medium and in a two-layer system

method an arbitrary value for limiting displacement is chosen regardless of the stresses in the materials. Calculation of stress distribution in layered pavements is very involved, but with the use of computers, efforts are now being made to extend the number of combinations previously considered.[11]

The effect of introducing a layer of higher modulus of elasticity on the vertical stress distribution under a circular area with uniform loading can be seen in Figures 10.8 and 10.9. Figure 10.8 shows bulbs of pressure for a two-layer system in which the pavement layer has a thickness equal to the radius of the applied loading and a modulus of

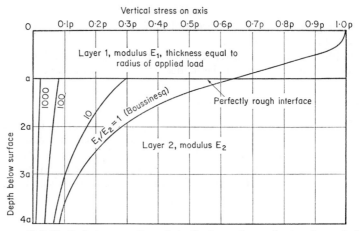

FIGURE 10.9 Vertical stress on the axis in the lower layer of a two-layer elastic system due to a circular uniform loading

elasticity ten times that of the subgrade, and comparison is made with the bulbs of pressure for the Boussinesq case. It can be seen that the pressure bulbs in the former case are concentrated within the pavement layer, and the maximum vertical stress at the pavement–subgrade interface is reduced from 65% to 30% of the applied pressure at the surface.

Figure 10.9 shows the vertical stress distribution beneath the centre of the loaded area for various ratios of moduli of elasticity for the pavement and subgrade layers, the thickness of the pavement layer being again equal to the radius of the applied loading. This demonstrates the very large reductions in subgrade stress that result from using material of high modulus of elasticity in the pavement layer.

10.10 *Application to existing pavement performance*

Although theoretical considerations have not yet reached the stage when they can be used as a complete design method, partly because of the

omplexities of the calculations involved but largely because of the
difficulties of allowing for the effect of non-elastic behaviour of the
pavement and subgrade under repetitive loading, use can be made of
these theories in comparing the performance of various pavement
materials and analysing road failures.

For example, analysis of the data published by Acum and Fox[10] for
three-layer elastic system shows that when the thickness and
modulus of elasticity of the surface layer and the elastic modulus of the
subgrade are held constant, the thickness of base h_2 to give a certain
vertical stress at the pavement–subgrade interface decreases as the
lastic modulus of the base E_2 is increased, the relation being[12]

$$h_2 = \text{Constant} \times E_2^{-0.42} \qquad (10.9)$$

Thus various types of road base materials can be compared experimentally under conditions which should be independent of the surfacing or the underlying subgrade and the relative performance can be
assessed.

REFERENCES

1. TANNER, J. S., 'Corrugations on Earth and Gravel Roads: their Formation,
   Treatment and Prevention', *Department of Scientific and Industrial
   Research, Road Research Overseas Bulletin No. 6* (Harmondsworth: Road
   Research Laboratory, 1957) also *Roads and Road Construction* (London:
   vol. 36, 1958, pp. 4–10 and 32–5)
2. SPARKES, F. N., 'Stresses in Concrete Road Slabs', *The Structural Engineer*
   (London: vol. 17, 1939, pp. 98–116)
3. HIGHWAY RESEARCH BOARD, 'Road Test One-MD, Final Report: Effects
   of Controlled Truck Axle Loadings on Concrete Pavement', *Highway
   Research Board Special Report 4* (Washington, D.C.: National Academy
   of Sciences—National Research Council, 1952)
4. HIGHWAY RESEARCH BOARD, 'The W.A.S.H.O. Road Test—Part 2: Test
   Data, Analyses, Findings', *Highway Research Board Special Report 22*
   (Washington, D.C.: National Academy of Sciences—National Research
   Council, 1955)
5. LAWTON, W. L., 'Static Load Contact Pressure Patterns under Airplane
   Tires', *Proceedings, Highway Research Board* (Washington, D.C.: vol. 36,
   1957, pp. 233–9)
6. TIMOSHENKO, S. and GOODIER, J. N., *Theory of Elasticity* (New York:
   McGraw-Hill, 1951 (2nd edition), p. 362)
7. BURMISTER, D. M., 'The Theory of Stresses and Displacements in Layered
   Systems and Applications to the Design of Airport Runways', *Proceedings, Highway Research Board* (Washington, D.C.: vol. 23, 1943, pp.
   126–44)
8. BURMISTER, D. M., 'The General Theory of Stresses and Displacements in
   Layered Soil Systems. III', *Journal of Applied Physics* (New York: vol. 16,
   1945, pp. 296–302)

9. FOX, L., 'Computation of Traffic Stresses in a Simple Road Structure' *Department of Scientific and Industrial Research, Road Research Technical Paper No. 9* (London: H.M.S.O., 1948)

10. ACUM, W. E. A. and FOX, L., 'Computation of Load Stresses in a Three Layer Elastic System', *Geotechnique* (London: vol. 2, 1951, pp. 293–300

11. JONES, A., 'Tables of Stresses in Three-Layer Elastic Systems', *Highway Research Board Bulletin 342* (Washington, D.C.: National Academy o Sciences—National Research Council, 1962, pp. 176–214)

12. WHIFFIN, A. C. and LISTER, N. W., 'The Application of Elastic Theory to Flexible Pavements', *Proceedings of the International Conference on Asphalt Pavements, University of Michigan, 1962* (Ann Arbor, Michigan University of Michigan, 1963, pp. 499–521)

11

Flexible Pavements: Design and Construction

Flexible road pavements rely on the load-spreading properties of a layered system to distribute the wheel loads to the subgrade. The overall pavement thickness and the thickness of the individual layers should be such that the stresses in any layer or at the pavement–subgrade interface will not cause permanent deformation of the material, resulting in an uneven running surface.

Because of the complexities encountered in the analysis of stresses in a multi-layered elastic system (see Chapter 10), together with the difficulty of allowing for cumulative plastic deformation of the subgrade as a result of repetitive loading, it is established practice to design flexible pavements on an empirical basis. These empirical design methods relate pavement thickness to certain subgrade properties as determined from a study of existing pavements which have proved satisfactory or otherwise.

11.1 Group index method

This design procedure is based on soil classification tests which when applied to the subgrade material produce a *group index* according to the following equation:[1]

$$GI = 0.2a + 0.005ac + 0.01bd \qquad (11.1)$$

where a is that portion of the percentage passing a No. 200 sieve greater than 35 and not exceeding 75, expressed as a positive whole number (0 to 40); b is that portion of the percentage passing a No. 200 sieve greater than 15 and not exceeding 55, expressed as a positive whole number (0 to 40); c is that portion of the numerical liquid limit greater than 40 and not exceeding 60, expressed as a positive whole number

183

(0 to 20); d is that portion of the numerical plasticity index greater than 10 and not exceeding 30, expressed as a positive whole number (0 to 20)

The group index varies from zero for excellent subgrades up to 20 for very poor subgrades.

The proposed method of design (Figure 11.1)[2] relates the thickness of the sub-base to the subgrade characteristics. The total thickness of the

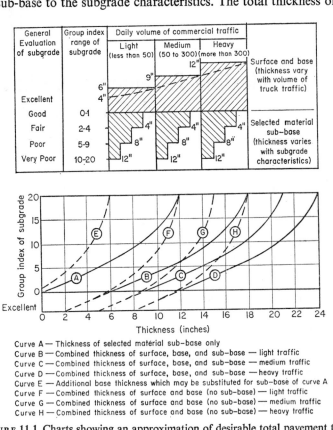

FIGURE 11.1 Charts showing an approximation of desirable total pavement thicknesses (surface, base, and sub-base) based on truck traffic volume and group index of subgrade[2]

base and surfacing is then determined from the intensity of traffic expressed in terms of commercial vehicles per day, so taking account of the effect of load repetition.

The method has been adopted by a number of American states but has a limited application, since it is assumed that subgrade performance is related only to its group index irrespective of the density and moisture content of the compacted material.

C.B.R. DESIGN METHOD

11.2 C.B.R. test

An alternative method of pavement design much more widely used than the group index method is based on the California bearing ratio (C.B.R.) value of the subgrade. The C.B.R. value is determined from a cylinder penetration test on a sample of subgrade prepared in the laboratory using a metal mould, 6 in internal diameter and 5 in high, with a detachable base plate (Figure 11.2).[3]

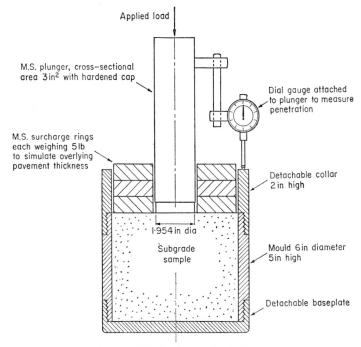

Applied load

M.S. plunger, cross–sectional area 3 in² with hardened cap

Dial gauge attached to plunger to measure penetration

M.S. surcharge rings each weighing 5 lb to simulate overlying pavement thickness

Detachable collar 2 in high

1·954 in dia

Subgrade sample

Mould 6 in diameter 5 in high

Detachable baseplate

FIGURE 11.2 Apparatus for C.B.R. test

To simulate actual site conditions, the sample must be compacted to a dry density corresponding to the minimum state of compaction which it is anticipated will be achieved in practice, the sample having been prepared at the maximum moisture content likely to be experienced subsequent to the completion of the roadworks. In many instances, this will be approximately the same as the natural moisture content of undisturbed soil samples taken from a depth of not less than 3 ft below existing ground level (below the level of seasonal fluctuations) and away from the roots of trees and shrubs, and thus in shallow cuttings the natural moisture content of the soil encountered at (or slightly below) formation level should be used to prepare the C.B.R. specimens. In deep clay cuttings, however, samples taken from the proposed formation level may have a reduced moisture content due to consolidation and 'wetting-up' may follow the release of overburden pressure during the construction of the cutting. For this reason, the C.B.R. test should be in this case be carried out on a sample of the same soil taken from a depth of 3 ft below existing ground level. Should this not be practicable, the

TABLE 11.1 *Estimated (laboratory) C.B.R. values for British soils compacted at the natural moisture content*[4]

Type of soil	Plasticity index (%)	C.B.R. (%)	
		Well-drained (water-table at least 2 ft below formation level)	*Poorly drained*
Heavy clay	70	2	1*
	60	2	1·5*
	50	2·5	2
	40	3	2
Silty clay	30	5	3
Sandy clay	20	6	4
	10	7	5
Silt	—	2	1*
Sand (poorly-graded)	Non-plastic	20	10
Sand (well-graded)	Non-plastic	40	15
Well-graded sandy gravel	Non-plastic	60	20

* Soils having C.B.R. values of less than 2% should preferably be removed and replaced by selected filling material

C.B.R. value can be estimated from the soil type as indicated in Table 11.1. Standard American practice is to soak C.B.R. specimens for 4 days before testing, but in this country this is considered to be generally too severe.

C.B.R. tests on fill material should be carried out on samples taken from a depth of 3 ft in the borrow area unless the soil survey shows that potentially weaker soils may be drawn from greater depths. If samples of these soils do not occur close to the surface, an estimate of the probable minimum C.B.R. value of the fill material can be made from Table 11.1.

The standard C.B.R. test procedure uses a cylindrical plunger having a cross-sectional area of 3 sq in which is forced into the sample at a constant rate of penetration of 0·05 in per minute following the application of an initial 10-lb seating load. Loads corresponding to penetrations of 0·025, 0·05, 0·075, 0·10, 0·15, 0·20, 0·25, and 0·30 in are recorded. Before the test commences, surcharge rings are placed on top of the sample to represent the weight of the overlying road pavement. One ring, weighing 5 lb, is used for each estimated 2½ in of constructional

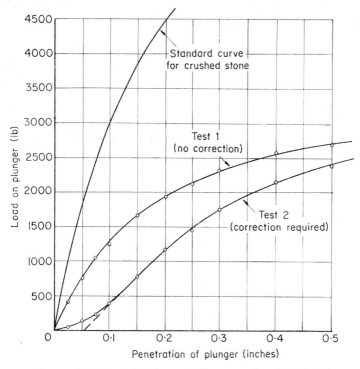

FIGURE 11.3 Typical load–penetration curves from C.B.R. test

thickness. Where a soaking procedure is being used prior to testing, the surcharge should be applied throughout the soaking period since this will affect the swelling of fine-grained soils.

The test results are plotted as a load–penetration diagram (Figure 11.3) and a smooth curve is drawn through the points. The curve is usually concave downwards, but if the initial part is concave upwards a correction has to be made. This consists of drawing a tangent to the curve at the point of steepest slope and producing the line backwards to cut the penetration axis at a point which is the corrected origin of the penetration scale. The loads required to produce penetrations of 0·1

G*

and 0·2 in are read off the curve and are expressed as percentages of the standard loads of 3,000 and 4,500 lb respectively which have been obtained for corresponding penetrations on a standard sample of high-quality crushed stone material. The higher of these two percentages is then termed the C.B.R. value of the subgrade. Typical values range from 2% for heavy clays to 50% or more for well-graded sand–gravel mixtures (see Table 11.1).

If desired, the C.B.R. test can be carried out in the field on *in situ* material using a lorry or mobile laboratory vehicle to obtain the necessary reaction load through a screw jack. The procedure is similar to that followed in the laboratory except that a plate 10 in in diameter with a centre hole for the plunger is placed on the soil before the addition of the surcharge weights. Care must be taken to mount the penetration-measuring dial gauge on members which are supported clear of the loaded area.

Correlation between field and laboratory test are good for claylike materials under the same moisture content and density conditions, but may be erratic for more granular soils as a result of the confining effect of the laboratory mould.

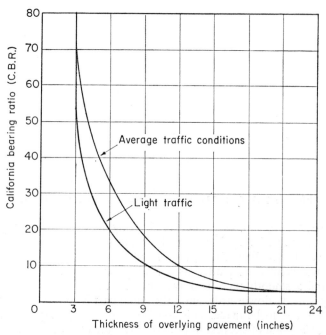

FIGURE 11.4 Original C.B.R. design curves from data collected by the California Division of Highways[6]

11.3 *Development of C.B.R. design method*

The C.B.R. method of design was first used by the California Division of Highways as a result of an extensive investigation of pavement failures during the period 1928–9. The survey showed that a relationship existed between the C.B.R. value of the subgrade or pavement material and the required thickness of construction above this level. From this study, design curves were produced corresponding to average and light traffic conditions relating the minimum thickness of the overlying pavement to the C.B.R. values of sub-base and subgrade materials. From these curves the required thickness of sub-base and base-plus-surfacing could be determined (Figure 11.4).

During the early years of the second world war, the U.S. Corps of Engineers adopted the C.B.R. method of design for airfield pavements. Allowing for the fact that airport runway loading is less channelized than on highways and taking account of the less frequent repetition of loading, it was considered that the two curves in Figure 11.4 could be assumed to represent 7,000 lb and 12,000 lb aircraft wheel loads. The latter curve was then extrapolated by calculating the shear stresses for various wheel loads in relation to depth and equating these to a required C.B.R. value, so obtaining tentative design curves for 25,000, 40,000,

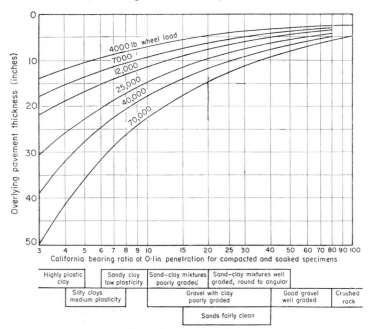

FIGURE 11.5 Tentative C.B.R. design curves for flexible airfield pavements[6]

and 70,000 lb wheel loads (Figure 11.5). At the same time a field and laboratory testing programme was set up, and from this the Corps of Engineers has developed more refined design curves taking into account wheel loads, tyre pressures, and landing gear configurations.

A review of the development of the C.B.R. method of design has been given in an American Society of Civil Engineers symposium.[5]

An example of the design procedure can be given with reference to Figure 11.5 for a 40,000 lb wheel load. If the pavement consists of a bituminous surfacing, a crushed limestone base (C.B.R. = 80%), and a fine sand sub-base (C.B.R. = 20%) overlying a clay subgrade (C.B.R. = 4%), then the total constructional thickness above each of these layers can be read off the 40,000 lb curve as follows:

Surfacing (above base with C.B.R. value of 80%)   = 5 in
Surfacing + base (above sub-base with C.B.R. value of 20%) = 12 in
Total thickness (above subgrade with C.B.R. value of 4%)   = 32 in

The pavement should thus be made up of a 20-in sub-base, a 7-in base, and 5 in of surfacing.

11.4 Current design practice

The normal maximum legally permitted axle load for vehicles in Great Britain is 9 tons (11 tons for multiple wheel axles with a minimum wheel spacing of 18 in), which corresponds to a maximum wheel load of 10,000 lb.[6] On this basis, making some allowance for overloading, a design curve for highway pavements could be produced. However, whilst this method of design is acceptable for airfield pavements which have relatively few repetitions of loading, it is desirable to introduce into the design procedure for highway pavements some factor which takes account of repeated load. For this reason, a modification of the original C.B.R. procedure has been introduced in which the design curves are related to a number of applications of wheel load rather than to specific wheel loads.

The current recommendations for British practice are set out in *Road Note No. 29*,[4] the revised edition of which now includes guidance on the design of housing-estate and other lightly trafficked roads previously given in *Road Note No. 20*.[7] For design purposes, traffic is considered in terms of the number of commercial vehicles per day (total two-way volume) and divided into the following categories:

More than 4,500 commercial vehicles per day
1,500–4,500 commercial vehicles per day
450–1,500 commercial vehicles per day
150–450 commercial vehicles per day
45–150 commercial vehicles per day
Less than   45 commercial vehicles per day

A commercial vehicle is defined as a goods or public service vehicle of unladen weight exceeding 30 cwt.

Traffic volumes are based on 24-hour counts or, where these are not available, on 16-hour counts plus 6% and volumes are averaged over 7 days. For design purposes, an estimate should be made of the traffic that will be carried by the road 20 years after construction, and to arrive at this figure the following formula may be used on major through routes in the absence of any other information:

$$A = P(1 + r)^{x+20}$$

where A is the number of commercial vehicles per day for design, P the number of commercial vehicles per day at the last census, r the annual rate of increase in the number of commercial vehicles, which may be taken as 0·04 (an average figure based on recent census data), and x the number of years between the last census and the year of construction.

The normal small number of notifiable heavy loads using heavily trafficked roads is provided for in the design charts, but where the number of these loads is likely to be high, such as on approach roads to docks and similar places, a design curve corresponding to a higher traffic intensity than that estimated as above should be used.

The design curves for the six traffic categories are given in Figure 11.6. In each case, a constant thickness of surfacing and base is recommended and the sub-base thickness only is varied according to the nature of the subgrade. Since in practice the sub-base thickness must remain constant over a considerable length, the design thickness will normally be that corresponding to the weaker subgrade occurring to any appreciable extent, pockets of lower quality material being replaced by selected filling. On larger contracts, however, it may prove economical to specify different thicknesses of sub-base corresponding to the main subgrade types encountered along the alignment, although in general it will not be convenient to make such changes more frequently than three or four times per mile of carriageway.

Where the C.B.R. value of the subgrade indicates that a sub-base is required, it is recommended that the thickness should not be less than 6 in for roads designed to charts 1–4 in order that the sub-base should be capable of carrying constructional traffic. For roads designed to charts 5 and 6, a minimum sub-base thickness of 3 in is recommended. If the subgrade is a material which is likely to be frost-susceptible (see page 138), the thickness of the sub-base should be increased, if necessary, to give a total pavement thickness of at least 18 in irrespective of the C.B.R. value of the subgrade. This requirement may be relaxed for roads designed to charts 3–6 at the discretion of the engineer where local experience during very severe winters has shown this to be permissible.

It is normal practice to use the same constructional thickness over the full width of the carriageway, despite the fact that most commercial

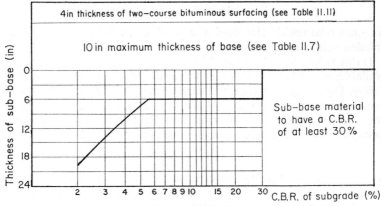

DESIGN CHART 1
(More than 4500 commercial vehicles per day 20 years after construction)

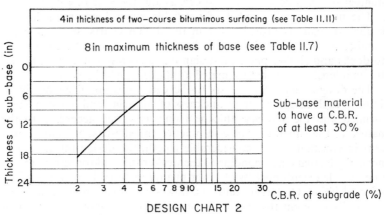

DESIGN CHART 2
(1500 to 4500 commercial vehicles per day 20 years after construction)

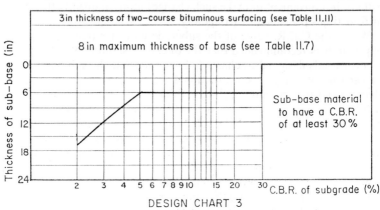

DESIGN CHART 3
(450 to 1500 commercial vehicles per day 20 years after construction)

FIGURE 11.6 Design curves for flexible road pavements[4]

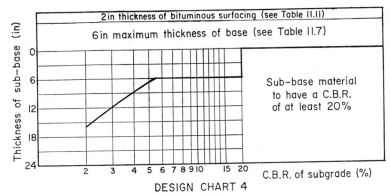

DESIGN CHART 4

(150 to 450 commercial vehicles per day 20 years after construction)

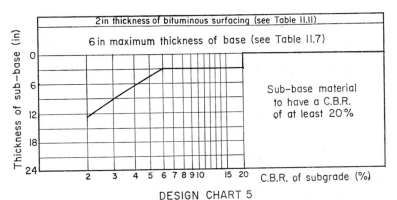

DESIGN CHART 5

(45 to 150 commercial vehicles per day 20 years after construction)

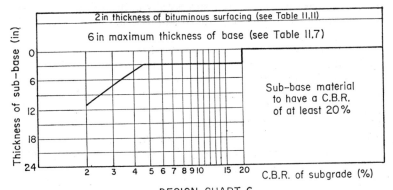

DESIGN CHART 6

(up to 45 commercial vehicles per day 20 years after construction)

FIGURE 11.6 (contd.)

vehicles travel in the nearside (or slow) lane on multi-lane roads. This is borne out by observations on traffic and by the fact that the maximum permanent deformation of the road surfacing occurs some 3–4 ft from the nearside kerb. It has been suggested that account could be taken of this by using a tapered sub-base as indicated in Figure 11.7. Apart from

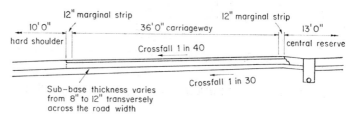

FIGURE 11.7

the saving in material costs, the tapered sub-base would allow a steeper crossfall to be used at formation level on non-superelevated sections of the alignment, so providing better drainage during construction.

BASE AND SUB-BASE MATERIALS

11.5 *Granular sub-base materials*

Essentially the sub-base should be constructed of frost-resistant material which will be structurally stable in all weather conditions. One method of construction is to increase the strength of the subgrade soil by the addition of cement or other stabilizing agent (see Chapter 9). This type of sub-base has been used successfully both in this country and overseas, but in recent years a granular sub-base has been preferred for most major road schemes.

The design charts given in *Road Note No. 29* are based on a minimum C.B.R. value for the sub-base of 30% (charts 1–3) or 20% (charts 4–6). Almost any low quality granular material will fulfil this requirement, but since it is desirable on most road contracts to use a sub-base material which is not susceptible to wet weather conditions, free-draining materials such as quarry overburden or crushed rock should be used in preference to materials containing large amounts of fines.

The current Ministry of Transport Specification[8] requires granular sub-base material to conform to the gradings specified in Table 11.2. Type 1 aggregates comprise crushed rock, crushed concrete, crushed slag, or well-burnt non-plastic shale. These materials will remain stable over a much wider range of moisture contents than type 2 aggregates which include well-graded natural sands, gravels, and rock or slag fines, and are therefore to be preferred in this country where site conditions are likely to be wet during construction. Since a considerable thickness of sub-base will be required on poor subgrades, the material must be readily available in large quantities and be relatively cheap (preferably not more than 9*d*. per sq yd per inch thickness at current prices), though cost should not be the primary consideration.

Where the sub-base material contains an appreciable amount coarser than ¾ in and the C.B.R. test cannot be used to measure its bearing capacity, the suitability of the material must be assessed either by visual examination or from the results of a field experiment.

TABLE 11.2 *Grading requirements for granular sub-base materials*[8]

B.S. sieve size	Percentage by weight passing	
	Type 1 aggregates	Type 2 aggregates
3 in	100	100
1½ in	85–100	85–100
⅜ in	—	45–100
3/16 in	25–45	25–85
No. 25	8–22	8–45
No. 200	0–2	0–10

Note: The proportion of material passing the No. 200 sieve for type 1 aggregates may be increased to 10% provided that all this material is non-plastic

All sub-base materials should be compacted in layers not exceeding 6 in thickness until the required dry density has been achieved. Compaction is best carried out with an 8–10-ton smooth-wheeled roller or a vibratory tandem roller with a similar effect. Generally, for compaction purposes, the moisture content of type 1 aggregates should not exceed 5% and lie within the range 5–8% for the type 2 materials.

11.6 Base materials

In general, any material which has a C.B.R. value of not less than 80% when compacted can be used for road base construction, provided that it remains stable in water and is unaffected by frost. Suitable materials for main road construction include crushed stone or blast-furnace slag, dry lean concrete, cement-bound granular material, and bituminous-bound materials, whilst for secondary roads and lightly trafficked roads overseas a less strong material such as stabilized soil or stabilized P.F.A. (see page 163) can be used, normally without a sub-base.

(i) *Dry-bound macadam*
Because of the difficulties encountered with segregation when dry graded materials are being transported, it is usual practice to supply dry material for base construction in two separate sizes; a single size coarse fraction (nominally 2 in or $1\frac{1}{2}$ in size) and a fine fraction graded $\frac{3}{16}$ in to dust. Dry crushed rock, preferably limestone, or crushed slag aggregate may be used in both cases.

The single size material is spread first in a 3–5-in layer, and, after preliminary compaction, a 1-in layer of the dry fine material is vibrated into the interstices of the coarser material using a vibrating-plate compactor or other suitable plant. Compaction is continued until no more fine material can be taken in, following which the layer is further compacted by a heavy smooth-wheeled roller. Other layers are then added in a similar manner until the required total base thickness has been achieved.

(ii) *Pre-mixed waterbound macadam (wet-mix)*
Segregation of graded material during transportation may also be reduced by pre-mixing with 2–5% water in an asphalt or concrete mixer, or by spraying during loading. The mixed material must be protected from the weather during transit to prevent evaporation of moisture or further wetting. The current Ministry of Transport Specification,[8] Clause 807, stipulates crushed rock or crushed slag aggregate with a grading as shown in Table 11.3, with the added provision that the percentage of material passing a No. 200 B.S. sieve may be increased to 10% provided that all this material is non-plastic.

The material is laid in layers 3–6 in finished thickness and compacted by heavy smooth-wheeled roller or by vibrating roller until the required

TABLE 11.3 *Grading requirements for pre-mixed waterbound macadam bases*[8]

B.S. sieve size	Percentage by weight passing
2 in	100
$1\frac{1}{2}$ in	95–100
$\frac{3}{4}$ in	60–80
$\frac{3}{8}$ in	40–60
$\frac{3}{16}$ in	25–40
No. 7	15–30
No. 25	8–22
No. 200	0–2

Note: The proportion of material passing the No. 200 sieve may be increased to 10% provided that all this material is non-plastic dry density has been achieved. Hand-spreading is satisfactory for small schemes, but preferably a mechanical spreader such as the Barber–Greene paver should be used. In addition to reducing segregation, the added water content assists compaction of the material to a high dry density.

Unlike dry-bound macadam, the laying of 'wet-mix' material is not so disrupted by wet weather, although, particularly with limestone, care must be taken to ensure that compaction is carried out immediately the material has been laid.

An interesting paper describing the development of 'wet-mix' construction in Lancashire has been presented by Hingley.[9]

(iii) *Dry lean concrete*
This material is similar to normal structural concrete except that the aggregate/cement ratio generally lies between 20 : 1 and 15 : 1, giving a

TABLE 11.4 *Grading requirements for aggregate for lean concrete bases*[8]

B.S. sieve size	Percentage by weight passing	
	$1\frac{1}{2}$ in nominal max. size	$\frac{3}{4}$ in nominal max. size
3 in	100	—
$1\frac{1}{2}$ in	95–100	100
$\frac{3}{4}$ in	50–80	80–100
$\frac{3}{16}$ in	30–40	35–45
No. 25	8–30	10–35
No. 100	0–6	0–6

cement content of between 170 and 230 lb/cu yd. Aggregates should comply with the requirements of B.S. 882[10] as regards freedom from clay, silt, and other impurities, or must be washed if this condition is not satisfied. Normally $1\frac{1}{2}$ in or $\frac{3}{4}$ in maximum size aggregate is used; this may be stockpiled separately in coarse and fine sizes or may be 'all-in' aggregate provided that the overall grading lies within the limits given in Table 11.4, although in certain cases the proportion passing the $\frac{3}{16}$-in sieve may be allowed to exceed or fall below these limits by 5%.

The water content of a lean concrete mix is determined by compaction requirements, as for soil–cement (see page 163), rather than by choosing a water/cement ratio from strength considerations. Compaction trials and experience on site have shown that for compaction by rolling, the optimum moisture content for maximum dry density and maximum compressive strength is about 6% of the total weight of dry materials.[11] If the mix is too dry, the surface of the lean concrete may shear under the roller during compaction and subsequently appear loose, whilst if the mix is too wet, the concrete will be picked up by the roller wheels.

The cement content of lean concrete is controlled by the strength requirements of the mix, the aim being to produce a material with an average 28-day cube strength of about 2,000 lb/sq in. For control purposes, the Ministry of Transport Specification[8] recommends that cubes be made in pairs at intervals, with three pairs for each 1,000 sq yd (or 2,000 sq yd) laid per day. One cube of each pair should be tested at 7 days and the other at 28 days. Whilst the latter form the essential basis for site control, the former serve to detect low strength concrete at an early age and allow remedial action to be taken prior to the 28-day strengths becoming available.

Applying a statistical approach to site control testing to take account of unavoidable variations in cube strength, the Specification requires that the average 28-day strength of each group of three cubes prepared as described above should fall below 1,400 lb/sq in on no more than one occasion in any five consecutive groups. Furthermore, the average strength of any consecutive five groups (15 cubes) should not be less than 1,600 lb/sq in at 28 days, nor should the average range of strength for the five groups exceed 50% of the overall average 28-day strength of these 15 cubes.

Test cubes of lean concrete should be prepared in a manner similar to those for normal structural concrete except that compaction should be by electric or pneumatic hammer applied directly onto each layer of the material until compacted to refusal. Comparative tests have shown that compaction of cubes either by hand tamping or by means of a vibrating table is quite unsuitable for lean concrete.

Since for lean concrete, as for soils and other granular materials, strength and density are interrelated, it is equally important that the density of the compacted material on site is subjected to control testing. Bulk density is normally determined by the sand-replacement method (see page 152). The test should be made within the period 4–24 hours after compaction and should be representative of the full depth of the compacted layer. One density measurement should be made corresponding to each pair of cubes, and the Specification requires that the average density of each group of three measurements should be not less than 95% of the theoretical density of the material compacted to zero air content as determined from the proportion of the constituent materials and their respective specific gravities.

Lean concrete can be produced by any of the batching and mixing plants used for ordinary structural concrete, including continuous mixing plants. Usually a mixer with a capacity in excess of 20 cu yd per hour is required to give the necessary output. Transportation of the material should be in vehicles with steel-lined bodies and the mixed material should be protected from the weather by sheeting. On small jobs, the material can be spread by hand, but on larger schemes a mechanical spreader such as a bituminous paver or box hopper spreader is required (Plate 11.1).

If necessary, the total base thickness should be built up in layers, normally not exceeding 8 in compacted thickness. Compaction should be carried out on each layer using either smooth-wheeled or vibrating rollers until the required density has been achieved (Plate 11.2). Following the completion of the base, the surface should be sprayed with a quick-breaking bitumen emulsion or with cut-back bitumen (see page 208) and blinded with sand so as to prevent the evaporation of moisture and allow curing to take place. Alternatively, the material can be cured by spraying with water and covering with polythene sheets.

(iv) *Cement-bound granular base material*

This material, often referred to as C.B.G.B., is in fact a high quality cement-stabilized soil in that the aggregate consists of naturally-occurring gravel–sand material or blended mixtures used in the 'as-dug' condition, although in many respects it is similar, though inferior, to lean concrete. Mixing is carried out by stationary plant assembled close to the borrow pit or stockpile from which the material is to be obtained. Because of the relatively high fines content of the material, the free-fall type batch mixers used for normal structural or lean concrete are unsuitable and pan, paddle, or continuous type mixing plant must be employed (see page 169).

Grading and strength requirements for cement-stabilized materials, together with methods of site control, have already been discussed in Chapter 9, but where the material is being used for base construction on moderately trafficked roads in this country, it is appropriate to introduce a more restrictive grading such as that given in Table 11.5.[12] As shown in Figure 11.8, these grading limits allow considerably greater

TABLE 11.5 *Grading requirements for cement-bound granular base material*[12]

B.S. sieve size	Percentage by weight passing
2 in	100
1½ in	95–100
¾ in	45–95
⅜ in	35–85
$\frac{3}{16}$ in	30–70
No. 7	25–60
No. 25	12–40
No. 52	5–30
No. 200	0–10

tolerance on the particle size distribution compared with lean concrete aggregates, particularly as regards the proportion passing the $\frac{3}{16}$-in B.S. sieve.

Apart from the type of mixing plant employed, the sequence of operations and the methods of constructing cement-bound granular bases are as for lean concrete, and the same precautions should be taken to ensure adequate curing and protection of the material until the required strength has been attained.

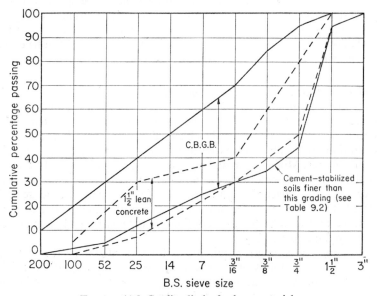

FIGURE 11.8 Grading limits for base materials

(v) Bituminous-bound base materials

These materials are essentially similar to those used for bituminous surfacings except that the binder content is somewhat lower. All are manufactured in accordance with British Standard Specifications and the Ministry of Transport Specification[8] (Clauses 809, 810, and 811 with subsequent minor amendment), and now form the basis of a separate specification (*Road Note No. 32*).[45] The main characteristics are listed in Table 11.6, but further description of their composition and properties is deferred until later in the chapter.

Bituminous-bound bases are constructed in layers of 2–3 in compacted thickness, each layer being uniformly compacted with a heavy smooth-wheeled roller (8–10-ton) as soon as rolling can be carried out without causing undue displacement of the mixed material but with the temperature of the material sufficiently high to allow a dense, compact

TABLE 11.6 *Bituminous-bound base materials*

Material	Relevant specification	Type of aggregate	Type of binder	Range of binder content (%)	Delivery temperature	Rolling temperature
rmacadam base	B.S. 802[13]	Crushed rock or slag	Tar to B.S. 76 with viscosity 50 or 54°C e.v.t.	3·8-5·8	70-90°C	60°C min.
rmacadam base	B.S. 1241[14]	Gravel		4·5-5·5		
tumen macadam base	B.S. 1621[15]	Crushed rock or slag	Bitumen or bitumen with 10% tar penetration 90/110 or 180/220	3·0-5·0	105-130°C 80°C min. (with 90/110 pen. bitumen)	
tumen macadam base	B.S. 2040[16]	Gravel		4·0-5·0	80-105°C 65°C min. (with 180/220 pen. bitumen)	
olled asphalt base	B.S. 594[17]	Crushed rock, slag, or gravel	Bitumen of 40/60 or 60/80 penetration	4·5-7·0	110-140°C 90-120°C (with 40/60 pen. bitumen) 100-130°C 80-110°C (with 60/80 pen. bitumen)	

material to be produced. This minimum temperature is related to the type of binder used in the material, and increases with the hardness of the binder.

11.7 Comparative performance of base materials

One of the accepted limitations of *Road Note No. 29* in its original form was that a given thickness of base and surfacing was specified for each traffic category irrespective of the nature and quality of the materials actually used in these layers.

Theoretical considerations of pavement design discussed in Chapter 10 have shown that the load-spreading properties of a road pavement are related to the elastic moduli of the respective layers. Thus, for a given stress allowable at the pavement–subgrade interface, the use of a material of higher modulus of elasticity should allow a decrease to be made in the overall pavement thickness. The elastic moduli of a limited number of types of pavement materials have been measured in the laboratory, but since these are likely to change during the life of the road as a result of compaction or breaking up by traffic, or, in the case of bituminous-bound materials, as a result of temperature changes, it is necessary to examine the relative performance of different materials in actual pavement structures constructed under controlled conditions before 'equivalent' thicknesses can be determined.

Such studies are at present being undertaken by the Road Research

Laboratory, both in a road machine at the laboratory and on a number of experimental sections along heavily trafficked roads. Similarly, full-scale experiments have been carried out in the United States during the past decade; the most publicized being the A.A.S.H.O. Road Test in which controlled truck traffic drove around specially prepared test roads for more than 18 hours a day over a period of two years ending in November 1960.[18]

The chief difference between the series of tests carried out in the two countries has been with regard to the method of applying load to the pavement structure. In Great Britain, the experimental sections normally form part of the national road network and are therefore subjected to a mixed composition of traffic loading such as occurs on any busy trunk road. By contrast, a number of specially constructed loops were used for the A.A.S.H.O. test and the testing programme was so arranged that every vehicle in any one of the ten traffic lanes had the same axle load and axle configuration. Loadings ranged from a 2,000-lb single axle load in one lane to a 48,000-lb tandem axle load in another. By including identical test sections in different lanes, it was possible to compare the number of load applications required to produce failure and also to express the tandem axle loading as an equivalent single axle load. For example, observations showed that the flexible pavement sections withstood approximately the same number of 33,000-lb tandem axle loads as 18,000-lb single axle loads. It should be appreciated, however, that these findings relate only to conditions similar to those experienced on the A.A.S.H.O. test and are not necessarily applicable to other areas, materials, and climates without supporting experimental evidence.

A feature common to both the British and the American full-scale tests has been the incorporation in the experiments of deliberately under-designed test sections in order to determine the extent by which, if any, the empirical methods of pavement design in current use over-estimate the required pavement thickness. For example, in the A.A.S.H.O. test approximately 70% of the pavement sections were under-designed by current American standards and were expected to fail or show signs of distress before the end of the test. In the event, 78% of the flexible sections had to be repaired at some stage.

The first of the British full-scale experiments began in 1949 on a section of the A1 trunk road in Yorkshire. Observations over a period of ten years showed that, of the three base materials examined, the open-textured tarmacadam bases performed much better than either the dry-bound stone bases or the hand-pitched bases. In addition, the latter type of base showed increased surface deformation with increasing base thickness in some cases, a factor which was attributed largely to further compaction of the base by traffic. On this account, and also because of the high labour costs involved, hand-pitched stone bases, a

TABLE 11.7 *Recommended base materials and thicknesses*[4]

Design chart 1	Design chart 2	Design chart 3	Design charts 4–6
10-in composite base, consisting of 3-in tar or bitumen macadam or rolled asphalt base on 7-in lean concrete or 7-in wet-mix (for roads other than motorways)	8-in lean concrete or wet-mix or dry-bound macadam	8-in lean concrete or wet-mix or dry-bound macadam or cement-stabilized material or other suitable material	6-in lean concrete or wet-mix or dry-bound macadam or cement-stabilized material or other suitable material
or	*or*	*or*	*or*
8-in tar* or bitumen macadam	6-in tar* or bitumen macadam	6-in tar or bitumen macadam	4-in tar or bitumen macadam
or	*or*	*or*	*or*
7-in rolled asphalt base	5-in rolled asphalt base	5-in rolled asphalt base	4-in rolled asphalt base

* Gravel tarmacadam is not recommended as a base on roads designed to charts 1 and 2

form of construction developed by Telford (see page 4) and used extensively in the 1930's, are no longer recommended.

A further experiment, also on the A1 at Alconbury Hill in Huntingdonshire, was initiated in 1957 to compare the performance of five different base materials laid to various thicknesses.[19] The base materials were cement-stabilized sand, wet-mix slag, lean concrete, tarmacadam, and hot-rolled asphalt. Experimental sections, each 200 ft long, were constructed on a sand sub-base of varying thickness. Results after 6 years show that the sections with rolled asphalt bases have performed the best (no replacements) whilst those with sand–cement bases are clearly the worst (six out of seven sections had failed and had to be replaced).

From these results and those obtained on other experimental sections, together with experience gained from non-experimental construction,

TABLE 11.8 *Comparative cost of various base materials*

Material	Cost per sq yd per in thickness s d
Hot-rolled asphalt base	3 3
Bitumen macadam base	2 0
Lean concrete	1 5
Wet-mix	1 5
Cement-bound granular base	1 4½
Dry-bound stone	11½
Soil–cement	11

specific recommendations are given in the revised edition of *Road Note No. 29* with regard to the type and thicknesses of base materials to be used with the various intensities of traffic specified in the design charts (Table 11.7). For roads carrying the heaviest intensity of traffic (design chart 1), it is recommended that the base be restricted to bituminous-bound materials or to a combination of bituminous-bound materials and lean concrete or wet-mix, but a wider range of base materials may be used on less heavily trafficked roads. Furthermore, a reduction of base thickness is now allowable with bituminous-bound bases provided that wherever the design charts require the use of a sub-base the overall pavement thickness is maintained by increasing the sub-base thickness accordingly. This represents an important step towards the introduction of a more rational design procedure which takes account of the quality of the materials used in the various layers of the pavement and further modifications to these recommendations can be anticipated as the results of other full-scale investigations now in progress become available.

A comparative cost of various base materials is given in Table 11.8, although it should be appreciated that these prices are dependent on the size and location of the roadworks and prices vary considerably between one contract and another. As can be seen, the cost of rolled asphalt is appreciably greater than that of the other materials shown, and hence some further reduction in base thickness must be allowed before the high quality bituminous-bound bases are competitive in price with other types of base material.

A second feature of interest is the small price difference between lean concrete and cement-bound granular base material. It is evident that the saving resulting from the use of lower quality aggregates in the latter case is offset by the need to provide special mixing plant and by the increased cement content normally required.

BITUMINOUS SURFACING MATERIALS

11.8 Function of road surfacing

The purpose of a road pavement, as stated in the preceding chapter, is to provide vehicles with a uniform running surface which has a high skidding resistance in all weather conditions.

Although the load-spreading characteristics of a flexible road pavement are essentially provided by the road base, the surfacing layer is subjected to the greatest intensity of stress from traffic, both directly and also as a result of vehicles braking and cornering, and therefore must consist of high quality material capable of resisting these deformation stresses. In addition, it is desirable that all bituminous surfacings should be made as impermeable as financial considerations will allow; firstly to reduce the weathering action of air and water on the surfacing itself and increase its durability, and secondly to limit the amount of moisture passing through the surfacing into the base and sub-base.

The other main function of the road pavement, that of providing a high resistance to skidding, is dependent solely on the characteristics of the running surface and is therefore one of the prime considerations in the selection of suitable surfacing materials. Other desirable properties of the surfacing include lightness in colour and high reflectivity for night driving.

For roads carrying a high intensity of traffic and on which resurfacing operations would cause a severe interference with traffic flow, it is essential that the road surfacing material chosen should have a long life and require little maintenance. Financial considerations obviously play a large part in the choice of surfacing materials, and in all cases it is important that expenditure be considered in terms of cost per year of effective life rather than be based solely on the initial outlay.

11.9 *Definitions*

The binder used in bituminous-bound materials is either *road tar*, which is obtained from crude tar subjected to further refining and blending processes and which must conform to the requirements of B.S. 76,[20] or *bitumen*, which is usually produced by the industrial refining of crude petroleum oil but which does occur naturally in association with mineral aggregate in various parts of the world. Occasionally a combination of the two binders may be employed.

A mixture of bitumen and inert mineral matter is termed *asphalt*. Asphalts can thus be produced artificially by mixing bitumen and aggregate or, as explained above, can be found occurring naturally in many different parts of the world. The most widely known of these natural deposits is without doubt the Trinidad Lake Asphalt, which is composed of bitumen and finely divided mineral matter, but several deposits of natural rock asphalt occur on the continent of Europe.

Some confusion in terminology exists with regard to British and American practice. In particular, the Americans commonly describe bitumen as asphalt and refer to hot-laid asphalt as asphaltic concrete (as opposed to Portland-cement concrete), and this should be borne in mind when consulting American literature dealing with bituminous materials. The definitions used throughout this book are in accordance with British practice and for convenience are listed below as abstracted from the relevant British Standard Specifications:

Bitumen—A viscous liquid, or a solid, consisting essentially of hydrocarbons and their derivatives, which is soluble in carbon disulphide; it is substantially non-volatile and softens gradually when heated. It is black or brown in colour and possesses waterproofing and adhesive properties. It is obtained by refinery processes from petroleum, and is also found as a natural deposit or as a component of naturally-occurring asphalt, in which it is associated with mineral matter.

Asphalt—A natural or mechanical mixture of bitumen with a substantial proportion of solid mineral matter.

Lake asphalt—A naturally-occurring asphalt found in well-defined surface deposits.

Refined lake asphalt—Lake asphalt from which unwanted materials, such as water and vegetable matter, have been removed.

Asphaltic cement—Bitumen, or the product resulting from a mixture of lake asphalt and bitumen or lake asphalt and flux oils, producing a binder having cementing qualities suitable for the manufacture of asphalt pavements.

Fluxed bitumen—Bitumen whose viscosity has been reduced by the addition of a diluent which is substantially non-volatile.

Cut-back bitumen—Bitumen whose viscosity has been reduced by the addition of a suitable volatile diluent.

Straight-run bitumen—A bitumen obtained after the final stage of distillation of a petroleum of a suitable type.

Natural rock asphalt—A rock of granular structure (usually limestone or sandstone) which in its natural state contains bitumen intimately dispersed throughout its mass.

Tar—A viscous liquid, black in colour, having adhesive properties, obtained by the destrictive distillation of coal, wood, shale, etc.

Road tar—Tar for use in road work prepared entirely from crude tars produced as a by-product of the high-temperature carbonization of coal in retorts or in coke ovens.

Emulsion—A relatively stable suspension of one liquid in a state of minute subdivision, dispersed throughout another liquid, in which it is not soluble.

Bitumen (or tar) emulsion—An emulsion in which bitumen (or tar) is suspended in a state of minute subdivision in water, or in an aqueous solution, with the aid of suitable emulsifying agents.

11.10 Binder characteristics

The viscosity of the binder determines the temperatures at which the bituminous material must be mixed, delivered to site, and compacted, and also affects the performance of the compacted material as regards its load-spreading properties and its durability. For a tar or bitumen to be used successfully as a binder in road surfacings it must be capable of being made sufficiently fluid, either by heating or by the addition of a volatile solvent, to be intimately mixed with aggregate or sprayed onto the road surface. In addition, it must be sufficiently viscous at high road temperatures (say 45°C in this country) to resist deformation but also sufficiently flexible at low road temperatures to resist fracture and disintegration. These two latter requirements set a lower and an upper limit respectively on the viscosity of the binder. It is customary to specify the binder in terms of equi-viscous temperature (e.v.t.) for tars and penetration for bitumens.

The *equi-viscous temperature* is the temperature in degrees Celsius at which 50 ml of the tar has a time of flow of 50 seconds through the orifice of a standard tar viscometer. The test should be carried out at a temperature which will keep the flow time within the range 33–75 seconds and a conversion chart is used to determine the temperature corresponding to a flow time of 50 seconds.[20] Since the flow time at a given temperature is longer for a more viscous binder, the e.v.t. *increases* with increasing hardness of the binder and usually lies in the range 24–54°C.

The *penetration* of a sample of bitumen is determined on a penetrometer by measuring the distance, expressed in units of tenths of a millimetre, that a standard needle will penetrate into the bitumen under a load of 100 g applied for 5 seconds with the sample at a standard temperature of 25°C. The method of test is described fully in B.S. 3235.[21] Contrary to e.v.t., penetration *decreases* with increasing hardness of the binder. In Great Britain, 'penetration-grade' bitumens are available in various grades between 10/20 and 400/500 penetration at 25°C.[22]

All these penetration-grade bitumens must be heated to varying degrees before mixing with hot or warm aggregate and the mixed material must be laid whilst it is still warm. In remote areas and in small scale 'patching' work, it is desirable to have a pre-mixed material which can be stored in bulk for short periods and laid when cold. This can be achieved by diluting a suitable penetration-grade bitumen with volatile oil either at the refinery or at the mixing plant so as to produce a *cutback bitumen*. As the volatile oil is lost by evaporation, the viscosity of the binder increases and eventually returns to that of the penetration-grade bitumen. Grades and properties of cut-back bitumens are also given in B.S. 3690.[22]

An alternative method of producing a low viscosity binder at normal air temperature is to create a *bitumen-in-water emulsion*, containing between 50 and 60% bitumen. Apart from the fact that they are cheaper than cut-back bitumens, emulsions have the added advantage that they can be applied to damp road surfaces and used for coating damp aggregate, an important factor in surface dressing operations. Emulsions can also be made from cut-back bitumens for use in pre-mixed materials which are to be stockpiled for some time before use, or from road tars.

Once the emulsion has been applied to the road surface or mixed with the particles of aggregate, it is essential that it should break down as quickly as possible. Breaking down signifies the separation of the particles of binder from the aqueous solution and their coalescence into a coherent film. The rate of breakdown is determined by the factors controlling the evaporation of the water (atmospheric temperature, relative humidity, and wind conditions), by the porosity of the surface to which the emulsion is being applied, and by the mechanical disturbance of the emulsion–aggregate system by rolling or by the action of traffic. The breakdown obtained during the initial stages of evaporation is reversible, so that heavy rain will result in further dilution of the emulsion. The diluted emulsion may then be washed from the road surface leaving insufficient binder to hold the chippings in place and resist their displacement by traffic. Once complete breakdown has taken place, however, the binder is unaffected by rain. The general properties of road emulsions are specified in B.S. 434,[23] and recommendations for their use are given in B.S. 2542.[24]

11.11 Types of surfacing materials

There is a wide, and at first somewhat confusing, range of bituminous surfacing materials, though all are similar in the sense that each consists of particles of aggregate (crushed natural rock, slag, gravel, or sand) bound together by tar or bitumen. The difference lies chiefly in the type, viscosity, and proportion of binder used, the maximum size and grading of the aggregate, the type of aggregate, and the presence or absence of a filler material such as limestone dust or Portland cement.

Surfacings on the more lightly trafficked roads may be laid as a single course up to $2\frac{1}{2}$ in thickness, but where a greater thickness of surfacing is required a two course construction must be used. In this case, the upper layer, termed the *wearing course*, is usually somewhat stronger and denser than the lower layer or *base course*. (The latter is additional to, and quite distinct from, the road base, and the two should not be confused.) Some materials can be used for both courses, though the composition generally varies slightly between the two, whilst other materials are suitable for either the wearing course or the base course only. In addition, further variations within each type are introduced to take account of such factors as traffic intensity and climatic conditions.

The main types of surfacing materials are listed in Tables 11.9 and 11.10 for wearing courses and base courses respectively. The binder contents shown indicate the overall range for each material and, together with other details, enable a general comparison to be made between different types of surfacing. For a particular type and grading of aggregate, the binder content, as measured by the percentage of soluble bitumen or tar, must be carefully controlled within much narrower limits, since experience has shown that a deficiency of binder will result in a loss of density and strength with consequent lack of durability whilst an excessive amount of binder will give an unstable material with a lower resistance to deformation. These 'optimum' binder contents are given in the relevant specification for the material to which reference should be made for full details of mix composition and aggregate grading. Where a lightweight blastfurnace slag is used, somewhat greater binder contents than shown in Tables 11.9 and 11.10 may be required to take account of the more absorbent characteristics of this aggregate.

(i) *Hot-rolled asphalt*

Hot-rolled asphalt is made by mixing a bitumen binder of low penetration with a graded aggregate consisting of crushed rock, slag, or gravel together with a natural or crushed sand. The material has a relatively high binder content and a filler such as limestone dust is added to stiffen the bitumen and give a dense, impermeable surfacing.

The binder, or asphaltic cement, used in hot-rolled asphalt may be bitumen or refined lake asphalt fluxed to a consistency suitable for use in this country or, as is frequently the case, equal proportions by weight of bitumen and refined lake asphalt. For general application 40/60 penetration is specified, but 60/80 penetration may be used in colder, wetter areas such as northern England and Scotland whilst 30/40 penetration

TABLE 11.9 *Bituminous wearing course materials*

Material	Relevant specification	Type of aggregate	Type of binder	Range of binder content (%)	Delivery temperature	Rolling temperature
Hot-rolled asphalt	B.S. 594[17]	Crushed rock, slag, or gravel with natural or crushed sand and filler	Bitumen or refined lake asphalt or equal proportions of the two. Normally 40/60 pen.	5·4–12·8	135–175°C	100–130°C
Dense tar surfacing	B.R.T.A. Spec.[25] (Tables 3 and 4)	Crushed rock, slag, or gravel with natural or crushed sand and filler	46–54°C e.v.t. tar (Grades B46, B50, or B54)	5·7–8·5	80–100°C (50 or 54°C e.v.t. tar) 65–90°C (46°C e.v.t. tar)	60–80°C e.v.t. tar) 50–70°C
Medium-textured tarmacadam	B.S. 802[13] (Table 3)	Crushed rock or slag with natural or crushed sand	37–42°C e.v.t. tar (summer), 34–38°C e.v.t. tar (winter)	4·5–6·75	Not specified, but vary according to the viscosity of the binder. Suitable ranges of rolling temperatures are: *Tars* 42°C e.v.t. 38°C e.v.t. 34°C e.v.t. *Bitumens*	40–60°C 30–45°C 20–35°C
Bitumen macadam	B.S. 1621[15] (Table 3)	Crushed rock or slag with natural or crushed sand	150–500 pen. bitumen or cut-back bitumen	3·5–6·0	90/110 pen. 190/210 pen. 280/320 pen. 400/500 pen.	80–100°C 65–85°C 55–75°C 45–65°C
Dense bitumen macadam	B.S. 1621[15] (Table 5)	Crushed rock or slag with natural or crushed sand	90–500 pen. bitumen or cut-back bitumen	4·0–6·0		
Fine cold asphalt	B.S. 1690[27]	Crushed rock or slag, all passing a ⅜-in B.S. sieve	180–500 pen. bitumen or cut-back bitumen	5·0–7·3	cut back	up to 40°C
Compressed natural rock asphalt	B.S. 348[28]	Natural rock asphalts containing between 7·5 and 13% of bitumen, ground to a powder and all passing a No. 7 B.S. sieve		7·5–12·5	110–140°C	—
Mastic asphalt	B.S. 1446[29]	Natural rock asphalt ground to powder and all passing a No. 7 B.S. sieve. Crushed rock chippings added later	Bitumen or refined lake asphalt or equal proportions of the two. 5–20 pen.	13·0–20·0 before the chippings are added	175–220°C	—
Mastic asphalt	B.S. 1447[30]	Limestone, ground to a powder and all passing a No. 7	Bitumen or refined lake asphalt or equal proportions	14·0–17·0 before the chip-	175–220°C	—

TABLE 11.10 *Bituminous base course materials*

Material	Relevant specification	Type of aggregate	Type of binder	Range of binder content (%)	Delivery temperature	Rolling temperature
Hot-rolled asphalt	B.S. 594[17]	Crushed rock, slag, or gravel with natural or crushed sand	Bitumen or refined lake asphalt or equal proportions of the two. 40/60 or 60/80 pen.	4·5-7·0	120-160°C	90-120°C (40/60 pen.) 80-110°C (60/80 pen.)
Open-textured bitumen macadam	B.S. 1621[15] (Table 1)	Crushed rock or slag, less than 10% passing a $\frac{1}{8}$-in B.S. sieve	150-500 pen. bitumen or cut-back bitumen	2·5-4·0	Not specified, but see Table 11.9	
Open-textured tarmacadam	B.S. 802[13] (Tables 1a or 1b)	Crushed rock or slag, less than 10% passing a $\frac{1}{8}$-in B.S. sieve	34-40°C e.v.t. tar (summer), 27-35°C e.v.t. tar (winter)	2·5-4·25		
Close-textured bitumen macadam	M.O.T. Spec.[8] (Clause 910)	Crushed rock, slag, or gravel, approx. 40% passing a $\frac{1}{8}$-in B.S. sieve	90/110 or 180/220 pen. bitumen or bitumen with 10% tar	3·5-6·0	105-130°C (90/110 pen. bitumen) 80-105°C (180/220 pen. bitumen)	80°C min. (bitumen) 65°C min. (bitumen)
Close-textured tarmacadam	M.O.T. Spec.[8] (Clause 911)	Crushed rock, slag, or gravel, approx. 40% passing a $\frac{1}{8}$-in B.S. sieve	50° or 54°C e.v.t. tar	4·5-6·5	70-90°C	60°C min.

H

may be preferred at bus stops and other sites subjected to heavy standing loads in districts having a more equable climate. In the latter cases, mixing, delivery, and rolling temperatures should be adjusted accordingly.

Wearing course mixtures vary from a 'sand carpet' having no stone content to a mixture with 55% coarse aggregate, but under present day conditions road surfacing materials invariably carry a proportion of coarse particles and a 30% stone content is often specified. For economic reasons, base course mixtures have a higher stone content (70% for crushed rock or slag, 65% for gravel) and a lower percentage of binder. Added filler is not often used. A similar composition is used for rolled asphalt bases (see page 201).

Because of the high viscosity binder used in the manufacture of hot-rolled asphalt, mixing must be carried out at a high temperature and the material must be laid and compacted within a comparatively short time. For this reason, asphalt mixing plants are often of a type that can be moved from time to time to suit the locality of the work and this necessarily increases the overall cost of the material (Plate 11.3).

(ii) *Dense tar surfacing*

Dense tar surfacing is a hot-process material consisting of a mixture of coarse and fine aggregate, filler, and high-viscosity tar, and thus is similar in composition to hot-rolled asphalt. The material was developed in this country at the Road Research Laboratory as a result of laboratory investigations into the mechanical properties of mixtures of tar, filler, sand, and stone, and found a particular use during the last war when bitumen was in short supply and a dense, strong surfacing was required on heavily trafficked roads. There is no British Standard covering the preparation of dense tar surfacing, but the British Road Tar Association (B.R.T.A.) have issued a general specification for the composition, manufacture, and laying of the material.[25]

The tar binder used in dense tar surfacing usually has a viscosity of 46–54°C e.v.t., this being the maximum that is generally practicable because of the fuming which occurs at the higher mixing temperatures which would otherwise be needed. This viscosity is lower than that of the bitumens used in hot-rolled asphalt and hence dense tar surfacing shows less resistance to deformation at maximum summer temperatures.

(iii) *Tarmacadam and bitumen macadam*

These materials, often referred to under the collective term *coated macadam*, form part of the structure of the majority of roads in Great Britain and are used as the running surface in a substantial proportion of them. The traditional materials consist of an interlocking mass of coarsely graded aggregate coated with a binder of relatively low viscosity, but in recent years denser mixtures with more viscous binders have been developed for use on roads carrying a medium-to-heavy intensity of traffic.

Tarmacadam was first used in this country to any appreciable extent from about 1890 onward to combat the dust nuisance caused by pneumatic-tyred vehicles travelling at higher speeds on water-bound macadam roads. Crude tar obtained as a by-product from the gas industry was used initially, but later 'road tars' of higher viscosity were introduced. About the same time, bitumen macadam first appeared, using the softer grades of petroleum bitumen as the binder instead of tar. The traditional open- and medium-textured materials contain between 2 and 7% tar or bitumen, slightly higher proportions of binder being used for wearing courses than for base courses or single course construction. Bitumen binders may be penetration-grade softer than 150 penetration, although a cut-back bitumen is often used. The material is very pervious to water when freshly laid and compacted, having a void content of the order of 25%, but becomes somewhat denser under the compacting action of traffic.

Because of the high void content, coated macadam is very susceptible to the weathering action of air and water. Exposure to air causes the binder to oxidize and become brittle in cold weather, resulting in disintegration of the surfacing and loss of stone, whilst the presence of water causes 'stripping' of bitumen binders from the stone. The displaced bitumen moves upwards under the action of traffic and collects at the surface, forming 'fat patches'. To reduce the effect of weathering and increase the life of the surfacing, a dense bitumen macadam wearing course has been included in the latest revision of B.S. 1621.[15] This material has a slightly higher binder content and an increased fines content compared with the open- and medium-textured wearing course materials and has gained widespread acceptance on roads carrying a medium intensity of traffic, particularly using slag aggregate.

Whilst the traditional base course materials are satisfactory under a wide variety of conditions, occasions arise when a denser, harder material is required. One instance of this is when a hot-laid wearing course of hot-rolled asphalt or dense tar surfacing is to be laid on a recently constructed coated macadam base course. The hot material will unduly soften a low-viscosity binder in the base course, giving rise to movement under the roller and making good riding quality impossible to achieve. For such conditions, mixtures with higher fines contents and harder binders are coming into more general use. These close-textured materials were originally specified in the first edition of *Road Note No. 29*, but are now included in the latest edition of the Ministry of Transport Specification[8] (Clauses 910 and 911 with subsequent minor amendment), and are to be published as a separate specification (*Road Note No. 38*).[48]

Because coated macadam requires only medium temperatures in its preparation, production can be centred at a large-scale mixing plant close to the source of the aggregate (Plate 11.4) and the mixed material can be transported very long distances before being laid. For this reason, it is generally the cheapest form of pre-mixed bituminous material.

In coated macadam, as with other types of pre-mixed materials, it is essential that the aggregate be dry and free from dust to ensure adhesion of the binder. Rotary driers are therefore provided in the mixing plant and perform the double function of removing the water and raising the temperature of the stone, thus enabling the binder to spread easily over the surface. In remote areas, however, it may not be practicable to dry the aggregate, and hydrated lime may be used to assist the coating of cold, wet aggregates to give surfacing materials suitable for light traffic. Recommendations for the *wet-aggregate process* are given in *Road Note No. 16*.[26]

(iv) *Fine cold asphalt*

Fine cold asphalt is a special form of fine-textured bitumen macadam used only as a wearing course and laid to a thickness not exceeding $\frac{3}{4}$ in. The composition of the material is covered by B.S. 1690.[27] The aggregate, which is normally blast-furnace slag, must be less than $\frac{1}{4}$ in maximum size, whilst the binder may range from penetration-grade bitumen (minimum 180 penetration) to a cut-back bitumen of low viscosity. Material made with the latter may be handled while cold and is frequently stored before laying. If a penetration-grade bitumen is used, the material must be laid warm, despite its name.

Fine cold asphalt is not impervious to water when first laid, although under heavy traffic it may become so after some time. Because of its fine texture and ease of laying, the material is particularly suited for covering over an existing surface with poor riding quality without the need to lift kerbs or remove the old surfacing.

(v) *Compressed natural rock asphalt*

Compressed natural rock asphalt was the original asphalt material used for surfacing city streets, and was extremely popular towards the end of the last century and for the first half of the present century. Its use has now been largely superseded by machine-laid hot-rolled asphalt.

Natural rock asphalt used in this country has been generally obtained from deposits in France and Switzerland and is specified in B.S. 348[28] to contain between 7·5 and 13% of bitumen. Preparation consists of grinding the rock to a powder passing a No. 7 B.S. sieve and heating in revolving drums to a temperature not exceeding 140°C. During the crushing process, rocks of varying bitumen content are blended to give a final bitumen content of between 7·5 and 12·5%. The hot powder is then spread onto the road surface with rakes and compressed with iron punners to a finished thickness of between $1\frac{1}{2}$ and $2\frac{1}{4}$ in.

(vi) *Mastic asphalt*

Mastic asphalt is an extremely durable, waterproof, hard-wearing surfacing material which is used as a wearing course of from 1 to 2 in thickness on city streets carrying intense traffic and on dock approaches. The material is hand-laid on a base course of hot-rolled asphalt or on concrete or sett pavings.

Mastic asphalt consists of a mixture of asphaltic cement, fine aggregate, and filler in proportions which give a voidless, impermeable mass. The asphaltic cement may be a low penetration-grade bitumen, fluxed lake asphalt, or a mixture of the two, whilst the aggregate may be natural rock asphalt (B.S. 1446[29]) or limestone (B.S. 1447[30]). The aggregate is ground to a powder passing a No. 7 B.S. sieve and blended with the asphaltic cement in a specially designed mixer for at least five hours at a temperature of approximately 200°C. At this stage, the soluble binder content should be of the order 13–20%, depending on the type and source of the aggregate.

Standard practice is to cast the mastic into blocks weighing about $\frac{1}{2}$ cwt for transporting to the site, unless the material is to be carried in a molten state in mechanically agitated mixers. At the site, the mastic asphalt is reheated, if necessary, to a temperature of between 175 and 220°C and mixed with fine gravel grit or rock chippings which are added to give increased stability and prevent distortion under traffic. For road surfacings, 35–45% of igneous rock chippings are commonly used.

Mastic asphalt is a difficult material to handle and requires considerable experience at all stages of preparation and laying. It is usually spread by hand with wooden floats and requires 'working' for a considerable period, particularly against joints and around manhole-covers. As with other smooth surfacing materials, pre-coated chippings should be spread over the surface and lightly rolled whilst the mastic asphalt is still sufficiently plastic to allow them to become partially embedded, thus producing a roughened finish.

11.12 *Transportation and laying*

With all pre-mixed bituminous materials, heat must be applied at the mixing plant; firstly to dry out the aggregate and secondly to make the binder sufficiently fluid to coat the aggregate particles. It is then necessary to retain much of this heat during transportation, other than with low-viscosity tars and cut-back bitumens, in order that the material, when laid, is sufficiently workable to permit thorough compaction. This applies particularly to the hot-process materials such as hot-rolled asphalt and dense tar surfacing which must be carried in lorries with suitably insulated metal bodies with the materials properly sheeted to minimize loss of heat.

With the exception of compressed natural rock asphalt and mastic asphalt, all pre-mixed bituminous material can be laid by machine, although hand laying may be preferred on smaller schemes. Before laying the surfacing, the base should be shaped approximately to the correct contour with appropriate crossfalls and gradients. On an existing road surface, high spots should be removed and low places made good with suitable material and thoroughly compacted. Adhesion may be improved by the application of a tack coat or by roughening the old surface. Each course of surfacing material should then be laid to give the required thickness when compacted by a 6–10-ton smooth-wheeled or vibrating roller (Plates 11.5 and 11.6).

The temperature for rolling is critical and depends on the viscosity of the binder. If the temperature i s too high the material will push excessively under the roller, forming bumps which cannot easily be removed, whilst too low a temperature will prevent a satisfactory state of compaction being attained. Temperature loss is related to atmospheric temperature and other climatic conditions and the delivery temperature should be adjusted accordingly to take account of these factors.

Common practice is to lay the wearing course as soon as possible after the base course and normally within a 3-day limit. Some authorities, however, prefer to use the base course as a temporary running surface for up to three years in order to allow compaction under traffic to take place. In this case, the temporary surface should be made waterproof by blinding with coated grit at the time of laying and a surface dressing should be applied shortly afterwards.

Dense wearing courses with a stone content of 45% or less, including cold asphalt, compressed rock asphalt, and mastic asphalt, present a smooth surface texture when compacted. To obtain a roughened surface with increased skid resistance, chippings, $\frac{3}{4}$ in or $\frac{1}{2}$ in size, are applied to the surface while it is still warm and lightly rolled to ensure partial embedment. The chippings are normally pre-coated with 2–3% tar or bitumen of the same viscosity as in the surfacing material and must be spread uniformly at the required rate. A machine has recently been designed at the Road Research Laboratory for this purpose (Plate 11.7). To facilitate the flow of surface water in the channels, a 6–9-in width should be covered temporarily when the chippings are being spread to maintain a smooth surface.

The overall accuracy of the finished surface should be within $\pm\frac{1}{4}$ in of the true surface level at any point and the maximum depression under a 10-ft straight edge placed on the surface parallel to the centre-line of the carriageway should not exceed $\frac{3}{16}$ in. In no case should the combined wearing course and base course thickness be more than $\frac{1}{2}$ in thinner than the total specified thickness.[8]

11.13 *Recommended surfacing materials*

With the exception of mastic asphalt which is expensive and therefore of limited use, hot-rolled asphalt is indisputably accepted as the best surfacing material. This reputation has been established by full-scale experiments on trial sections of road surfaced with different materials and by its satisfactory performance for periods of 30 years or more in city streets. Under heavy traffic conditions, the average life of hot-rolled asphalt before any treatment is required is about 20 years. On heavily trafficked roads (design charts 1 and 2, *Road Note No. 29*) hot-rolled asphalt to B.S. 594 is the only material recommended at present for wearing course construction. The wearing course in this instance should be made with crushed rock or slag aggregate (30% stone content) bound with an asphaltic cement made up of equal proportions by weight of refinery bitumen and refined lake asphalt, or, alternatively, a pitch–bitumen binder may be used (see page 221). The base course material may be either hot-rolled asphalt or the cheaper close-textured bitumen macadam or tarmacadam more recently authorized by the Ministry of Transport for use on heavily trafficked roads (Plate 11.8). Other recommendations for roads covered by design charts 3–6 are given in Table 11.11. It should be recognized, however, that new materials of improved composition are continually being developed and tested by full-scale experiment, and that these recommendations will be subject to revision from time to time.

Experience has shown that dense tar surfacing can form a durable surfacing with a life of 15 years or more when traffic is not unduly heavy. Coated macadam wearing courses and cold asphalt are somewhat less durable, having average lives of 5 and 10 years respectively without further treatment, though, being considerably cheaper to lay, these materials are often preferred on roads carrying a light or medium volume of traffic.

In general, tar-bound materials are more affected by temperature than are bitumen-bound materials, becoming softer on hot summer days and more brittle in winter. In addition, the temperature range for laying and compacting is more critical.

On the other hand, tar requires lower temperatures for mixing and spraying and has better adhesive properties than bitumen. Tar-bound materials are more resistant to the softening action of oil droppings from vehicles and are therefore often preferred for car parks and other areas where vehicles are stationary for considerable periods. A further advantage of tar is that it weathers more than refinery bitumen, leaving the aggregate in a dense material exposed to give a skid-resistant surfacing. This disadvantage of bitumen can be overcome, however, by using a blend of lake asphalt or a pitch–bitumen mixture.

TABLE 11.11 *Recommended bituminous surfacings for newly constructed flexible pavements*[4]

Design chart 1 (total thickness 4 in)	*Design chart 2 (total thickness 4 in)*	*Design chart 3 (total thickness 3 in)*	*Design charts 4–6 (total thickness 2 in minimum—see Notes 3 and 5)*
Wearing course (1½ in) Rolled asphalt (crushed rock or slag coarse aggregate only)	*Wearing course* (1½ in) Rolled asphalt (crushed rock or slag coarse aggregate only)	*Wearing course* (¾–1¼ in) Rolled asphalt Dense tar surfacing Cold asphalt Medium-textured tarmacadam Dense bitumen macadam Bitumen macadam	*Single course* Rolled asphalt Dense tar surfacing Medium-textured tarmacadam Dense bitumen macadam 2½ in tarmacadam to B.S. 802 or B.S. 1241 (1½ in single course material) 2½ in bitumen macadam to B.S. 1621 or B.S. 2040 (1½ in single course material)
Base course (2½ in) Rolled asphalt (crushed rock or slag coarse aggregate only) Close-textured bitumen macadam or tarmacadam (crushed rock or slag only)	*Base course* (2½ in) Rolled asphalt Close-textured bitumen macadam or tarmacadam (see Note 4)	*Base course* (1¾–2¼ in) Rolled asphalt Close-textured bitumen macadam or tarmacadam Open-textured bitumen macadam or tarmacadam (see Note 2)	*Two course* (*a*) *Wearing course* (¾–1 in) Cold asphalt Medium-textured tarmacadam Dense bitumen macadam Bitumen macadam (*b*) *Base course* (2–2¼ in) Open-textured bitumen macadam or tarmacadam

Notes:
1. When the wearing course is neither rolled asphalt nor dense tar surfacing and where it is not intended to apply a surface dressing immediately to the wearing course, it is essential to apply a surface dressing seal either to the base or the base course.
2. Under a wearing course of rolled asphalt or dense tar surfacing the base course should consist of rolled asphalt or of close-textured bitumen macadam or tarmacadam.
3. Charts 4–6 call for a nominal thickness of 2-in surfacing. This thickness is only applicable when the finish of the base is strictly in accordance with the specification requirements and the surface is firm and free from loose material. In some cases, it will be necessary to lay the surfacing with a greater nominal thickness of at least 2½ in, using either single course material or in two courses.
4. Gravel tarmacadam is not recommended as a base course for roads designed to chart 2.
5. On certain types of road, e.g. housing estate roads, the laying of the wearing course is often delayed until construction traffic has finished using the road. In such cases, any temporary surfacing should be [illegible]

11.14 *Control and testing of bituminous materials*

With the possible exception of dense tar surfacing, the compositions of the various surfacing materials discussed in the preceding sections have been derived from the results of many years of experience rather than from laboratory tests on bituminous mixtures. Site control in this country is therefore normally confined to checking that the delivered material conforms to the specification and that the temperatures at which the material is mixed, delivered, and compacted are within the specified limits.

Complete analysis of the material involves the determination of

1. The nature and viscosity of the binder.
2. The nature of the mineral aggregate.
3. The proportion of binder.
4. The grading of the mineral aggregate.

The first two factors can be checked at the mixing plant from time to time and would not normally be expected to cause any difficulty. Errors can occur, however, in the proportioning of the materials, even with well-maintained automatic mixing plants, and consequently an analysis giving the binder content and aggregate grading should be carried out at frequent intervals.

A number of methods of determining binder content and aggregate grading are available and are described in B.S. 598.[31] All depend on the removal of the soluble part of the binder by means of a suitable solvent such as toluene, leaving the aggregate and filler for a grading test. The method employed in a particular instance depends on the type of material being examined and the speed at which it is desired to obtain the result. Thus the sieving-extractor method (Method D, B.S. 598) giving a rapid analysis may be preferred in a small, mobile laboratory attached to a mixing plant, whilst one of the other methods which are slower but require less attention would normally be more suitable for a central laboratory carrying out routine testing on a large number of samples daily (Plate 11.9).

While the above method of analysis is satisfactory for determining the composition of bituminous mixes, many engineers feel that it would be desirable to have a mechanical method of testing the mixed material, both for the purpose of site control and for designing bituminous mixes. A number of such tests have been devised, all of which are empirical in the sense that observed values are correlated in the first place with field performance of the various materials under study. Many of these tests measure resistance to deformation of specimens compacted in a standard manner and loaded at a constant rate of strain, and of these the Marshall test,[32] which is widely used in America, is probably the best known.

In this test, a cylindrical specimen, 4 in diameter and $2\frac{1}{2}$ in long, is

H*

compressed between two curved holders which are brought together at the standard rate of 2 in per minute. The normal temperature of the test in America is 60°C, but a test temperature of 45°C would perhaps be more applicable to conditions in Great Britain, since observations have shown that this temperature is only exceeded in surfacing materials for a few hours during the year. The maximum load (lb) sustained by the specimen is termed the *Marshall stability value* and the compression undergone at this load, expressed in units of 0·01 in, is the *Marshall flow value*.

Tests with mixes at various binder contents show a maximum stability value and a maximum density occurring at an optimum binder content. However, the flow value increases with increasing binder content, and whilst it is true to say that a mix with a binder content in excess of the optimum will lack resistance to deformation, a mix leaner than the optimum will show a lower stability value but also a lower flow value, and may therefore prove to be a more satisfactory mix in practice.

Another laboratory test of a completely different nature is the immersion wheel-tracking test,[33] used to measure stripping of the binder in samples of coated macadam. The test specimens, 12 in long, 4 in wide, and 1¼ in thick, are held horizontally just below the surface of a constant temperature water bath maintained at 40°C and subjected to the reciprocating movement of a loaded wheel. Susceptibility to stripping is determined in terms of the time to the failure point, which is marked by a sharp break in the time–penetration curve.

11.15 Skidding resistance

Adequate skidding resistance is an essential requirement for any surfacing material, particularly in these days of increasing vehicle speeds. With open-textured materials the resistance to skidding depends largely on the 'polished-stone value' of the aggregate, but with dense surfacing materials with low stone content, the surface texture is dependent on the nature of the binder and the type of chippings applied to the finished surface.

In the accelerated polishing test,[34] specimens consisting of ⅜-in chippings mounted in a sand–cement mortar are clamped onto the periphery of a 16-in diameter wheel and subjected to the polishing action of a pneumatic-tyred wheel fed with fine abrasives. Experiments have shown that the state of polish after a six-hour test run is similar to that reached by the same type of stones in the road surface after a year or more of traffic. The polished-stone value is then determined for the specimen using a pendulum-type portable skid-resistance tester (see below). Measurements have shown that this value may range from 30 for a stone liable to become highly polished to 80 or more for a stone likely to remain rough under heavy traffic conditions.[35]

With dense surfacing materials, binder is brought up to the surface by the action of traffic. Unless this binder hardens sufficiently on exposure to the atmosphere to be abraded by traffic so as to reveal the texture of the sand, a smooth surface with low skid resistance will eventually be produced and treatment by surface dressing will be necessary. Observations on hot-rolled asphalt surfacings made with different types of binder, but otherwise of the same composition, have shown that refinery bitumens give a characteristic smooth surface after many years traffic whilst sections containing Trinidad lake asphalt have a 'sandpaper' texture.[36] This is considered to be largely a result of the greater susceptibility of the Trinidad mixtures to atmospheric oxidization and has led to the recommendation that refinery bitumen and lake asphalt be used in equal proportions for heavy-duty rolled asphalt wearing courses (M.O.T. Specification, Clause 901). A similar improvement in surface texture has been obtained by using binders containing up to 30% coal-tar pitch in refinery bitumen.[37]

The skidding resistance of an existing road surface can be expressed in terms of its sideways force coefficient (see page 59). Measurements taken on sections of road involving skidding accidents or for which complaints of slipperiness in wet weather had been made showed that at 90% of these sites the sideways force coefficient, measured at a speed of 30 m.p.h. with smooth tyres on a wet surface, was less than 0·4. This compares with only 30% below this figure on a random sample of roads in the same area and suggests that any section of road surface with a sideways force coefficient of less than 0·4 at 30 m.p.h. may give rise to skidding accidents in wet weather.[38]

An alternative method of checking skidding resistance is by use of the portable skid-resistance tester.[39] The apparatus measures the frictional resistance between a rubber slider mounted on the end of a pendulum arm and the road surface or, in the case of the accelerated polishing test described above, between the slider and the polished stone specimen. The pendulum is adjusted to be in contact with the surface of the road (or stone specimen) and is then lifted to a fixed height and allowed to fall. The slider passes over the surface and rises to the other side, taking a pointer with it. The pointer measures the skidding resistance as a number varying from below 45 (very poor) to over 65 (very good). A reading above 55 would be generally satisfactory on all but the most difficult sites such as roundabouts, sharp bends, steep gradients, and approaches to traffic lights on derestricted roads. Full instructions for using the apparatus are given in *Road Note No. 27*.[40]

11.16 *Surface dressing*

Surface dressing is a low-cost form of treatment which is used to seal existing surfaces against the entry of water and to provide a new wearing surface with increased skidding resistance. The treatment consists of spraying the road surface with a film of hot tar, hot cut-back bitumen, or bitumen emulsion and rolling in a layer of stone chippings to give a shoulder-to-shoulder cover.

Over half of the roads in this country are maintained by surface dressing and with modern techniques the treatment should be effective for five years or more. Although surface dressing is a relatively inexpensive form of treatment, it has now been realized that a large sum of money could be saved annually by giving more careful attention to control and supervision, and a considerable amount of research has recently been directed towards determining the factors affecting the life of surface dressings.[41]

TABLE 11.12 *Recommended size of chippings for surface dressing*[42]

Surface characteristics	Light traffic (under 1,000 tons per day)	Medium traffic (1,000–10,000 tons per day)	Heavy traffic (over 10,000 tons per day)
Hard	$\frac{1}{4}$ in	$\frac{1}{4}$ in or $\frac{3}{8}$ in	$\frac{3}{8}$ in or $\frac{1}{2}$ in
Normal	$\frac{1}{4}$ in or $\frac{3}{8}$ in	$\frac{3}{8}$ in or $\frac{1}{2}$ in	$\frac{1}{2}$ in or $\frac{3}{4}$ in
Soft	$\frac{3}{8}$ in or $\frac{1}{2}$ in	$\frac{1}{2}$ in or $\frac{3}{4}$ in	$\frac{3}{4}$ in

Approximate rate of spread:

$\frac{3}{4}$-in chippings   60–80   sq yd per ton
$\frac{1}{2}$-in chippings   80–100 sq yd per ton
$\frac{3}{8}$-in chippings 100–130 sq yd per ton
$\frac{1}{4}$-in chippings 140–180 sq yd per ton

The binder used in surface dressing operations must be sufficiently fluid at the time of application for spraying onto the road surface and wetting the chippings, yet sufficiently viscous as soon as possible afterwards to hold the chippings in place against the displacing forces of traffic. Hot binders are therefore normally used and the viscosity must be a compromise between these two requirements. For tar, experience has shown that a viscosity of 34–38°C e.v.t. is generally suitable for use during spring and autumn and 38–42°C e.v.t. during the summer months. Surface dressing is not normally carried out during the winter months because the lower viscosity binder which would be needed to secure adhesion of the chippings at low road temperatures would soften unduly in the summer. The binder should be sprayed uniformly over the road surface at the required rate, using a mechanical tank sprayer (Plate 11.10) in preference to hand spraying.

The chippings should be of hard, tough rock, gravel, or slag and not susceptible to polishing. Experience has shown that the size of chippings depends on the amount of traffic and on the hardness of the existing road surface, a larger size being necessary with a heavier traffic intensity or with an old surface rich in binder, since in either case the chippings will be embedded further. Recommendations for the size of chippings and suitable rates of spread of tar binder are given in Tables 11.12 and 11.13.[42]

The success of any surface dressing treatment is largely dependent on a satisfactory bond between the chippings and the binder being achieved at an early stage. If wet chippings are used, there will be no adhesion of the stones until the film of water separating the binder and the chippings has evaporated, and during this time considerable displacement of the stone may be expected if traffic travelling at more than 15 m.p.h. is allowed to use the road. With high-viscosity binders, adhesion difficulties can be overcome by using chippings pre-coated with about 1% of their weight of tar or by using heated chippings.

TABLE 11.13 *Recommended rate of spread of tar for surface dressing*[42]

Size of chippings	Rate of spread (sq yd per gallon) at spraying temperature								
	Hard surface			Normal surface			Soft surface		
	L	M	H	L	M	H	L	M	H
¾ in	*	*	*	*	*	4	*	4	5
½ in	*	*	4	*	4	5	4	5	*
⅜ in	*	4	5	4	5	*	5	*	*
¼ in	4	5	*	5	*	*	*	*	*

The above figures are for crushed rock or slag. With gravel use rate of spread from ¼ to 1 sq yd per gallon *heavier* than above rates (e.g. where 5 is specified use 4).
* Not recommended
L = Light traffic, M = Medium traffic, H = Heavy traffic

Even when satisfactory adhesion has been achieved, cold wet weather within the next few days may lead to displacement of the binder from the chippings by water. This type of damage can be prevented by dispersing an adhesion agent in the binder immediately before spraying.[43]

HARD SHOULDERS

11.17 Shoulder construction

Hard shoulders form a continuous strip alongside the carriageway onto which vehicles can be driven when an emergency stop is necessitated. These shoulders are constructed on motorways and occasionally on

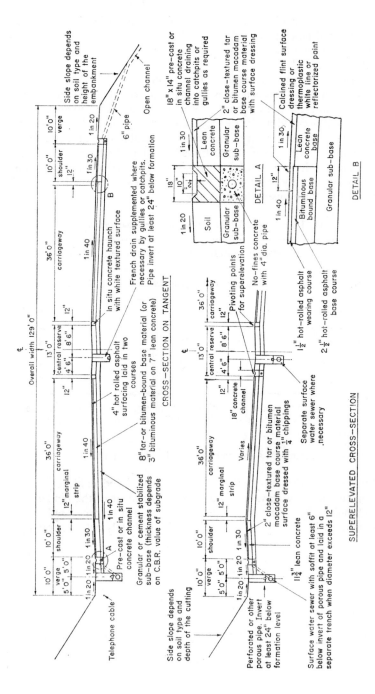

FIGURE 11.9 Typical motorway cross-section for flexible construction

other heavily trafficked roads built to 'motorway standards' and have a standard width of 10 ft.

On the earlier motorways, shoulders were constructed to an overall thickness of 9 in made up of a $4\frac{1}{2}$-in broken stone, slag, or gravel base surfaced with a $4\frac{1}{2}$-in thick mixture of stone, sand, and loamy topsoil, the surface being sown with grass seed. Unfortunately, experience soon showed that this form of construction was unsuitable for the heavy use to which they were subjected and paved shoulders contrasting in colour with the main carriageway are now specified. Paved shoulders have the additional advantage of reducing substantially the amount of moisture movement between the verge and the subgrade underlying the carriageway (see page 134).

Current practice for paved shoulders is to continue the base and sub-base under the shoulder using the same construction, except that where a rigid concrete slab or a composite base of lean concrete and bituminous-bound material is used for the main carriageway a lean concrete or cement-bound granular base is used for the shoulder. The surfacing consists of 2-in close-textured tarmacadam or bitumen macadam base course material surface dressed with $\frac{1}{4}$-in light coloured chippings to give a colour contrasting with that of the carriageway. Alternatively, a bitumen-coated sand product known as 'Schlamme' which has a distinctive red colour has been used on the Lancashire section of the M.6 motorway in place of chippings to give a clear demarcation between the hard shoulder and the carriageway. Typical cross-sectional details showing shoulder construction are given in Figures 11.9 and 12.13.

Recent work has indicated that a concrete hard shoulder with an exposed aggregate finish will provide a satisfactory construction contrasting both in colour and texture with the carriageway surfacing material.[44]

REFERENCES

1. HIGHWAY RESEARCH BOARD, 'Report of Committee on Classification of Materials for Subgrades and Granular Type Roads', *Proceedings, Highway Research Board* (Washington, D.C.: vol, 25, 1945, pp. 375–88)
2. STEELE, D. J., 'Application of the Classifications and Group Index in Estimating Desirable Sub-Base and Total Pavement Thicknesses', *Proceedings, Highway Research Board* (Washington, D.C.: vol. 25, 1945, pp. 388–92)
3. AMERICAN SOCIETY FOR TESTING AND MATERIALS, 'Tentative Method of Test for Bearing Ratio of Laboratory-Compacted Soils. Test D 1883–61T', *1966 Book of A.S.T.M. Standards, Part 11* (Philadelphia: American Society for Testing and Materials, 1966, pp. 576–81)

4. ROAD RESEARCH LABORATORY, 'A Guide to the Structural Design of Flexible and Rigid Pavements for New Roads', *Ministry of Transport, Road Research Road Note No. 29* (London: H.M.S.O., 1965 (2nd edition))
5. AMERICAN SOCIETY OF CIVIL ENGINEERS, 'Development of C.B.R. Flexible Pavement Design Method for Airfields: a Symposium', *Proc. Amer. Soc. civ. Engrs.* (New York: vol. 75, 1949, pp. 3–104)
6. KITCHIN, L. D. (Revised by WENLOCK, E. K.), *Road Transport Law* (London: Iliffe Books Ltd, 1964 (14th edition), p. 135)
7. ROAD RESEARCH LABORATORY, 'Construction of Housing-Estate Roads Using Granular Base and Sub-Base Materials', *Department of Scientific and Industrial Research, Road Research Road Note No. 20* (London: H.M.S.O., 1955)
8. MINISTRY OF TRANSPORT, *Specification for Road and Bridge Works* (London: H.M.S.O., 1963 (3rd edition))
9. HINGLEY, C. E., 'Waterbound Macadam', *J. Instn. Highw. Engrs.* (London: vol. 5, 1958, pp. 136–45)
10. BRITISH STANDARDS INSTITUTION, 'Concrete Aggregates from Natural Sources', *B.S. 882: 1954* (London: British Standards Institution, 1954)
11. CEMENT AND CONCRETE ASSOCIATION, *Lean Concrete Bases for Roads* (London: Cement and Concrete Association, 1962)
12. STONE, M. A., 'Cement-Bound Granular Bases', *J. Instn. Highw. Engrs.* (London: vol. 8, 1961, pp. 314–24)
13. BRITISH STANDARDS INSTITUTION, 'Tarmacadam with Crushed Rock or Slag Aggregate', *B.S. 802: 1958* (London: British Standards Institution, 1958)
14. BRITISH STANDARDS INSTITUTION, 'Tarmacadam and Tar Carpets (Gravel Aggregate)', *B.S. 1241: 1959* (London: British Standards Institution, 1959)
15. BRITISH STANDARDS INSTITUTION, 'Bitumen Macadam with Crushed Rock or Slag Aggregate', *B.S. 1621: 1961* (London: British Standards Institution, 1961)
16. BRITISH STANDARDS INSTITUTION, 'Bitumen Macadam with Gravel Aggregate', *B.S. 2040: 1953* (London: British Standards Institution, 1953)
17. BRITISH STANDARDS INSTITUTION, 'Rolled Asphalt (Hot Process)', *B.S. 594: 1961* (London: British Standards Institution, 1961)
18. HIGHWAY RESEARCH BOARD, 'The A.A.S.H.O. Road Test. Report 7: Summary Report', *Highway Research Board Special Report 61G* (Washington, D.C.: National Academy of Sciences—National Research Council, 1962)
19. CRONEY, D. and LOE, J. A., 'Full-Scale Pavement Design Experiment on A.1 at Alconbury Hill, Huntingdonshire', *Proc. Instn. civ. Engrs.* (London: vol. 30, 1965, pp. 225–70)
20. BRITISH STANDARDS INSTITUTION, 'Tars for Road Purposes', *B.S. 76: 1964* (London: British Standards Institution, 1964)
21. BRITISH STANDARDS INSTITUTION, 'Test Methods for Bitumen', *B.S. 3235: 1964* (London: British Standards Institution, 1964)
22. BRITISH STANDARDS INSTITUTION, 'Bitumens for Road Purposes', *B.S. 3690: 1963* (London: British Standards Institution, 1963)
23. BRITISH STANDARDS INSTITUTION, 'Bitumen Road Emulsion (Anionic)', *B.S. 434: 1960* (London: British Standards Institution, 1960)

24. BRITISH STANDARDS INSTITUTION, 'Recommendations for the Use of Bitumen Emulsions (Anionic) for Roads', *B.S. 2542: 1960* (London: British Standards Institution, 1960)

25. BRITISH ROAD TAR ASSOCIATION, *Dense Tar Surfacing* (London: British Road Tar Association, 1966)

26. ROAD RESEARCH LABORATORY, 'Bituminous Surfacings made by Wet-Aggregate (Hydrated Lime) Process', *Department of Scientific and Industrial Research, Road Research Road Note No. 16* (London: H.M.S.O.,1953)

27. BRITISH STANDARDS INSTITUTION, 'Cold Asphalt', *B.S. 1690: 1962* (London: British Standards Institution, 1962)

28. BRITISH STANDARDS INSTITUTION, 'Compressed Natural Rock Asphalt', *B.S. 348: 1948* (London: British Standards Institution, 1948)

29. BRITISH STANDARDS INSTITUTION, 'Mastic Asphalt (Natural Rock Asphalt Aggregate) for Roads and Footways', *B.S. 1446: 1962* (London: British Standards Institution, 1962)

30. BRITISH STANDARDS INSTITUTION, 'Mastic Asphalt (Limestone Aggregate) for Roads and Footways', *B.S. 1447: 1962* (London: British Standards Institution, 1962)

31. BRITISH STANDARDS INSTITUTION, 'Sampling and Examination of Bituminous Mixtures for Roads and Buildings', *B.S. 598: 1958* (London: British Standards Institution, 1958, p. 56)

32. AMERICAN SOCIETY FOR TESTING AND MATERIALS, 'Standard Method of Test for Resistance to Plastic Flow of Bituminous Mixtures Using Marshall Apparatus. Test D 1559–65', *1966 Book of A.S.T.M. Standards, Part 11* (Philadelphia: American Society for Testing and Materials, 1966, pp. 450–7)

33. ROAD RESEARCH LABORATORY, *Bituminous Materials in Road Construction* (London: H.M.S.O., 1962, pp. 85–7)

34. BRITISH STANDARDS INSTITUTION, 'Methods for Sampling and Testing of Mineral Aggregates, Sands, and Fillers', *B.S. 812: 1960* (London: British Standards Institution, 1960, with Amendment No. 3 dated 16 March 1965)

35. MACLEAN, D. J. and SHERGOLD, F. A., 'The Polishing of Roadstone in Relation to the Resistance to Skidding of Bituminous Road Surfacings', *Department of Scientific and Industrial Research, Road Research Technical Paper No. 43* (London: H.M.S.O., 1958)

36. ROAD RESEARCH LABORATORY, *Bituminous Materials in Road Construction* (London: H.M.S.O., 1962, p. 184)

37. LEE, A. R., 'Pitch–Bitumen Mixtures', *Road Tar* (London: vol. 16, No. 1, March 1962, pp. 5–7)

38. ROAD RESEARCH LABORATORY, *Research on Road Safety* (London: H.M.S.O., 1963, pp. 526–39)

39. GILES, C. G., SABEY, B. E., and CARDEW, K. F. H., 'Development and Performance of the Portable Skid-Resistance Tester', *Department of Scientific and Industrial Research, Road Research Technical Paper No. 66* (London: H.M.S.O., 1964)

40. ROAD RESEARCH LABORATORY, 'Instructions for Using the Portable Skid-Resistance Tester', *Department of Scientific and Industrial Research, Road Research Road Note No. 27* (London: H.M.S.O., 1960)

41. LEE, A. R. and FUIDGE, G. H., *The Technique of Surface Dressing with Tar* (London: British Road Tar Association, 1959 (Revised edition))

42. ROAD RESEARCH LABORATORY, 'Recommendations for Tar Surface Dressings', *Ministry of Transport, Road Research Road Note No. 1* (London: H.M.S.O., 1965 (4th edition))

43. ROAD RESEARCH LABORATORY, 'Prevention of Wet-Weather Damage to Surface Dressings by the Use of Surface-Active Agents', *Department of Scientific and Industrial Research, Road Research Road Note No. 14* (London: H.M.S.O., 1964 (3rd edition))

44. LILLEY, A. A., 'The Use of Concrete for Hard Shoulders for Motorways', *Cement and Concrete Association Technical Report TRA/381* (London: Cement and Concrete Association, 1964)

45. ROAD RESEARCH LABORATORY, 'Specification for Dense Tarmacadam and Dense Bitumen Macadam for Use as Road Bases', *Ministry of Transport, Road Research Road Note No. 32* (in preparation)

46. ROAD RESEARCH LABORATORY, 'Specification for Dense Tarmacadam and Dense Bitumen Macadam Basecourses', *Ministry of Transport, Road Research Road Note No. 38* (in preparation)

12

Rigid Pavements: Design and Construction

- -

A rigid pavement consists essentially of a concrete slab resting on a relatively thin granular base, and distributes wheel loads over a wide area of subgrade by virtue of its rigidity and high modulus of elasticity. The major factor considered in the design of rigid pavements is the structural strength of the concrete in relation to the stresses imposed upon it. These stresses can arise from a variety of causes including, in addition to wheel loads, changes in temperature and moisture content. The criterion for design is usually the maximum tensile stress developed at the top or bottom face of the slab as a result of these factors, although compressive stresses may be critical in hot weather if expansion is unduly restricted.

STRESSES IN CONCRETE SLABS

12.1 *Westergaard analysis*

Although the stress analysis of two- and three-layer elastic systems can be applied to both flexible and rigid pavements, the theoretical approach to rigid pavement design has generally been based on the earlier work of Westergaard,[1] who derived expressions for the maximum tensile stresses in a concrete slab of finite extent resting on a uniform subgrade with interior, edge, and corner loading. Westergaard considered the slab to be a homogeneous, elastic, isotropic solid, and assumed that the subgrade reaction was vertical and proportional to the deflexion of the slab at any point. This is equivalent to assuming that the subgrade acts as a dense fluid and hence has no shear strength. This assumption simplifies the stress calculations compared with the Burmister analysis (see page 177) and, although it is less accurate, Westergaard's method has the added advantage of including edge and corner loading conditions.

Westergaard considered the case of a single static wheel load uniformly distributed over a circular contact area and found that with the load at the edge or at the interior of the slab, the maximum tensile stresses were produced in the bottom of the slab, but with the load at the corner the maximum tensile stresses occurred in the top of the slab. Formulae were derived for these stresses, but were later modified by Westergaard[2] and by Teller and Sutherland[3] in the light of field experience to take account of an increase in the subgrade reaction immediately underneath the loaded area and for variations in subgrade support at the edges and corners of the slab as a result of warping. The modified formulae are as follows:

$$\sigma_I = \frac{0 \cdot 275P}{h^2}(1+\nu)\left[\log_{10}\left(\frac{Eh^3}{kb^4}\right) - 54 \cdot 54\left(\frac{l}{L}\right)^2 Z\right] \tag{12.1}$$

$$\sigma_E = \frac{0 \cdot 529P}{h^2}(1+0 \cdot 54\nu)\left[\log_{10}\left(\frac{Eh^3}{kb^4}\right) + \log_{10}\left(\frac{b}{1-\nu^2}\right) - 1 \cdot 0792\right] \tag{12.2}$$

$$\sigma_C = \frac{3P}{h^2}\left[1 - \left(\frac{a\sqrt{2}}{l}\right)^{1 \cdot 2}\right] \tag{12.3}$$

where σ_I is the maximum tensile stress at the bottom of the slab due to loading at the interior, σ_E the maximum tensile stress at the bottom of the slab due to loading at the edge, σ_C the maximum tensile stress at the top of the slab due to loading at the corner, P the applied wheel load, a the radius of the circular contact area, h the slab thickness, E the modulus of elasticity of the concrete slab, ν Poisson's ratio of concrete, k the modulus of subgrade reaction (see below), b the radius of equivalent distribution of pressure, given by

$$b = \sqrt{(1 \cdot 6a^2 + h^2)} - 0 \cdot 675h \text{ for } a < 1 \cdot 724h$$
or $\qquad b = a \qquad\qquad\qquad\qquad\text{ for } a \geqslant 1 \cdot 724h$

and l is the radius of relative stiffness, given by

$$l^4 = Eh^3/12(1 - \nu^2)k$$

L and Z are correction factors to allow for a redistribution of subgrade reaction immediately under the load.

These correction factors vary with pavement and subgrade stiffness, but Teller and Sutherland[3] have suggested conservative values $Z = 0 \cdot 2$ and $L = 5l$ where conditions are not known.

Owing to local depressions of the subgrade or warping of the slab, the corner may become unsupported in extreme circumstances and behave as a cantilever. In this case, Equation 12.3 becomes

$$\sigma_C = \frac{3P}{h^2} \tag{12.4}$$

12.2 Modulus of subgrade reaction

The elastic property of the subgrade used in Westergaard's analysis is termed the modulus of subgrade reaction k and is defined as the vertical reaction of the subgrade per unit deflexion, expressed in lb/sq in/in. The modulus of subgrade reaction is determined by a plate-loading test on the subgrade using a standard 30-in diameter steel plate.

It is essential that the plate should be perfectly level at the start of the test, and to ensure an even bearing surface on coarse-grained soils the plate is bedded on a thin layer of fine sand or plaster of Paris. Dial gauges, supported clear of the loaded area, should be placed close to the periphery of the plate, preferably using three or more gauges spaced at equal intervals. To minimize bending effects, it is standard practice to use a series of stacked plates of decreasing diameter (for example, 24 in, 18 in, and 12 in diameter) on top of the 30-in diameter plate. The reaction load is then applied to the upper plate by means of a hydraulic jack.

In theory, for an elastic soil, the vertical deflexion under a loaded rigid circular plate is given by

$$\Delta = \frac{1 \cdot 18pa}{E} \qquad (12.5)$$

where p is the average contact pressure und er the plate, a the radius of the plate, and E the modulus of elasticity o f the subgrade.

Since, by definition, $k = p/\Delta = E/1 \cdot 18a$, the load/deformation curve should be linear. In practice, the subgrade does not behave elastically and therefore it is necessary to define how the value of k should be measured.

There is no British Standard testing procedure for plate-loading tests, but standard American practice[4] is to apply a load of 10 lb/sq in (7,070 lb for a 30-in diameter plate) and maintain this until the rate of settlement is less than 0·002 in per minute. The corresponding deflexion is then used to calculate k.

It should be noted from Equation 12.5 that the deflexion is directly proportional to the diameter of the plate used in the test, and therefore if a smaller plate is used in the test for convenience, a correction factor must be applied to determine the correct value of k corresponding to a 30-in diameter plate.

As with all other tests on the subgrade, the modulus of subgrade reaction should be measured with the subgrade compacted to the same dry density and at the maximum moisture content that is likely to be experienced during the life of the pavement. If the existing subgrade does not satisfy this condition, tests can be made on an area where the required degree of compaction has been obtained by hand-tamping in thin layers.

12.3 *Effect of subgrade on slab thickness*

Typical values of k range from 100 lb/sq in/in for highly plastic clays to 1,000 lb/sq in/in for well-graded gravel–sand–clay subgrades. Experience has shown, however, that the load-carrying capacity of a concrete slab is virtually independent of the character of the underlying subgrade, and this fact is borne out by Figure 12.1 in which the maximum tensile stresses for interior and corner loading conditions calculated from Equations 12.1 and 12.3 respectively are given for various combinations of slab thickness and modulus of subgrade reaction.

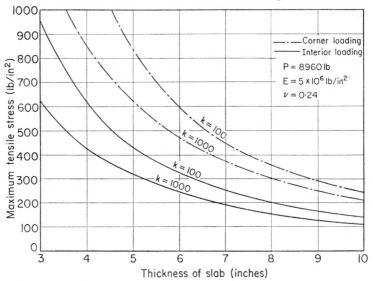

FIGURE 12.1 Tensile stresses due to loading at interior and corner of slab for various subgrades

It should be noted that this same conclusion could be reached from Burmister's analysis, since for a pavement material such as concrete with a relatively high modulus of elasticity, the vertical stress at the pavement–subgrade interface will be extremely small irrespective of the nature of the subgrade (Figure 10.9). This is in marked contrast to flexible pavement design (see page 191) where a poor quality subgrade requires a considerable thickness of sub-base in order to reduce the magnitude of these stresses to a value acceptable to the subgrade.

12.4 *Stresses due to restraint of subgrade*

Changes in air temperature and direct radiated heat bring about changes in the mean temperature of a concrete slab and cause the slab to expand or contract. A perfectly smooth subgrade would offer no restraint to this movement, and provided that joints filled with a compressible material were formed in the slab at suitable intervals to take up expansion, no stresses would be set up in the slab. In practice, all subgrades offer a considerable resistance to movement of the slab and in so doing develop tensile and compressive stresses within the slab which can be of the same order of magnitude as those resulting from applied wheel loads.

Observations have shown that the frictional restraint of the subgrade increases with longitudinal displacement up to a maximum value at which slipping occurs. This value may range from 100 lb/sq ft at a displacement of 0·01 in for smooth subgrades of compacted sand or gravel covered with a sheet of waterproof paper to 300 lb/sq ft at a displacement of 0·05 in for rough subgrades,[5] although lower values of frictional restraint can be achieved by incorporating a 'sliding layer' of fine sand or asphalt between the underside of the concrete slab and the subgrade.

The maximum stress occurs at the mid-point of the slab length where there is no longitudinal displacement, and its magnitude can be determined if the relation between the frictional restraint of the subgrade and the longitudinal displacement of the slab is known. For example, calculations show that with a maximum frictional restraint of 100 lb/sq ft, a 6-in slab, 400 ft long, would develop a stress of more than 250 lb/sq in as a result of a 10°C change in temperature. Tensile stresses of this order of magnitude combined with those resulting from applied wheel loading may be sufficient to cause failure of the concrete and would, in any case, give rise to critical conditions during the initial curing period.

12.5 Stresses due to restrained warping

In addition to producing a change in the mean temperature of the slab, changes in atmospheric temperature are invariably associated with the establishment of a temperature gradient through the slab. Thus a falling air temperature will cause a greater lowering of temperature in the upper part of the slab compared with the lower portion and consequently the greatest contraction will take place at the upper surface.

If the slab were weightless and free from restriction at the joints, then the slab would deform as indicated in Figure 12.2 without producing any change of stress (apart from that resulting from a non-linear distribution of temperature). In practice the weight of the slab and the restraint of load-transfer devices or friction at the slab joints will prevent free warping, so producing in the above example tensile

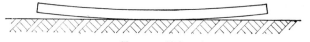

FIGURE 12.2

stresses in the top of the slab. Similarly, a rising air temperature will give compressive stresses in the top of the slab but tensile stresses at the bottom.

The magnitude of these stresses can be calculated from Westergaard's original work,[6] which assumed a linear temperature gradient, or, more accurately, by Thomlinson's method[7] in which a harmonic variation of temperature is assumed for the upper surface of the slab and the temperature at any depth is deduced from this variation and from the thermal properties of concrete. From this theory, Thomlinson derived expressions enabling the internal stress in the slab to be calculated, firstly when warping only is fully restrained and secondly when both warping and longitudinal movements are restrained.

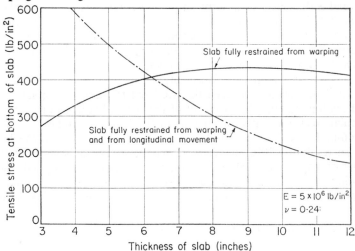

FIGURE 12.3 Tensile stresses at bottom of slab due to curved gradient of daytime temperature (Thomlinson's method)[8]

Applying Thomlinson's method to a specific example of a slab subjected to a temperature cycle at the exposed surface of amplitude 17°C, daytime conditions will produce tensile stresses at the bottom of the slab as indicated in Figure 12.3. Maximum night-time stresses will be about one-third of these values and will be reversed in direction. Again, it can be seen that these stresses are of the same order of magnitude as those produced by loading on the slab, although the net effect would be to reduce the maximum tensile stresses in some instances but increase them in others.

Differential shrinkage of the slab may also occur during the time immediately following the placing of the concrete as a result of the upper part of the slab drying out far more quickly than the lower portion. Such movement is again restrained by the weight of the slab, with the result that tensile stresses are produced in the top of the slab. Since the flexural strength of the concrete will be very low at this early age, severe cracking may occur on hot days if sufficient care is not taken to cure the concrete properly. Subsequent changes in moisture content during the life of the road will cause some shrinkage or swelling in much the same way as do changes in temperature, but indications are that these moisture movements are small and in any case tend to oppose those resulting from temperature changes.

CURRENT DESIGN PRACTICE

12.6 Slab thickness

Two important points have emerged from the theoretical study of stresses in concrete slabs. Firstly, the stresses produced by wheel loads in a slab of a given thickness are largely independent of the nature of the underlying subgrade and, secondly, the stresses arising from temperature changes can be just as severe as those produced by wheel loads. In order to reduce the effects of temperature, joints must be provided in the slab to allow for expansion, contraction, and warping movements. The slab thickness can then be determined largely by consideration of the applied wheel loads.

Westergaard's analysis has been confined to a study of the stresses produced by a single wheel load, but it would not be difficult to extend this to determine the worst possible combination of loading from a given wheel configuration and so calculate the maximum tensile stresses produced by a particular vehicle. It must be appreciated, however, that Westergaard's theory, like most others, entails certain basic assumptions, one of which is that the subgrade behaves perfectly elastically and is in continuous contact with the slab. In fact, all subgrades are to some extent inelastic in their behaviour and successive applications of load produce progressive plastic deformation, thus creating unsupported areas of slab which are spanned by virtue of the tensile strength of the concrete. It is therefore necessary in practice to relate slab thickness to the number of applications of heavy wheel loads, as for flexible pavement design.

The design recommendations for concrete roads currently employed in this country were originally set out in *Road Note No. 19*[9] and its Addendum, but these have since been incorporated into *Road Note No. 29*.[10] As with flexible pavements (see page 190), traffic intensity is measured in terms of the number of commercial vehicles per day which it is anticipated will be using the road 20 years after construction. A commercial vehicle is again defined as a goods or public service vehicle of unladen weight exceeding 30 cwt. Traffic is divided into the following categories:

> More than 3,000 commercial vehicles per day
> 1,500–3,000 commercial vehicles per day
> 450–1,500 commercial vehicles per day
> 150–450 commercial vehicles per day
> 45–150 commercial vehicles per day
> Up to 45 commercial vehicles per day

These volumes again represent the total two-way flow, even on divided highways.

The recommended design thicknesses for concrete slabs with reinforcement are given in Table 12.1. For unreinforced slabs, recommended

TABLE 12.1 *Design thickness of reinforced concrete slabs (in)*[10]

Type of subgrade	Traffic intensity (commercial vehicles per day) 20 years after construction					
	*More than 3,000**	*1,500– 3,000*	*450– 1,500*	*150– 450*	*45– 150*	*Less than 45*
Very stable subgrades	9	8	7	6	5	4
Normal subgrades	10	9	8	7	6	5
Subgrades very susceptible to non-uniform movement	11	10	9	8	7	6

* For traffic in excess of about 6,000 commercial vehicles per day it will generally be desirable to increase the thickness of the slab by 1 in

slab thicknesses should be increased by 1 in for traffic intensities of less than 450 commercial vehicles per day.[37]

Whilst acknowledging the fact that the same thickness of slab is suitable for the majority of subgrade types, as indicated by Westergaard's analysis, the design provides for a slight reduction in thickness on very stable subgrades where non-uniform movement is very small. These subgrades are defined to include well-compacted and undisturbed foundations of old roads, rock, and well-graded sandy gravels compacted to an air voids content of 5% or less (see page 151) and having a C.B.R. value of not less than 60% (see page 185) at the highest moisture content likely to occur in the road. Similarly, a slight increase in thickness is recommended on subgrades of organic soils and highly plastic clays having a C.B.R. value of 2% or less or containing pockets of peat within a depth of 15 ft below the surface, since such subgrades are known to be susceptible to very large non-uniform movements.

Wherever practicable, the water table should be prevented from rising to within 2 ft of formation level either by providing subsoil drainage or by raising the formation level by means of a low embankment. Where local conditions make this impossible, the slab thickness on a normal subgrade should be increased by 1 in and made equal to that for a subgrade very susceptible to non-uniform movement.

In America, concrete pavements have often been constructed with thickened edges as a means of compensating for the increased loading stresses at the slab edges. This method of construction suffers from the disadvantage that difficulties occur in shaping and compacting the formation, and drainage problems are introduced. The same effect can be obtained more easily by extending the slab for some 12 in beyond the face of the kerb and bedding the latter on the slab.

12.7 Base thickness and function

The load-spreading capacity of a rigid pavement lies mainly in the concrete slab surfacing and is little affected by the provision or omission of a base. Bases are, however, commonly provided, except on very stable subgrades. The function of the base is chiefly to assist drainage and allow construction to proceed during wet weather without damage to the subgrade, but in addition a base prevents pumping of fine-grained soils and provides a blanket for frost-susceptible subgrades.

Pumping is defined as 'the ejection of water and subgrade soil through joints, cracks, and along the edges of pavements caused by downward slab movement actuated by the passage of heavy axle loads over the pavement after the accumulation of free water on or in the subgrade'.[11] Pumping occurs only with fine-grained soils such as clays and silts which do not have free draining properties and therefore allow water to collect under the pavement. Excessive pumping is marked by the ejection of muddy water from the joint or the edge of the pavement during the passage of a vehicle, so creating an even larger void until failure of the pavement occurs by cracking. An open-graded base course, properly compacted, will control pumping by allowing water to percolate through it. Pumping is not possible with flexible pavements, since in this case deformation of the subgrade produces a corresponding deformation of the road surface rather than the creation of a void.

Recommended thicknesses of bases under concrete pavements are given in Table 12.2. The normal recognized thickness is 3 in, but on poorer subgrade materials where constructional traffic may damage the formation and its protective seal, a 6- or 9-in base may be required. In any case, on frost-susceptible subgrades, a thicker base may be necessary to give an overall pavement thickness of 18 in and so reduce the risk of frost heave (see page 138). No base is required on a well-graded gravel subgrade which has been thoroughly compacted and protected by surface dressing.

Base materials should be hard, durable, and capable of being compacted to a high density. Frost-susceptible materials or materials subject to shrinkage, swelling, or loss of stability with increasing moisture content should be excluded. Suitable materials include graded gravels, hard clinker, crushed stone or slag, well-burnt hard colliery shale, stabilized soil, or lean concrete. As with sub-base materials for flexible pavements (see page 194), the ability to carry heavy constructional traffic in all weather conditions usually determines whether or not the material is satisfactory, and an otherwise suitable material such as hoggin (a well-graded gravel–sand–clay mixture which is liable to become unstable in wet weather) may be rejected on this account.

TABLE 12.2 *Recommended thickness of bases for concrete pavements (in)*[10]

Type of subgrade	Traffic intensity (commercial vehicles per day) 20 years after construction					
	More than 3,000	1,500– 3,000	450– 1,500	150– 450	45– 150	Less than 45
Very stable subgrades	—	—	—	—	—	—
Normal subgrades	3	3	3	3	3	3
Subgrades very susceptible to non-uniform movement	6	6	3–6	3–6	3	3

Note: Where, for roads carrying more than 1,500 commercial vehicles per day, construction traffic is to use the base under one carriageway it is recommended that this base should be type 1 aggregate (see page 195), lean concrete, or cement-stabilized material, and the base thickness should be increased by 3 in from that given above. Alternatively, the base thickness may be increased by 6 in and the slab thickness may be decreased by 1 in. Where type 1 materials are difficult to obtain, type 2 aggregate may be used by traffic without stabilization during the months April to September inclusive provided that the thickness of base is increased by 6 in and no reduction is made to the thickness of the slab

12.8 *Joint spacing and reinforcement*

Joints are formed in concrete slabs for the purpose of allowing expansion, contraction, and warping movements of the slab to take place, so reducing to acceptable limits the stresses produced by changes of temperature. The absence of joints would result in irregular cracking of the concrete which, apart from being unsightly in appearance, would give rise to excessive deflexion of the slab at these points with further cracking and spalling of the concrete.

Since it is desirable for constructional purposes that joints should be spaced as far apart as economically possible, a light fabric reinforcement is normally included in the slab to prevent the opening of cracks beyond the 'hair crack' stage at positions intermediate between the joints. Experience has shown that transverse joints are required in unreinforced slabs at approximately 20-ft centres, but this distance can be increased to between 40 and 80 ft if the slabs are reinforced to control cracking. At one time it was common practice to use an even greater spacing of joints in conjunction with a heavier weight of reinforcement, but developments in techniques of forming joints have now made this increased spacing uneconomical.

Transverse joints in concrete pavements may be either expansion or contraction joints. The former allow for expansion, contraction, and warping movements of the slab, whilst the latter allow for contraction,

TABLE 12.3 *Reinforcement and joint spacing for concrete pavements*

Traffic intensity (commercial vehicles per day) 20 years after construction	Minimum weight of oblong-mesh reinforcement (lb/sq yd)	Maximum spacing of expansion joints (ft)	Maximum spacing of contraction joints (ft)
(a) Reinforced concrete slabs[10]			
More than 3,000	9	240 (160)	80
1,500–3,000	6·5	240 (180)	60
450–1,500	6·5	240 (180)	60
150–450	4·5	160 (120)	40
45–150	4·5	160 (120)	40
Less than 45	3·5	120 (80)	40
(b) Unreinforced concrete slabs[37]			
5–8 in slab (limestone aggregate)		180 (120)	18
ditto (gravel or igneous rock)		90 (60)	15
9–11 in slab (limestone aggregate)		230 (160)	23
ditto (gravel or igneous rock)		120 (100)	20

Note: The figures given in brackets are to be used in cold weather only

warping, and only a limited amount of expansion. Since concrete is strong in compression but relatively weak in tension, expansion joints can be spaced more widely apart than contraction joints and it is usual practice to have two or three contraction joints between each pair of expansion joints. Recommended maximum joint spacings are given in Table 12.3. The spacing in fact depends on several factors including the temperature at which the concrete is placed, the frictional restraint of the subgrade, and the slab thickness. A somewhat closer spacing of expansion joints is thus recommended for concrete placed during cold weather, although it is not practicable to take account of day-to-day variations in temperature. For high-speed roads, the desirability of varying the spacing of contraction joints, using spacings between those given for reinforced slabs and about 20 ft less depending on the length of the reinforcing mat, should be considered as a method of avoiding the possibility of producing a resonant vibration in vehicles travelling at certain speeds.

Expansion joints are difficult to form when mechanized construction is being used and established practice in the United States and in certain continental countries is to omit them altogether (except where adjacent to structures), since the risk of 'blow-up' or buckling of the concrete is slight. Current practice in this country is to include expansion joints, although on certain experimental sections of road they have been omitted and a greater spacing than shown in Table 12.3 (600 ft maximum) has been permitted on the Preston to Lancaster section of the M.6 motorway.[12]

Fabric mesh reinforcement should be in accordance with B.S. 1221[13] with the heavier bars placed in the longitudinal direction. One layer of

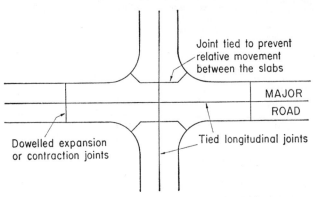

FIGURE 12.4 Bay layout at a four-way intersection[14]

reinforcement is used in all but exceptional circumstances and it is usually placed in the top of the slab with a cover of $2\frac{1}{2}$ in. Flat sheets of fabric reinforcement are preferred to continuous rolls since the latter have a tendency to curl upwards at the ends when laid. Recommended minimum weights of reinforcement are given in Table 12.3.

Longitudinal joints are required in all slabs exceeding 15 ft width since the amount of transverse steel in the type of reinforcing fabric used is negligible. In most cases, warping joints with tie-bars to prevent opening of the joint are suitable, since it is seldom necessary to provide for transverse expansion and contraction of the slab. In practice, longitudinal joints are usually formed to coincide with the lane markings which in most cases on new roads will be 12 ft apart.

Transverse joints should be continued in line across longitudinal joints rather than be staggered, since experience has shown that the latter arrangement often induces cracking in line with the joint in the adjacent slab. Joints should also be formed in kerbs or marginal strips to coincide with transverse joints in the slab, otherwise cracking will occur at these points.

Particular attention should be paid to joint layout at intersections with the object of ensuring that no slabs are constructed with acute-angled corners. If this is not possible, additional reinforcement should be placed in the top of the slab at the corner to prevent cracking. Guidance on slab layout at intersections is given in a Cement and Concrete Association publication,[14] from which Figure 12.4 has been taken.

JOINT DESIGN AND CONSTRUCTION

12.9 Expansion joints

The function of an expansion joint is to permit unrestrained horizontal movements of the concrete slabs, both expansive and contractive, and therefore the joint must contain some compressible filler material and be sealed at the surface to exclude the entry of grit and moisture. In addition, differential vertical movements of the slabs must be prevented by incorporating load-transfer devices such as dowel bars. These dowel bars are usually placed at 12-in centres and vary in size with slab thickness, being $1\frac{1}{4}$ in diameter by 28 in long for slabs 10–12 in thick, 1 in diameter by 24 in long for 8- and 9-in thick slabs, and $\frac{3}{4}$ in diameter by 20 in long for 5–7-in thick slabs. To allow free horizontal movement of the slabs, the dowel bar on one side of the joint must be given a thin coating of bitumen or be covered with a close-fitting polythene sheath and be provided with a cardboard or metal cap partly filled with cotton waste or other compressible material. A typical section through an expansion joint is given in Figure 12.5.

On smaller schemes where the concrete slabs are being constructed in single bays or where 'alternate-bay construction' is being employed,

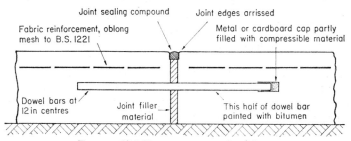

FIGURE 12.5 Transverse expansion joint

expansion joints present little trouble and can be formed by placing the filler material against the formwork and forming a groove to take the sealing compound at a later date (Figure 12.6). To ensure that the dowel bars are aligned parallel to the centre-line, a second row of split forms, suitably drilled at the appropriate spacing, should be set behind the first. After the concrete on one side of the joint has been placed and has hardened, the formwork can be removed and the second slab can then be cast against the joint filler material, using a timber capping of width equal to that of the joint sealer to form a groove.

Where fully-mechanized construction is being used on a larger scheme, expansion joints must be designed so as to allow continuous placing of the concrete without interrupting the progress of the work. This requires that the filler material and dowel bars be supported on the formation or base ahead of the concreting train and held rigidly in

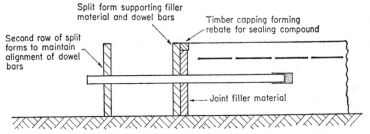

FIGURE 12.6 Forming expansion joint in alternate-bay construction

position to resist the displacing forces from the spreading and compacting machines.

Various techniques have been devised to enable construction to proceed smoothly over the joints and almost every contract employs a slightly different procedure. Common practice is to support the dowel bars on wire cradles or prefabricated cages fixed either side of the filler material.[12] Alternatively, a method at present being used experimentally is to weld the dowel bars onto T-section steel stems set in a transverse concrete sleeper beam (Plate 12.1). Prior to welding, the dowel bars are held rigidly in position by temporary wooden jigs running transversely across the road. The steel stems are designed to shear at the bottom of the slab, so allowing expansion and contraction movements of the slab to take place.

It is normal practice to set the top of the filler material about 1 in below the finished surface level and place concrete over the top of the joint. A groove is then formed in the surface of the slab down to the filler material and subsequently filled with joint sealing compound. This groove may be formed either by cutting the wet concrete with a traversing wheel (Plate 12.2) or by sawing the semi-hardened concrete some

PLATE 12.1   Expansion joint assembly ready for concreting of slab

PLATE 12.2   Traversing eccentric wheel cutting groove in newly laid concrete slab on Newark By-Pass

PLATE 12.3 Concut joint sawing mach cutting transverse joint in concrete p ment slab

PLATE 12.4 Contraction joint assem used on Salzburg–Linz–Vienna autoba the crack inducers are plastic moulding

PLATE 12.5   S.G.M.E. 4 cu yd spreader distributing the top layer of concrete
on the Chiswick–Langley section of the M.4 motorway

PLATE 12.6   Screw spreader fed by slewing conveyor: Preston–Lancaster
section of the M.6 motorway

PLATE 12.7 General view of the concreting train assembly used on the Preston–Lancaster section of the M.6 motorway

PLATE 12.8　Slewing conveyor spreading bottom course of concrete on the Preston–Lancaster section of the M.6 motorway

PLATE 12.9　Rex compacting unit supported on marginal haunches

PLATE 12.10　Finished slab showing brushed texture and sawn joints

PLATE 12.11   General view of the Guntert and Zimmerman slip-form paver at work on the Autoroute du Sud, near Fontainebleau

PLATE 12.12   Rear view of the Guntert and Zimmerman slip-form paver showing the completed slab of fresh concrete

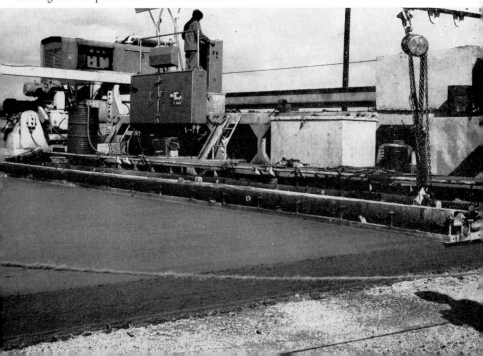

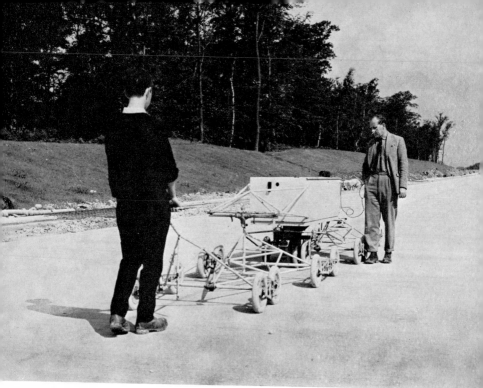

PLATE 12.13   Multi-wheel profilometer

PLATE 12.14   Wet-surface profilometer

12–24 hours after placing using a joint sawing machine (Plate 12.3). Both methods have their advantages, and the choice is often determined by economic considerations. Recommended dimensions of sealing grooves are given in Table 12.4.

TABLE 12.4 *Dimensions of sealing grooves for joints in concrete slabs*[10]

Type of joint	Spacing (ft)	Minimum width (in)	Depth of groove (in)
Expansion joints	All spacings	$\frac{1}{4}$ in greater than the thickness of the filler	$1-1\frac{1}{4}$
Contraction joints	15	$\frac{1}{4}$	$\left.\begin{array}{c}\\\end{array}\right\}$ $\frac{3}{4}-\frac{7}{8}$
	40	$\frac{1}{2}$	
	60	$\frac{3}{4}$	$\left.\begin{array}{c}\\\end{array}\right\}$ $1-1\frac{1}{4}$
	80	1	
Longitudinal joints	—	$\frac{1}{4}$	$\frac{3}{4}-\frac{7}{8}$

12.10 *Contraction joints*

In alternate-bay construction, contraction joints are formed in a similar manner to expansion joints except that the filler material is omitted. Dowel bars are again required to provide load-transfer across the joint and one half of these bars should be painted with a thin coating of bitumen to allow contractive movements of the slabs to take place. For the same reason, the interface between the two slabs should also be painted with bitumen before the second slab is cast. The completed joint is shown in Figure 12.7.

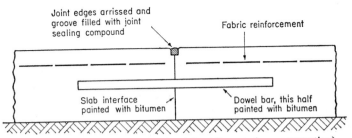

Joint edges arrised and groove filled with joint sealing compound

Fabric reinforcement

Slab interface painted with bitumen

Dowel bar, this half painted with bitumen

FIGURE 12.7 Transverse contraction joint (alternate-bay construction)

With continuous construction, 'dummy' contraction joints are formed by creating planes of weakness in the slab at the required spacings. To induce cracking of the slab at these points, a timber fillet

I

or plastic moulding (Plate 12.4) can be fixed to the base or the formation and a groove is formed or sawn on the surface of the slab directly over the fillet. This groove is then filled and sealed as shown in Figure 12.8.

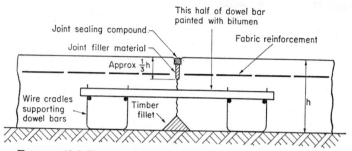

FIGURE 12.8 Dummy contraction joint (continuous construction)

On account of the irregular nature of the crack which will develop at a dummy contraction joint, some degree of load transfer may be considered to be provided by the interlocking of the particles of aggregate but dowel bars should be included as an additional safeguard where it is essential to prevent any differential movement between the adjacent slabs.

12.11 Longitudinal joints

Longitudinal joints in concrete pavements normally provide only for small angular movements of the two slabs, thus reducing in magnitude the stresses arising from restrained warping. As previously indicated, longitudinal joints are formed in all slabs exceeding 15 ft width, and are usually positioned so as to correspond to the lane-line markings.

When the carriageway is being constructed a single lane width at a time, the longitudinal warping joint may be of the form shown in

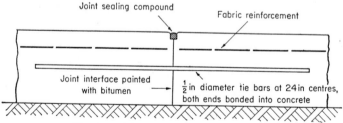

FIGURE 12.9 Longitudinal warping joint

Figure 12.9. Tie-bars $\frac{1}{2}$ in diameter by 3 ft 6 in long at 24-in centres are used to prevent lateral movement of the two slabs and these are particularly essential on clay subgrades which are subject to seasonal shrinkage and swelling. A keyed joint may be used in preference to a butt joint to give additional capacity for transference of load across the joint. In either case, the face of the joint should be painted with bitumen after the forms have been removed from the first line of slabs concreted, and a groove should be formed at the surface for sealing the joint.

Projecting tie-bars which are misaligned will give difficulty in the removal and re-use of longitudinal road forms, in addition to which it may be necessary to bend aside all projecting tie-bars and later straighten them to avoid interference with constructional traffic. These difficulties can be avoided by casting a threaded coupling into the first slab adjacent to the form and screwing in the second half of the tie-bar immediately prior to concreting the adjoining slab (Figure 12.10).

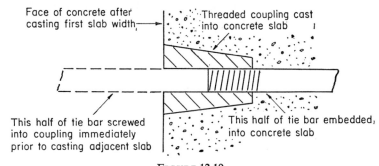

Face of concrete after casting first slab width

Threaded coupling cast into concrete slab

This half of tie bar screwed into coupling immediately prior to casting adjacent slab

This half of tie bar embedded into concrete slab

FIGURE 12.10

On larger schemes, it is common practice to cast the full width of the carriageway at the same time and a machine capable of laying the 36-ft wide three-lane carriageways has been used on the recently completed section of the M.6 motorway.[12] In such cases, dummy warping joints are formed longitudinally along the slab by sawing the hardened concrete in the same manner as for transverse contraction joints. A timber fillet fixed to the base or formation will again help to locate the plane of weakness and tie-bars should be provided to prevent the joint opening (Figure 12.11). Alternatively, a mat of reinforcement fabric may be used in place of tie-bars.

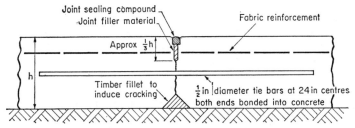

Joint sealing compound
Joint filler material
Fabric reinforcement
Approx $\frac{1}{3}$h
h
Timber fillet to induce cracking
$\frac{1}{2}$ in diameter tie bars at 24 in centres both ends bonded into concrete

FIGURE 12.11 Dummy warping joint (full-width construction)

12.12 Joint filler and sealing materials

The requirements of filling and sealing materials for joints in concrete roads are given in *Road Note No. 7*.[15] Joint filler material must be capable of being compressed without forcing out the joint sealer and must have elastic properties of recovery. In addition, it should be durable and rot-proof, and also be sufficiently rigid to stand upright on the base or formation with a minimum of support. Satisfactory materials include knot-free timber, fibreboard impregnated with creosote, and cork.

Joint sealing compounds must adhere well to the concrete and have considerable tensile strength to resist fracture when the slabs on either side are contracting away from the joint. On the other hand, the material must be of sufficient viscosity to resist the penetration of grit and must not be susceptible to the softening effect of hot weather. Other essential properties are durability and ease of application. The most suitable materials are hot-poured rubber–bitumen compounds which give a compromise between the conflicting requirements stated above. Full-scale trials[16] have shown that compounds meeting the requirements of United States Federal Specification SS-S-164[17] are more satisfactory where large movements are anticipated than those complying with B.S. 2499.[18]

CONSTRUCTIONAL PRACTICE

12.13 Concrete mix design and quality control

The current Ministry of Transport Specification[19] requires that the concrete used in pavement construction should have a minimum cube crushing strength of 4,000 lb/sq in at 28 days when tested in accordance with B.S. 1881,[20] with not more than 1% of the cubes tested failing below this value. In addition, the mix proportions should be such that the water/cement and aggregate/cement ratios do not exceed 0·55 and 7·0 respectively by weight.

The water/cement ratio for the mix will be determined by the mean strength for which the mix must be designed in order to achieve this required minimum strength. This in turn will depend on the type of batching equipment used on site and the amount of site supervision. One of the earliest, yet still widely used, methods of mix design is given in *Road Note No. 4*.[21] To achieve a minimum 28-day compressive strength of 4,000 lb/sq in, *Road Note No. 4* requires the mix to be designed for a mean 28-day strength of 5,350 lb/sq in or more, depending on the degree of control exercised on site. From a study of a large number of works test cube results obtained from different sites,

Erntroy[22] has shown that even on the best controlled sites with servo-operated weigh-batching equipment, a mean strength of 5,600 lb/sq in is normally required to ensure that only one cube in every hundred fails below 4,000 lb/sq in, and a higher mean strength of up to 7,000 lb/sq in is necessary to achieve the same result on sites subjected to less rigorous control.

Within the limit of aggregate/cement ratio not exceeding 7·0 by weight, the mix should be designed to have the lowest workability compatible with the type of compaction equipment available on site, so as to produce the greatest economy in the use of cement and also reduce the amount of drying shrinkage. For small contracts where the concrete is laid by hand, a mix of 'medium' workability will be required, but on larger schemes where power-operated compactors are available, a 'low' or 'very low' workability can be used.

The aggregate/cement ratio can be obtained from the tables given in *Road Note No. 4*, having first decided upon the water/cement ratio and the degree of workability acceptable. Alternatively, one of the more refined methods of mix design, such as that given by Murdock,[23] may be used. It should be appreciated, however, that the workability of a concrete mix depends, amongst other things, on the shape of the aggregate particles, particularly that of the fine aggregate, and since this cannot be readily assessed by eye it is usually necessary to make up a series of trial mixes on site, keeping the water/cement ratio constant and increasing or decreasing the aggregate/cement ratio until the desired workability has been obtained.

To control the quality of the concrete, the Specification requires test cubes to be made up in pairs, each pair from a different batch of concrete. At the start of the work, six pairs should be made up each day, but this number can be reduced later when sufficient results are available. One cube of each pair should be tested at 28 days, after curing in the prescribed manner, whilst the other can be used to estimate the suitability of the mix at an earlier age by 7-day tests or by accelerated curing methods.

With a normal (or Gaussian) distribution of results, the effective minimum strength of the mix (only 1% of results below this value) will be 2·33 standard deviations below the mean. A check on the suitability of the mix can thus be obtained when a number of the 28-day cube results have become available by calculating the mean strength and the standard deviation for this sample and subtracting 2·33 standard deviations from the mean. If this value exceeds 4,000 lb/sq in it may be assumed that the Specification is being met. If this minimum crushing strength is not attained, cores with a height/diameter ratio of 2 may be cut from the hardened concrete and a core strength of not less than 3,000 lb/sq in at 28 days is accepted as taking precedence over the cube strengths.[19]

The use of compressive strength to control the quality of the concrete may be questioned, since compressive strength is of itself of little importance in concrete pavements, although it is generally recognized that concrete satisfying the above strength requirements would have adequate durability and impermeability—properties which are themselves much more difficult to measure. It has been suggested, however, that more attention should be paid to the tensile and flexural strengths of concrete, and that flexural strength rather than compressive strength could be used as a basis for mix design and quality control.[24] In this case a minimum flexural strength of 450 lb/sq in at 28 days would be appropriate.

12.14 *Admixtures*

Admixtures are substances which are added in small quantities to a concrete mix in order to modify various properties of the concrete. The principal admixtures of concern to highway engineers are accelerators, retarders, and air-entraining agents.

Accelerators increase the rate of hardening of the concrete, thus allowing the earlier removal of formwork. They are particularly useful in cold weather since the rate of hydration of the cement is increased, thus enabling concreting to be carried out when the air temperature is close to freezing point. This property is of reduced value in roadworks, however, where a large exposed area of slab allows heat to be rapidly dissipated.

The commonest accelerator is calcium chloride which is used in the concentration of between 1 and 2% of the weight of the cement and is usually dissolved in the mixing water. Calcium chloride approximately halves the setting time of the concrete and similarly reduces the curing time, giving an increase of strength at early ages in much the same manner as does rapid-hardening Portland cement compared with ordinary Portland cement.

Retarders are used to delay the setting of concrete and may be of use in roadworks when concrete is being transported over a considerable distance from a central mixing plant, since a breakdown of the spreading and compaction plant would result in a considerable quantity of concrete being held up in transit and possibly wasted.

Many commercial retarders increase the workability of the concrete and therefore act also as water-reducing admixtures, allowing the mix proportions to be adjusted to give concrete of the same workability as an untreated mix but with increased compressive and flexural strength. The amount of admixture added is usually between 0·05 and 0·5% of the weight of the cement. Recent investigations have shown that ordinary granulated sugar added to a concrete mix in the proportion 0·05% of the weight of cement will act as a set-retarding, water-reducing admixture in a manner similar to proprietary retarders and at a fraction of the cost.[25]

Air-entraining agents increase the resistance of concrete to frost damage and to the destructive action of de-icing salts which result in surface scaling of the concrete. Air-entrained concrete is thus particularly useful for pavement construction and its use has been widespread in the United States for almost thirty years. In Great Britain, however, possibly because of the less severe winters and the general use of drier mixes, frost damage to concrete pavements has been a lesser problem and air-entrainment has only been used to any appreciable extent in recent years but is now specified on most roads for at least the top two inches of slab thickness.

The mechanism of air-entrainment is not fully understood, but it is known that materials such as animal and vegetable fats and oils and natural wood resins when added to concrete mixes in small amounts will produce a large number of minute air bubbles ranging in size from 0·002 to 0·05 in. The presence of these air bubbles in the hardened concrete prevents the concrete becoming saturated by capillary attraction along the pores and relieves the pressures developed during the initial stages of freezing by accommodating the excess water in the voids, thus preventing the disruption which would otherwise occur with saturated concrete.[26]

In addition to frost protection, air-entrainment has other effects on the properties of the concrete. In the first place, entrained air reduces the strength of concrete in the same way as air included by lack of thorough compaction. Wright[27] has shown that the reduction in compressive strength is 5·5% for each 1% of air present. However, it has been further shown that air-entrained concrete is more workable than plain concrete of the same mix proportions—a fact which allows the mix proportions to be adjusted by reducing the water/cement ratio of the air-entrained mix. The strength increase thereby obtained offsets to some extent the loss of strength resulting from the increased air content. To obtain optimum advantage of frost resistance without excessive loss of strength, the concrete should contain about 4–6% of air by volume.

The air content of the freshly compacted concrete can be measured using a pressure-type air meter. Pressure is applied by a bicycle pump, and, by observing the decrease in volume of a sample of concrete subjected to a known pressure, the air content can be obtained directly. The test procedure is covered by A.S.T.M. Standard C231-62.[28]

12.15 *Slab construction*

Once the base or subgrade has been prepared and compacted to the required density and surface tolerance, construction of the overlying concrete slab can proceed. In some instances a 'sliding layer' of fine sand, approximately 1 in thick, is placed on top of the base or subgrade to take out surface irregularities and reduce the magnitude of the frictional restraint. In addition, it is normal practice to use a waterproof underlay immediately under the slab to reduce friction and prevent the loss of cement grout. Polythene sheeting is invariably used for this underlay nowadays (see Plate 12.1).

In alternate-bay construction, formwork is set up for a number of separate bays, leaving the intermediate slabs to be cast at a later date. The maximum length of each bay is governed by the spacing of the joints and would thus normally be 40 ft in reinforced construction and 15 ft with unreinforced slabs. Concrete is spread by hand over the slab area and the reinforcement is positioned when the concrete has reached the required level. The top surface of the slab is then compacted either by hand-tamping or by using a tamping beam on which has been

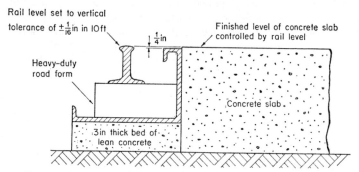

FIGURE 12.12 Form and rail assembly for mechanized construction

mounted a small vibrator. To enable tamping to be carried out transversely across the slab, the side forms must be set initially to the finished surface level.

On most road schemes, mechanized construction must be employed to reduce the cost of construction and increase the rate of progress. Mechanized construction allows the use of drier concrete and thus the cement content of the mix can be reduced for a given strength requirement. However, greater attention must be paid to the formwork, and, as previously explained, the making of joints is more difficult in continuous construction, which is the only method suited to fully-mechanized work.

In mechanized construction the spreading and compacting machines run along the steel side forms or on rails set alongside the formwork (Figure 12.12). To prevent excessive deflexion of the forms under the weight of the concreting train, with consequent effect on the riding quality of the finished surface, the forms should be set on a bed of soil-cement or lean concrete laid at least 24 hours in advance of concreting operations. On motorway construction, flush marginal strips can be cast in advance, as is the normal practice with flexible construction, and used to support the spreading, compacting, and finishing machines.

Spreading machines may be of the hopper type mounted on a chassis which is capable of being moved longitudinally and transversely over the slab (Plate 12.5). Concrete is tipped into the hopper from the side of the road and is then distributed over the formation. Alternatively, a reciprocating blade or screw-type spreader may be used (Plate 12.6), in which case the concrete is deposited directly onto the formation ahead of the machine.

A general view of the concrete train assembly used on the Preston to Lancaster section of the M.6 motorway is shown in Plate 12.7. Agitator truck mixers were used to transport the concrete from a central batching and mixing plant and these discharged into hopper units running alongside the train which in turn fed the concrete onto the formation via a transfer hopper and a slewing conveyor (Plate 12.8). As is normal practice with reinforced slabs, concrete was spread to the level of the reinforcement before the fabric mats were placed in position and a second spreader and compactor unit was used to place the top layer of concrete. With this arrangement, it was thus practicable to use an air-entrained mix made with a granite aggregate of high polished stone value (see page 220) for the top course and a normal concrete mix made with a cheaper aggregate of lower quality for the bottom course. Final compaction was carried out by a separate oscillating beam (Plate 12.9) followed by an articulated oscillating beam and a finishing drag float.

To allow for subsequent compaction of the slab, the top surface of the concrete must be struck off to a level somewhat higher than the finished slab level. The amount of surcharge depends on the workability of the concrete, but for mixes of very low to low workability (compacting factor 0·80–0·84) it is usually between 25 and 20% of the slab thickness, decreasing as the workability increases.[29] Insufficient surcharge will result in incomplete compaction, whilst excessive surcharge will cause a build-up of concrete.

After compaction, a surface texture to the concrete can be produced by brushing the surface transversely with a steel wire broom. This brushed texture increases skidding resistance and also gives a more pleasant and uniform appearance to the surface, with better light-reflecting qualities (Plate 12.10). Curing of the slab is carried out by applying a resinous curing compound (preferably light in colour to reduce thermal stresses) to the finished road surface at the rate of between 20 and 25 sq yd per gallon, using a fine spray.

Constructional techniques used on eleven major road contracts have been reviewed by Blake and Brook,[29] and a typical cross-section of a concrete road is given in Figure 12.13.

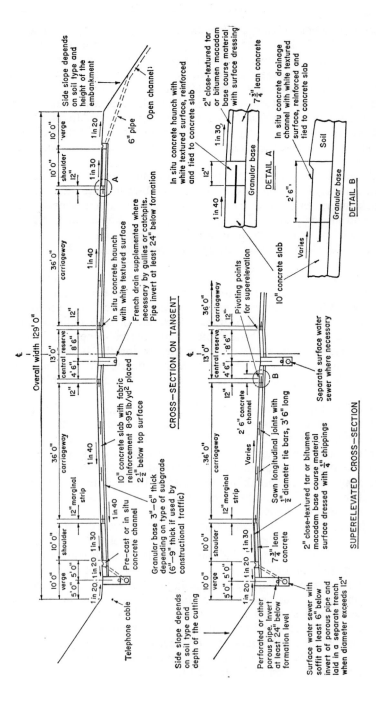

FIGURE 12.13 Typical motorway cross-section for rigid construction

12.16 Slip-form pavers

Considerable interest is at present being focused on the use of slip-form pavers for concrete road construction. These machines are capable of a high output and have been used extensively in the United States and, more recently, on the Continent with considerable success.[30, 31] A slip-form paver has also been used experimentally in Great Britain for the construction of the Cromwell By-pass in Nottinghamshire.

One of these machines, the Guntert and Zimmerman paver (Plate 12.11), is mounted on crawler tracks and is capable of laying pavings to widths ranging from 12 to 60 ft at speeds of up to 7 ft per minute. No side forms are required, apart from short lengths which are integral with the machine. The concrete is tipped into receiving boxes at the front of the machine, subjected to high frequency vibration, and moulded to the required thickness under a heavily loaded beam. The newly moulded concrete is then extruded from the rear of the machine and left unsupported as the paver moves forwards (Plate 12.12).

Automatic control of line and level for the finished slab is obtained by using electronically operated sensing probes at each corner of the machine. These probes straddle a length of tensioned piano wire attached to steel pegs set to the correct gradients and levels. Any variation of level resulting from irregularities of the base is detected by the probes and automatically corrected by the operation of hydraulic jacks. Directional control is achieved by a fifth sensing probe mounted on one of the front corners of the machine.

Applied to British practice, slip-form pavers do present some difficulty with the incorporation of reinforcement, expansion joints, and dowelled contraction joints in the slab. Continental practice has been to use unreinforced slabs without expansion joints and with dummy contraction joints sawn at approximately 25-ft centres. No dowel bars have been incorporated in the slab at contraction joints. There is no reason why these technical problems should not be overcome, however, and provided that sufficient continuity of work is available to justify the purchase of an expensive machine, slip-form pavers should provide an economical method of constructing concrete pavements.

12.17 Prestressed concrete roads

Concrete road slabs constructed by traditional methods require the use of reinforcement and closely spaced joints to control the formation of cracks. If an initial compressive stress is applied to the slab shortly after casting, the magnitude of tensile stresses resulting from loading and temperature changes will be greatly reduced, and thus joints can be spaced more widely apart and the need for reinforcement no longer exists. This is the argument for prestressed concrete roads.

Disadvantages arise in prestressed construction, however, from the extra safety precautions and supervision required on site, particularly during stressing operations, and from the fact that jacking bays may have to be left between slabs, so preventing continuity of construction. Furthermore, any maintenance of services beneath the road which necessitates a trench being cut through the prestressed slab will cause additional difficulties.

A number of prestressed concrete roads have been constructed experimentally, both in Great Britain and abroad, using slab lengths up to about 1,000 ft.[32] The advantages of prestressing have diminished in recent years, however, with the introduction of methods of sawing contraction joints in the hardened concrete and the subject is now receiving less attention, although an international symposium has recently been devoted to this topic.[33]

RIDING QUALITY OF ROADS

12.18 *Measurement of riding quality*

The riding quality of a road surface is to a large extent the criterion by which the layman assesses the work of the highway engineer. Failure to appreciate the importance of any one of a number of factors, either at the design stage or later during construction, may result in unevenness of the running surface with consequent discomfort to drivers using the road.

Specifications usually require the finished road surface to be such that the gap under a 10-ft straightedge placed parallel to the carriageway centre-line at any point does not exceed $\frac{1}{8}$ in for rigid pavements or $\frac{3}{16}$ in for flexible construction.[19] Whilst this is suitable as a method of control during construction, it is desirable to have some means of assessing the overall riding quality of a length of road, both initially and after several years of trafficking. The multi-wheel profilometer (Plate 12.13) developed at the Road Research Laboratory provides a means of doing this.

The profilometer[34] consists of a 16-wheeled articulated carriage arranged so as to support the recording gear at a constant height above the continuously averaged level of the road surface at these 16 wheel points. The recording wheels, situated centrally, actuate a profilometer which records a continuous longitudinal profile of the road surface. In addition, the recording gear includes an integrator, which totals all the upward vertical movements of the recording wheel, and a classifier, which registers automatically the number of irregularities within the ranges 0·1–0·2 in, 0·2–0·3 in, and so on up to 1·4–1·5 in. The irregularity index q is the sum of the products of the number of irregularities in each range and the average size of the irregularity for that range. Experience has suggested that this gives a better assessment of overall unevenness than the total irregularity registered by the integrator.

A comparison of measured values of q with the opinions of experienced road users has indicated that a road with 'good' riding quality will have a q value of less than 75 in per mile, whilst one with 'fair' riding quality will have a q value not exceeding 130 in per mile.

12.19 Factors affecting the riding quality of concrete roads

Although most concrete roads constructed in the late 1930's and compacted by hand-tamping achieved a reputation for good riding quality, the introduction of mechanical spreading and finishing of the concrete produced a deterioration in riding quality which had an adverse effect on the development of concrete road construction in this country. It was observed, however, that good riding quality had been achieved on substantial lengths of mechanically constructed road and this suggested that better results might have been obtained from closer control of constructional operations. A programme of research was therefore initiated to examine the factors affecting the riding quality of machine-laid concrete roads.[35, 36]

These investigations covered such factors as the methods used for spreading and finishing the concrete, the effect of different types of joint formation, the irregularities resulting from poor setting of the formwork, and the effect of variations in the workability of the concrete mix. To separate those irregularities caused by misaligned and badly supported forms from those resulting from other causes, a wet-surface profilometer was used to record the surface profile of the road relative to that of the forms.

The wet-surface profilometer (Plate 12.14) consists essentially of a rigid frame having the same wheel base as the finishing machine. The frame carries two recorder wheels (four for full-width construction of a two-lane carriageway) which are set in the same position relative to the chassis wheels as that occupied by the trailing edge of the vibrating beam (or of the finishing screed if the latter is fitted). The recording wheels are counter-balanced so that the pressure on the concrete is only just sufficient to cause rotation, and the vertical movement of each is recorded autographically. Thus a continuous record of the surface profile is obtained while the concrete is still plastic and serious irregularities can be corrected by further passes of the finishing machine. Errors resulting from poor setting of the formwork cannot be detected by the wet-surface profilometer, however.

At the beginning of the investigation, average irregularity index values of 115 in per mile had been recorded on concrete roads constructed by mechanical plant, of which 25 in per mile was estimated to be caused by poor form setting and the remaining 90 in per mile by faulty constructional techniques. Measurements taken at the four experimental sites showed that careful spreading of the concrete to reduce pre-compaction and give a more uniform density reduced the irregularity index by 20 in per mile. A further reduction of 40 in per mile was achieved by redesigning the finishing screed, by attaching it to the back of the compacting machine, and by making repeated passes of the finishing machine where necessary. Other improvements in riding quality resulted from the use of articulated bogies to support the finishing screed, so reducing the effects of variations in form level, and from improved methods of constructing joints. These reductions were estimated as 15 in per mile and 5 in per mile respectively. Variations in the workability of the concrete, within practical limits, gave no significant difference in riding quality.

An overall examination of the above results suggests that machine-laid concrete roads can be constructed with an irregularity index as low as 35 in per mile provided that sufficient attention is paid to spreading and finishing the concrete. This denotes a very high standard of riding quality and compares favourably with that achieved in flexible construction.

REFERENCES

1. WESTERGAARD, H. M., 'Stresses in Concrete Pavements Computed by Theoretical Analysis', *Public Roads* (Washington, D.C.: vol. 7, 1926–7, pp. 25–35)

2. WESTERGAARD, H. M., 'Analytical Tools for Judging Results of Structural Tests of Concrete Pavements', *Public Roads* (Washington, D.C.: vol. 14, 1933–4, pp. 185–8)

3. TELLER, L. W. and SUTHERLAND, E. C., 'The Structural Design of Concrete Pavements. Part 5: An Experimental Study of the Westergaard Analysis of Stress Conditions in Concrete Pavement Slabs of Uniform Thickness', *Public Roads* (Washington, D.C.: vol. 23, 1942–4, pp. 167–212)

4. YODER, E. J., *Principles of Pavement Design* (New York: Wiley; London: Chapman and Hall, 1959, p. 196)

5. ROAD RESEARCH LABORATORY, *Concrete Roads: Design and Construction* (London: H.M.S.O., 1955, p. 170)

6. WESTERGAARD, H. M., 'Analysis of Stresses in Concrete Roads Caused by Variations of Temperature', *Public Roads* (Washington, D.C.: vol. 8, 1927–8, pp. 54–60)

7. THOMLINSON, J., 'Temperature Variations and Consequent Stresses Produced by Daily and Seasonal Temperature Cycles in Concrete Slabs', *Concrete and Constructional Engineering* (London: vol. 35, 1940, pp. 298–307 and 352–60)

8. ROAD RESEARCH LABORATORY, *Concrete Roads: Design and Construction* (London: H.M.S.O., 1955, p. 166)

9. ROAD RESEARCH LABORATORY, 'The Design Thickness of Concrete Roads', *Department of Scientific and Industrial Research, Road Research Road Note No. 19* (London: H.M.S.O., 1955, with Addendum dated November, 1957)

10. ROAD RESEARCH LABORATORY, 'A Guide to the Structural Design of Flexible and Rigid Pavements for New Roads', *Ministry of Transport, Road Research Road Note No. 29* (London: H.M.S.O., 1965 (2nd edition))

11. HIGHWAY RESEARCH BOARD, 'Final Report of Committee on Maintenance of Concrete Pavements as Related to the Pumping Action of Slabs', *Proceedings, Highway Research Board* (Washington, D.C.: vol, 28, 1948, pp. 281–310)

12. ANON, 'The M.6 Motorway. Preston–Lancaster Section Approaches Completion', *Roads and Road Construction* (London: vol. 42, 1964, pp. 354–9 and 403–8)

13. BRITISH STANDARDS INSTITUTION, 'Steel Fabric for Concrete Reinforcement', *B.S. 1221: 1964* (London: British Standards Institution, 1964)

14. CEMENT AND CONCRETE ASSOCIATION, *Bay Layout for Concrete Roads* (London: Cement and Concrete Association, 1964)

15. ROAD RESEARCH LABORATORY, 'Filling and Sealing Materials for Joints in Concrete Roads', *Department of Scientific and Industrial Research, Road Research Road Note No. 7* (London: H.M.S.O., 1955 (2nd edition))

16. WRIGHT, P. J. F., 'Full-Scale Tests of Materials for Sealing Expansion Joints in Concrete Roads', *Roads and Road Construction* (London: vol. 41, 1963, pp. 138–46)

17. UNITED STATES FEDERAL SPECIFICATION BOARD, 'Sealer: Hot Poured Type, for Joints in Concrete', *United States Federal Specification SS-S-164* (Washington, D.C.: United States Federal Specification Board, 1956)

18. BRITISH STANDARDS INSTITUTION, 'Tests to Assess the Properties of Hot Applied Joint Sealing Compounds for Concrete Pavements', *B.S. 2499 1954* (London: British Standards Institution, 1954)

19. MINISTRY OF TRANSPORT, *Specification for Road and Bridge Works* (London: H.M.S.O., 1963 (3rd edition))

20. BRITISH STANDARDS INSTITUTION, 'Methods of Testing Concrete', *B.S. 1881: 1952* (London: British Standards Institution, 1952)

21. ROAD RESEARCH LABORATORY, 'Design of Concrete Mixes', *Department of Scientific and Industrial Research, Road Research Road Note No. 4* (London: H.M.S.O., 1950 (2nd edition))

22. ERNTROY, H. C., 'The Variation of Works Test Cubes', *Cement and Concrete Association Research Report No. 10* (London: Cement and Concrete Association, 1960)

23. MURDOCK, L. J., *Concrete Materials and Practice* (London: Edward Arnold, 1960 (3rd edition), pp. 99–115)

24. WRIGHT, P. J. F., 'The Flexural Strength of Plain Concrete—Its Measurement and Use in Designing Concrete Mixes', *Department of Scientific and Industrial Research, Road Research Technical Paper No. 67* (London: H.M.S.O., 1964)

25. ASHWORTH, R., 'Some Investigations into the Use of Sugar as an

Admixture to Concrete', *Proc. Instn. civ. Engrs.* (London: vol. 31, 1965, pp. 129–45)

26. SHACKLOCK, B. W., 'Air-Entrained Concrete: Properties, Mix Design and Quality Control', *The Surveyor* (London: vol. 119, 1960, pp. 969–71)

27. WRIGHT, P. J. F., 'Entrained Air in Concrete', *Proc. Instn. civ. Engrs.* (London: vol. 2, Part I, 1953, pp. 337–58)

28. AMERICAN SOCIETY FOR TESTING AND MATERIALS, 'Standard Method of Test for Air Content of Freshly Mixed Concrete by the Pressure Method. Test C231-62', *1965 Book of A.S.T.M. Standards, Part 10* (Philadelphia: American Society for Testing and Materials, 1965, pp. 163–9)

29. BLAKE, L. S. and BROOK, K. M., 'The Construction of Major Concrete Roads in Great Britain, 1955–60', *J. Instn. Highw. Engrs.* (London: vol. 10, 1963, pp. 31–47)

30. BROOK, K. M., 'Construction of Concrete Paving with a Slip-Form Paver', *Cement and Concrete Association Technical Report TRA/376* (London: Cement and Concrete Association, 1964)

31. WALKER, B. J. and JOHNSON, B. W., 'Current Mid-European Concrete Road Construction', *J. Instn. Highw. Engrs.* (London: vol. 11, 1964, pp. 177–88)

32. STOTT, J. P., 'Prestressed Concrete Roads', *Proc. Instn. civ. Engrs.* (London: vol. 4, Part II, 1955, pp. 491–511)

33. FÉDÉRATION INTERNATIONALE DE LA PRÉCONTRAINTE and PERMANENT INTERNATIONAL ASSOCIATION OF ROADS CONGRESSES, *Symposium on Prestressed Concrete Roads and Airfield Runways, Naples, 1962* (London: Fédération Internationale de la Précontrainte, 1964)

34. SCOTT, W. J. O., 'Roads and their Riding Qualities', *Instn. civ. Engrs. Road Engineering Division Paper No. 25* (London: Instn. civ. Engrs., 1948)

35. KIRKHAM, R. H. H., 'The Riding Quality of Concrete Roads', *Department of Scientific and Industrial Research, Road Research Technical Paper No. 60* (London: H.M.S.O., 1963)

36. KIRKHAM, R. H. H., 'Recent Research into the Construction of Concrete Pavements', *Proc. Instn. civ. Engrs.* (London, vol. 27, 1964, pp. 241–62)

37. ROAD RESEARCH LABORATORY, 'Design Recommendations for Unreinforced Concrete Pavements', *Road Research Laboratory Report LR 192* (Crowthorne: Road Research Laboratory, 1968)

13

Surface Water Drainage

- -

The provision of adequate surface water drainage facilities is an essential feature of any road scheme. In addition to measures for dealing with the surface water run-off from the carriageways, footways, shoulders, and verges, the drainage scheme must take account of the run-off from adjacent catchment areas affected by the new construction works by providing cut-off drains, culverts, and bridges as required.

Before any detailed drainage scheme can be prepared, it is necessary to determine the design flow for each part of the drainage system. This in turn depends on the intensity of rainfall, the size of the catchment area concerned, the impermeability factors for the various types of surface within that area, the duration of the storm, and the time of concentration; the latter being the time taken for rain falling at the most distant point in the catchment area to reach the point in the drainage system where the flow is being calculated.

13.1 *Intensity of rainfall*

Studies of storm characteristics show that the storms having the greatest average intensity of rainfall are normally those of short duration. Relationships between intensity of rainfall and storm duration, based on British rainfall statistics, have been proposed by a Ministry of Health committee as follows:[1]

$$i = \frac{30}{t + 10} \quad \text{(for storms having a duration between 5 and 20 minutes)} \tag{13.1}$$

$$i = \frac{40}{t + 20} \quad \text{(for storms having a duration between 20 and 120 minutes)} \tag{13.2}$$

where i is the average intensity of rainfall (inches per hour) and t the duration of the storm (minutes).

Whilst these formulae are acceptable in many instances for design purposes, they take no account of the much heavier storms which occur only occasionally but which may have to be taken into consideration when designing storm water drainage systems in certain areas. For this reason, the Bilham formula,[2] which relates the average intensity of a storm not only to its duration but also to the frequency at which a storm of that intensity may be expected, is preferable. Bilham's formula is as follows:

$$N = 1 \cdot 25t(r + 0 \cdot 1)^{-3 \cdot 55} \tag{13.3}$$

where N is the number of occurrences of storms of this intensity in

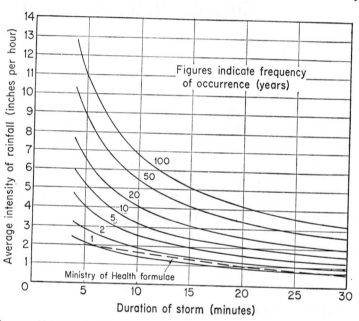

FIGURE 13.1 Relation between average intensity of rainfall and storm duration

10 years, t the time of duration of the storm (hours), and r the rainfall during time t (inches). Owing to the compressed time-scale used in the records from which the information was derived, the formula is not considered to be reliable for durations of less than 4 minutes.

Tables have been produced giving values of the mean rate of rainfall calculated by Bilham's formula for a range of frequencies and durations,[3] and specific values are given in Figure 13.1. Thus, for example, a storm lasting for 15 minutes with an intensity of 1·1 inches per hour may be expected to occur every year, but one of similar duration with twice this intensity would be expected only once in every seven years. These figures apply only to Great Britain, of course, and far greater intensities are frequently recorded in tropical countries.

On most road schemes occasional flooding, although hindering traffic, will not cause widespread damage and therefore can be tolerated. Thus for reasons of economy, a 'one-year storm' forms the usual basis of design for rural and suburban development schemes, in which case Bilham's formula gives virtually the same intensity as that given by the Ministry of Health formulae (Figure 13.1). In urban areas where there are older types of properties with basements, however, repeated flooding could not be contemplated and the design must be based on a greater intensity of rainfall such as that occurring every ten or possibly even every hundred years.

In this connection, it is of interest to note that 2·20 in of rain fell during a 15-minute period at Bolton, Lancashire, during a thunderstorm in July 1964. This intensity is far in excess of that given by the Ministry of Health formula, and according to Bilham's formula may be expected to occur only once every six hundred years or more.

13.2 Determination of design flow

(i) Lloyd-Davies method

Lloyd-Davies[4] has suggested that the design flow for any section of storm water drain should be based on a storm of duration equal to the time of concentration for the particular section under consideration. This means that surface run-off from every part of the catchment area is then contributing to the flow in this section of drain. Any storm having a duration in excess of this time would be expected to have a lower average intensity of rainfall and hence the maximum flow would be smaller.

The time of concentration is made up of the time of flow through the drainage system plus the time of entry. The latter is the time taken by rain to run over impermeable surfaces and, in the case of urban areas, through the drains of premises to the storm water sewer, and is usually assumed to be 2 or 3 minutes. The time of flow is dependent on the size of pipe, its gradient, and its internal roughness. Several empirical formulae have been derived to determine velocity, and hence the time of flow, for values of these various parameters, but *Road Note No. 35*[3] recommends that the Colebrook–White equation be used for this purpose. Charts and tables have been produced to simplify the use of this equation.[5, 6]

The design procedure is thus essentially one of trial and error, each section of storm water drain between manholes being considered in turn, starting at the upstream end. For this first length, a pipe diameter, normally not less than 6 in, is assumed and the time of flow through the length is calculated for the pipe running full. The time of concentration is then determined by adding the time of entry, and the average intensity of rainfall corresponding to a storm of this duration is calculated from Bilham's formula or abstracted from the published tables.[3] The total flow which the pipe must be capable of passing is then given by the product of the impermeable area of the catchment for this particular length of pipe and the intensity of rainfall. If these are expressed as A acres and i inches per hour respectively, then the total run-off Q cu ft per sec (cusecs) is given by:

$$Q = (4{,}840 \times 9 \times A)(i/3{,}600 \times 12)$$
$$= 121Ai/120$$

which for all practical purposes

$$= Ai \tag{13.4}$$

Should this exceed the capacity of the pipe, the design must be repeated using the next largest pipe size.

The next section of drain is treated in a similar manner, determining the new time of concentration (and hence critical storm duration) by adding the calculated time of flow through this second length to the time of concentration previously determined for the first length. The total run-off for the new catchment area is calculated from Equation 13.4 and compared with the capacity of the pipe. If the sewer is inadequate or excessively large, the designer chooses another size and repeats the calculation. Subsequent sections, including branches, are treated in a similar manner until the complete length down to the outfall has been designed.

(ii) Area–time diagrams

Whilst the Lloyd-Davies method can be considered to form a satisfactory basis for the design of surface water drainage systems in a small, compact area, errors in estimating the maximum rate of flow can occur where there is a long length of drain at the head of the system which

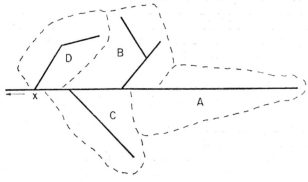

FIGURE 13.2

contributes little to the total flow. In such circumstances, the time of concentration calculated for any point in the drainage system below this length will be increased beyond that which would give the maximum flow, and the pipe size so determined may not be capable of dealing with the peak rate of flow.

This can be illustrated with reference to Figure 13.2. If the required size of sewer at point X is being determined, then rain falling in area A may be considered to start arriving at this point after a time t_1 min and the contributing area may be assumed to increase linearly with time until a time t_2 min, when the whole area is contributing to the flow at X.

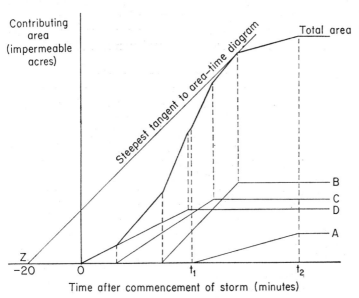

FIGURE 13.3 Area-time diagram

The area–time graph will be as shown in Figure 13.3 for area A. Similarly for areas B, C, and D, area–time graphs can be constructed. A summation of these individual graphs shows the actual area (in terms of impermeable acres) contributing to the flow at X at any time after the commencement of the storm.

The critical condition for design purposes is when Q $(= Ai)$ is a maximum. Using the Ministry of Health formula for a storm of duration exceeding 20 min (Equation 13.2), $Ai = 40A/(t + 20)$ and hence the maximum rate of flow occurs when the slope of a line drawn from a point on the area–time diagram to a point at minus 20 min on the time scale is at its maximum. The graphical solution is thus obtained by drawing the steepest line from point Z (Figure 13.3) which just touches the area–time diagram, and the maximum rate of flow (cusecs) is 40 times the slope of this line.

In many cases this maximum slope will occur when the whole impermeable area is contributing to the flow at point X and thus the maximum rate of flow is exactly that given by the original Lloyd-Davies method. On the other hand, the curve may be convex as shown in Figure 13.3, in which case the maximum rate of flow occurs with a storm of somewhat shorter duration.

The above method is applicable only when the Ministry of Health formulae are used to estimate rainfall intensity in terms of the storm duration. When the more accurate Bilham formula (Equation 13.3) is being employed, a series of tangent curves for equal rates of run-off can be drawn on a transparent overlay to the same scale as the area–time diagram and used to determine the maximum rate of flow.[7]

(iii) *Road Research Laboratory hydrograph method*

Experience with drainage schemes designed in accordance with the foregoing methods has indicated that in many cases the design has been unduly conservative, whilst in others—although far less frequently—insufficient drainage capacity has been provided, with consequential flooding. Following requests from local authorities, the Road Research Laboratory began in 1951 a programme of extensive research into the relation between the rate of rainfall and the rate of run-off from urban areas with the object of producing a method of calculation which would be more accurate and reliable over as wide a range of conditions as possible. Twelve urban areas were investigated, comprising areas of both old and new development and housing and factory areas, and ranging in size from a length of road having a total paved surface of just over 1 acre to a natural catchment of over 5,000 acres.

The investigations[8, 9] covered continuous measurements of rainfall and run-off, and the subsequent analysis of data relating to 286 storms. A special rainfall recorder was developed to enable the rate of rainfall to be obtained in addition to the total rainfall falling in a given time. From these rainfall records, calculations of maximum run-off were made by various methods and compared with the recorded run-off. These calculations were based in the first instance on the Lloyd-Davies method of design which gave values for the peak rate of run-off only, but complete run-off hydrographs were later obtained by using the area–time diagram in conjunction with the incremental rates of rainfall actually recorded during the storm.

A comparison of these calculated hydrographs with those recorded showed that, without exception, the calculation overestimated the rate of run-off and the recorded peak occurred later than the calculated peak. This difference is considered to result from errors implicit in the method of design which assumes full-bore velocities in the sewer system throughout the storm, irrespective of the actual depth of flow. The velocity of flow naturally decreases when the pipe is only partially full, thus increasing the time of concentration beyond that assumed in the calculations and resulting in a 'retention' of surface water run-off within the drainage system. Revised hydrographs which allowed for this retention showed good agreement between the calculated and recorded values.

It was therefore concluded from the investigation that the Lloyd-Davies method of sewer design is only suitable for relatively small areas such as housing estates and villages in which there are no sewers larger than 24 in diameter. For larger areas the Road Research Laboratory hydrograph method which takes account of the varying quantity of water retained in the sewers should be used. Where the Lloyd-Davies method has been found to give a reasonably accurate estimate of the peak flows, the research indicated that this was because there was, for the particular area concerned, a rough balance between the error introduced by neglecting the shape of the area–time diagram and that introduced by neglecting retention. The use of the 'tangent' method of design would correct the first error only, leading to an overestimation of the peak flow and is therefore not recommended.

Although the data required for the Road Research Laboratory hydrograph method of design are exactly the same as for the Lloyd-Davies method, the complexity of the subsequent calculations has necessitated the use of an electronic digital computer. Programmes have been devised for use with a Ferranti Pegasus computer which enable the design of a new sewer system to be carried out or an existing system to be examined for incorrect sizes. Details of these programmes are given in *Road Note No. 35*.[3]

It should still be appreciated, however, that the close agreement between the calculated and measured run-off obtained in the above investigations was to some extent influenced by the use of the actual storm profile for run-off calculations. For design purposes, in the absence of such data, a storm profile must be assumed. The Road Research Laboratory hydrograph method uses a storm profile which is related to the design frequency of occurrence and which has been obtained by the Meteorological Office from a preliminary analysis of storm data. These storm profiles are only provisional, and may give a somewhat different run-off hydrograph from that which would occur in practice with an actual storm profile of different shape but having the same average intensity overall. Further research is being carried out into the nature of storm profiles measured at a single point and efforts are also being made to relate the distribution of rainfall over an area to that measured by a point recorder. In addition, it is hoped that sufficient data will eventually be available to specify different storm intensities and frequencies for different parts of the country.

13.3 *Impermeable area*

All calculations for surface run-off involve the measurement of the catchment in terms of impermeable area. Since the critical storms for design purposes in Great Britain normally occur during the summer months, often after a prolonged dry period, natural surfaces can be considered sufficiently permeable to absorb a large proportion of the rainfall falling or running onto them, and the total surface area contributing to the flow in the storm water sewers should be taken to be only the area of paved surfaces directly connected to the sewer system.[3] This will include footways from which the surface run-off passes directly into the channels, but will exclude those from which the run-off flows over unpaved surfaces such as grass verges.

Two principal exceptions to this recommendation are where the road is in a cutting and where the area of unpaved surface is large compared with the area of paved surface, such as a natural catchment. In the former case, it is recommended that the whole plan area of the cutting slope should be added to the area of the road surface, although it is recognized that this will probably overestimate the impermeable area in the case of deep cuttings in open country. For large natural catchments, an accurate estimation of the percentage run-off is impossible but research suggests that winter conditions with the soil relatively impervious will be the criterion for design and that an impermeable area of from 40 to 70% of the gross area should be assumed.

Since it is impossible to estimate the time of entry for unpaved surfaces with any great accuracy, it is recommended that as a reasonable practical assumption the time of entry should normally be taken to be 1 hour. A satisfactory design value for the corresponding rate of rainfall under winter conditions has been estimated as $\frac{1}{4}$ in per hour. This is about one-half the value given by the Bilham formula which was derived mainly from records of summer storm rainfall.

13.4 *Surface water drainage on urban roads*

Surface water run-off from the carriageway in a built-up area is collected into the channels and discharged at intervals through gullies into the storm water sewers. Gullies are usually sited at approximately 100-ft centres, the exact spacing depending on the road width and whether a crowned section or one with straight crossfall has been used. In the latter case, gullies are required only along the outer channels of a dual carriageway layout except when the road cross-section is superelevated.

Storm water sewers should preferably be sited under the footways or verges rather than under the carriageway to facilitate maintenance and avoid the need to raise manhole covers prior to resurfacing. A single sewer can be used, with cross-connections under the carriageway from gullies on the opposite side of the road, but a separate storm water sewer down each side of the road with infrequent cross-connections is preferable for maintenance purposes.

Paved footways alongside the carriageway are normally graded to fall towards the channel, and a side-entry gully opening set into the line of the kerb (Figure 13.4) should be used in preference to one set into the channel, since the latter, although more efficient, will effectively reduce the carriageway width and thus affect the capacity of the road. Where the longitudinal gradient of the road exceeds 1 in 250, the same gradient can be used for the channels, but on flatter gradients summits must be

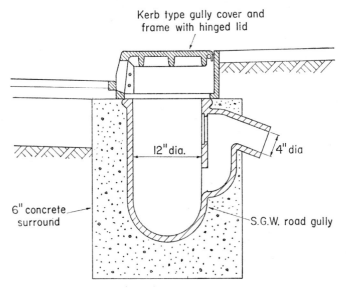

FIGURE 13.4 Side-entry gully opening

introduced along the channels to give a suitable fall to the gully openings. This should be done in such a way that the flattest road crossfall at the summit points is not less than 1 in 60 and the steepest crossfall at the gully openings does not exceed 1 in 30. Particular attention must be paid to the siting of gullies at road intersections.

13.5 Surface water drainage on rural roads

Most minor roads passing through open country have verges which are raised above the carriageway level, and surface water drainage is effected by grips which are cut through the verges and lead into open ditches or french drains. This method is sometimes used for main roads also, but, more frequently, raised kerbs, gullies, and piped sewer systems are

K*

constructed, as in urban areas. With the use of flush kerbs and hard shoulders in motorway construction it became necessary to reconsider the most suitable method of collecting surface water run-off from the carriageways.

On some of the earlier motorways, surface run-off in cuttings was collected in a turf- or concrete-lined channel at the toe of the cutting slope, or, in some cases, allowed to filter through to a porous subsoil drain sited at this same point. These channels or subsoil drains discharged into glazed storm water drains through catchpits, generally at 360-ft centres, which in turn discharged into open channels at the end of the cutting sections. From there the run-off passed to existing watercourses. On embankment sections, drainage channels were provided at the toe of the embankment to accommodate both run-off from the motorway and overland flow towards the embankment. Cut-off ditches were provided along the tops of cuttings where necessary.

Subsequent experience has shown this form of drainage system to be unsatisfactory for a number of reasons. Firstly, although a large proportion of the carriageway run-off was carried away in the channels or subsoil drains and from there to the storm water drains, a considerable amount penetrated into the verge and into the soil surrounding the subsoil drain during times of storm, thereby affecting the load-bearing properties of the subgrade to some extent. In addition, on embankment sections, the heavy surface water flow down the face of the embankment and its subsequent softening effect on the underlying soil increased the risk of slips. A modified surface water drainage system has therefore been used on more recently completed motorways.

The aim of this improved drainage system is to collect all surface water run-off from the paved carriageways and hard shoulders before it has the opportunity to soak into subgrade. Channels have therefore been formed between the shoulder and the verge or, in the case of superelevated sections, between the carriageway and the central reserve. Alternatively, a raised concrete or mastic asphalt edging, 3–4 in high, has sometimes been used at the outside edge of the shoulder. In either case, gully inlets or catchpits are provided, spaced as required, and the surface run-off is taken into storm water sewers when the road is in a cutting or discharged through a 6-in pipe into an open channel running down the face of embankments. On superelevated lengths of the alignment, a separate storm water sewer is required under the central reserve, cross-connected at intervals to the main storm water sewers sited under the verges. Typical drainage details are shown in Figures 11.9 and 12.13.

As previously mentioned, a one-year storm has usually been taken as the basis for the design of surface water drainage systems for rural roads in Great Britain. An exception to this has been made for culverts passing through road embankments, for which a 25-year storm intensity has formed the design criterion. In any case, no culvert should be less than 3 ft 6 in diameter so as to provide access for maintenance.

13.6 Carriageway crossfall

The purpose of providing crossfall or camber to the road surface is to obtain a rapid rate of surface water run-off from the carriageway during times of heavy rainfall. Delayed drainage will cause a considerable depth of water to form on the road surface, giving rise to the possibility of accidents resulting from the decreased skidding resistance of the road surface or from the heavy spray thrown up by fast-moving vehicles. This problem is particularly apparent on motorways where vehicle speeds are high, even in adverse weather conditions, and the surface run-off from a 36-ft carriageway is taken to one side of the road. In Great Britain, the original standard crossfall for motorways was 1 in 48, but this has now been increased to 1 in 40 in an attempt to decrease the amount of surface water retained on the carriageway.

The Road Research Laboratory is at present carrying out investigations into the problem of carriageway run-off in relation to rate of rainfall, crossfall, and surfacing material, using a 36 ft long by 15 ft wide steel platform which can be set at a range of crossfalls up to 1 in 20 from the horizontal position. The surfacing is laid on this platform, and a system of spraybars is used to simulate different rates of rainfall. Measurements are made of the rate of run-off at the lower edge of the platform and of the depth of water at various points on the surface and photographic records are used to compare the amounts of spray thrown up by vehicles travelling at different speeds.[10]

REFERENCES

1. MINISTRY OF HEALTH DEPARTMENTAL COMMITTEE ON RAINFALL AND RUN-OFF, 'Rainfall and Run-Off', *J. Instn. munic. Engrs.* (London: vol. 56, 1930, pp. 1172–6)
2. BILHAM, E. G., 'Classification of Heavy Falls in Short Periods. Revisions of the Curves Showing the Lower Limits of "Noteworthy", "Remarkable", and "Very Rare" Falls', *British Rainfall, 1935* (London: H.M.S.O., 1936, pp. 262–80)
3. ROAD RESEARCH LABORATORY, 'A Guide for Engineers to the Design of Storm Sewer Systems', *Department of Scientific and Industrial Research, Road Research Road Note No. 35* (London: H.M.S.O., 1963)
4. LLOYD-DAVIES, D. E., 'The Elimination of Storm-Water from Sewerage Systems', *Min. Proc. Instn. civ. Engrs.* (London: vol. 164, 1905–6, pp. 41–67)
5. ACKERS, P., 'Charts for the Hydraulic Design of Channels and Pipes',

Department of Scientific and Industrial Research, Hydraulics Research Paper No. 2 (London: H.M.S.O., 1958)

6. ACKERS, P., 'Tables for the Hydraulic Design of Storm-Drains, Sewers, and Pipelines', *Department of Scientific and Industrial Research, Hydraulics Research Paper No. 4* (London: H.M.S.O., 1963)

7. ESCRITT, L. B., *Sewerage and Sewage Disposal* (London: Contractors Record Ltd, 1962, p. 80)

8. WATKINS, L. H., 'The Design of Urban Sewer Systems', *Department of Scientific and Industrial Research, Road Research Technical Paper No. 55* (London: H.M.S.O., 1962)

9. WATKINS, L. H., 'Research on Surface Water Drainage', *Proc. Instn. civ. Engrs.* (London: vol. 24, 1963, pp. 305–30)

10. DEPARTMENT OF SCIENTIFIC AND INDUSTRIAL RESEARCH, *Road Research 1963* (London: H.M.S.O., 1964, p. 119)

Appendix I

Relation between Vertical Curve Length and Visibility Distance

- -

Two cases must be considered depending on whether the curve length is greater than or less than the visibility distance. In either case, the vertical curve is parabolic and extends an equal distance either side of the vertical intersection point.

Let L be the curve length (ft), s the visibility distance between two points each a height h above the road surface (ft), and G be the algebraic difference between the grades.

Case (a): $L \geqslant s$
Referring to Figure A.1, the vertical distance $BC = LG/200$, where

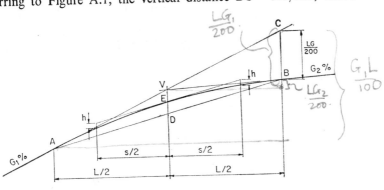

FIGURE A.1

$G = G_1 - G_2$. By similar triangles, $DV = \frac{1}{2}BC$ and by the properties of a parabola, $EV = \frac{1}{4}BC$. Thus $DE = \frac{1}{4}BC = LG/800$.

Since the curve is parabolic, $h/DE = (s/L)^2$

271

i.e.
$$L^2 = s^2\left(\frac{DE}{h}\right) = \frac{s^2 LG}{800h}$$

or
$$L = s^2 G/800h$$

In British practice, $h = 3$ ft 6 in $= 3\cdot50$ ft
and therefore $L = s^2 G/2,800$ metric equiv.   (4.14)

Case (b): $L \leqslant s$

Referring to Figure A.2, BC is again equal to $LG/200$, and

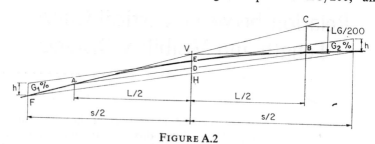

FIGURE A.2

$DE = EV = LG/800$.

Triangles FVH and AVD are similar and therefore $HV/DV = s/L$.
Now $HV = EV + h = (LG/800) + h$ and therefore

$$\frac{(LG/800) + h}{(LG/400)} = \frac{s}{L}$$

i.e.
$$1 + (800h/LG) = 2s/L$$

or
$$L = 2s - 800h/G$$

Since h is again $3\cdot5$ ft in British practice,

$$L = 2s - 2,800/G \qquad\qquad (4.15)$$

Appendix II

Calculations of Cross-sectional Areas and Prismoidal Corrections from Slope Stake Coordinates

----

Cross-sectional areas

(a) Section wholly in cut or fill
Let Figure A.3 represent the cross-section, where b is the formation

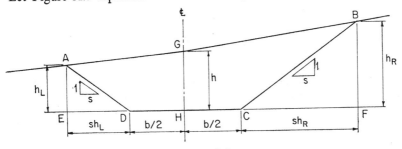

FIGURE A.3

width, assumed horizontal, h_L is the level difference between the left-hand slope stake and formation level, h_R the level difference between the right-hand slope stake and formation level, h the level difference between the original ground level along the centre-line and the formation level, and s the side slope, expressed as 1 (vertically) in s (horizontally).

Then the cross-section area A is given by:

$$A = \text{Area of trapezium AGHE} + \text{Area of trapezium GBFH} - \text{Area of triangle ADE} - \text{Area of triangle BFC}$$

$$= \tfrac{1}{2}(h_L + h)(\tfrac{1}{2}b + sh_L) + \tfrac{1}{2}(h + h_R)(\tfrac{1}{2}b + sh_R) - \tfrac{1}{2}sh_L^2 - \tfrac{1}{2}sh_R^2$$

$$= \tfrac{1}{4}b(h_L + 2h + h_R) + \tfrac{1}{2}sh(h_L + h_R) \tag{7.2}$$

273

(b) Section in sidelong ground
Let Figure A.4 represent the cross-section in sidelong ground.

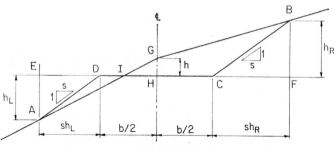

FIGURE A.4

Using the same notation as above, the area of cut A_C is given by:

A_C = Area of triangle GHI + Area of trapezium GBFH − Area of triangle BFC

$$= \tfrac{1}{2}IH(h) + \tfrac{1}{2}(h + h_R)(\tfrac{1}{2}b + sh_R) - \tfrac{1}{2}sh_R^2$$

Now by similar triangles, IH/EH = GH/(GH + EA)

and therefore $$\text{IH} = \frac{h}{(h + h_L)}(\tfrac{1}{2}b + sh_L)$$

Hence $$A_C = \frac{h^2}{2(h + h_L)}(\tfrac{1}{2}b + sh_L) + \tfrac{1}{2}(h + h_R)(\tfrac{1}{2}b + sh_R) - \tfrac{1}{2}sh_R^2$$

$$= \tfrac{1}{4}b\left[\frac{h^2}{(h + h_L)} + h + h_R\right] + \tfrac{1}{2}sh\left[\frac{hh_L}{(h + h_L)} + h_R\right] \qquad (7.3)$$

Similarly, the area of fill A_F is given by:

$$A_F = \text{Area of triangle EIA} - \text{Area of triangle EDA}$$

$$= \tfrac{1}{2}EI(h_L) - \tfrac{1}{2}sh_L^2$$

Now $$\text{EI} = \frac{h_L}{(h + h_L)}(\tfrac{1}{2}b + sh_L)$$

Therefore $$A_F = \frac{h_L^2}{2(h + h_L)}(\tfrac{1}{2}b + sh_L) - \tfrac{1}{2}sh_L^2$$

$$= \tfrac{1}{4}b\left[\frac{h_L^2}{(h + h_L)}\right] - \frac{shh_L^2}{2(h + h_L)} \qquad (7.4)$$

Prismoidal corrections

(c) Sections wholly in cut or fill
Let Figure A.3 represent a typical cross-section of the prismoid such that h_L, h, and h_R are the level differences between the original ground surface and the formation at one end of the prismoid and h_L', h', and

h_R' are the corresponding values at the other end section. The end areas from Equation 7.2 are

$$A_1 = \tfrac{1}{4}b(h_L + 2h + h_R) + \tfrac{1}{2}sh(h_L + h_R)$$

and $\qquad A_2 = \tfrac{1}{4}b(h_L' + 2h' + h_R') + \tfrac{1}{2}sh'(h_L' + h_R')$

Midway between the two ends the cross-section area is

$$M = \tfrac{1}{4}b[\tfrac{1}{2}(h_L + h_L') + 2 \times \tfrac{1}{2}(h + h') + \tfrac{1}{2}(h_R + h_R')]$$
$$+ \tfrac{1}{4}s(h + h')[\tfrac{1}{2}(h_L + h_L') + \tfrac{1}{2}(h_R + h_R')]$$

From equation 7.6, the prismoidal correction is $\tfrac{1}{3}L(A_1 - 2M + A_2)$

$$= \tfrac{1}{3}L[\tfrac{1}{4}b(h_L + 2h + h_R) + \tfrac{1}{2}sh(h_L + h_R)$$
$$- \tfrac{1}{4}b(h_L + h_L' + 2h + 2h' + h_R + h_R')$$
$$- \tfrac{1}{4}s(h + h')(h_L + h_L' + h_R + h_R')$$
$$+ \tfrac{1}{4}b(h_L' + 2h' + h_R') + \tfrac{1}{2}sh'(h_L' + h_R')]$$

All terms containing b cancel, leaving prismoidal correction

$$= \tfrac{1}{12}Ls[2hh_L + 2hh_R - (hh_L + hh_L' + hh_R + hh_R'$$
$$+ h'h_L + h'h_L' + h'h_R + h'h_R') + 2h'h_L' + 2h'h_R']$$
$$= \tfrac{1}{12}Ls(h - h')[(h_L - h_L') + (h_R - h_R')] \qquad (7.7)$$

(d) Sections in sidelong ground

Let Figure A.4 represent a typical cross-section of the prismoid such that h_L, h, and h_R are the level differences between the original ground surface and the formation at one end section and h_L', h', and h_R' are the corresponding values at the other end section.

At the first end section, the net area of cut $A_1 = A_C - A_F$

$$= \tfrac{1}{4}b\left[\frac{h^2}{(h + h_L)} + h + h_R\right] + \tfrac{1}{2}sh\left[\frac{hh_L}{(h + h_L)} + h_R\right]$$
$$- \tfrac{1}{4}b\left[\frac{h_L{}^2}{(h + h_L)}\right] + \frac{shh_L{}^2}{2(h + h_L)}$$

$$= \tfrac{1}{4}b(2h + h_R - h_L) + \tfrac{1}{2}sh(h_L + h_R)$$

Similarly, $\qquad A_2 = \tfrac{1}{4}b(2h' + h_R' - h_L') + \tfrac{1}{2}sh'(h_L' + h_R')$

and

$$M = \tfrac{1}{4}b[2 \times \tfrac{1}{2}(h + h') + \tfrac{1}{2}(h_R + h_R') - \tfrac{1}{2}(h_L + h_L')]$$
$$+ \tfrac{1}{4}s(h + h')[\tfrac{1}{2}(h_L + h_L') + \tfrac{1}{2}(h_R + h_R')]$$

The prismoidal correction $= \tfrac{1}{3}L(A_1 - 2M + A_2)$

$$= \tfrac{1}{3}L[\tfrac{1}{4}b(2h + h_R - h_L) + \tfrac{1}{2}sh(h_L + h_R)$$
$$- \tfrac{1}{4}b(2h + 2h' + h_R + h_R' - h_L - h_L')$$
$$- \tfrac{1}{4}s(h + h')(h_L + h_L' + h_R + h_R')$$
$$+ \tfrac{1}{4}b(2h' + h_R' - h_L') + \tfrac{1}{2}sh'(h_L' + h_R')]$$

All terms containing b again cancel, leaving prismoidal correction

$$= \tfrac{1}{12}Ls(h - h')[(h_L - h_L') + (h_R - h_R')]$$

as before.

Appendix III

Relation between Dry Density, Moisture Content, and Percentage Air Voids for a Compacted Soil

----

Let V_S, V_W, and V_A represent the volumes of soil, water, and air respectively in a sample of soil of total volume V (Figure A.5).

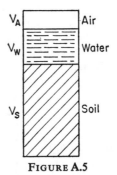

FIGURE A.5

Then
$$V = V_S + V_W + V_A$$

If a is the percentage air voids, then by definition
$$a/100 = V_A/V$$
or
$$V_A = Va/100$$
Hence
$$V(1 - a/100) = V_S + V_W$$

If the density of water is γ_W and the specific gravity of the soil particles is G, then the moisture content m, which by definition is weight of water/weight of soil, is given by:

$$m = \frac{V_W \gamma_W}{V_S G \gamma_W} = \frac{V_W}{G V_S}$$

276

Therefore $$V_{\mathrm{W}} = mGV_{\mathrm{S}}$$

and $$V(1 - a/100) = V_{\mathrm{S}}(1 + mG)$$

The dry density of the soil is, by definition, the weight of soil per unit volume.

i.e. $$\gamma_{\mathrm{D}} = \frac{V_{\mathrm{S}}G\gamma_{\mathrm{W}}}{V} = \frac{G\gamma_{\mathrm{W}}}{1 + mG}\left(1 - \frac{a}{100}\right)$$

For zero air voids,

$$\gamma_{\mathrm{D}} = \frac{G\gamma_{\mathrm{W}}}{1 + mG} \tag{8.1}$$

Index